Chemistry:
An Atoms-Focused Approach

D1511213

Chemistry:
An Atoms-Focused Approach

Thomas R. Gilbert, Rein V. Kirss, Natalie Foster

Karen S. Brewer
HAMILTON COLLEGE

W • W • NORTON & COMPANY • NEW YORK • LONDON

W. W. Norton & Company has been independent since its founding in 1923, when William Warder Norton and Mary D. Herter Norton first published lectures delivered at the People's Institute, the adult education division of New York City's Cooper Union. The Nortons soon expanded their program beyond the Institute, publishing books by celebrated academics from America and abroad. By mid-century, the two major pillars of Norton's publishing program—trade books and college texts—were firmly established. In the 1950s, the Norton family transferred control of the company to its employees, and today—with a staff of four hundred and a comparable number of trade, college, and professional titles published each year—W. W. Norton & Company stands as the largest and oldest publishing house owned wholly by its employees.

Media Editor: Rob Bellinger
Associate Media Editor: Jennifer Barnhardt
Assistant Media Editor: Paula Iborra
Production Manager: Eric Pier-Hocking

ISBN 978-0-393-25011-4

W. W. Norton & Company, Inc., 500 Fifth Avenue, New York, NY 10110

www.wwnorton.com

W. W. Norton & Company Ltd., Castle House, 75/76 Wells Street, London W1T 3QT

1 2 3 4 5 6 7 8 9 0

CONTENTS

PREFACE

You might be starting this introductory course in chemistry with a little trepidation and want to know the secret formula for success. The simple answer (admittedly hard to put into practice) is for you to engage fully with the course in the classroom and in laboratories, during office hours, and by working problems outside of class on your own or with friends. We hope that this solutions manual will help you with the last of these.

The textbook has introduced you to the COAST method as an approach to solving problems and answering conceptual questions. This method encourages you to assemble all relevant information and to plan an approach for any new problem you encounter, on an exam let's say, before you start calculating an answer. After you answer, this method also guides you to think further about the problem to extend your knowledge. We use the COAST method as summarized below throughout this manual:

COLLECT AND ORGANIZE Restatement of the problem to delineate exactly what information has been provided and what is being asked.

ANALYZE Strategy to solve the problem including what formulas are relevant and what unit conversions are necessary.

SOLVE Application of the strategy to solve a problem numerically or answer a conceptual question.

THINK ABOUT IT Reminders to check the answer or consider whether the answer makes sense. In this manual, we sometimes use this step to add factual information extending the context of the question.

In this manual you will see the worked-out solutions to all the odd-numbered problems at the end of each of the textbook's chapters. In general, this manual uses the conventions for significant figures as outlined in Chapter 1 of the textbook except where an additional significant figure in the answer would clarify the difference between what you might show on your calculator and what strict adherence to the significant figure rules would give us as an answer. For most calculations presented, all significant digits were kept in the calculator for intermediate values in a multistep calculation.

As you use this *Student's Solutions Manual*, keep in mind that often more than one valid approach exists to solving a particular problem in chemistry. Neither your professor nor you will always solve the problem in exactly the way presented here. In class, you may be shown additional approaches to solving the many problems that you will encounter in introductory chemistry. That's okay as long as those methods are applicable to the range of problems of that type.

When you sit down to solve a set of problems from the textbook, make sure that you have all the relevant tools (textbook, periodic table, and calculator) and that you are ready to dig in. Sometimes working alone is best, but you might find that you learn more when discussing solutions with a study group. You will be more successful in the course if you work the end-of-chapter problems on a regular basis, not just on weekends or right before a test. Doing 8–10 problems every other day is less overwhelming (so you will accomplish more) than trying to do 30 per week or more than 100 right before a test. If you solve problems steadily and conscientiously throughout your chemistry course, you will be amazed by how much you are learning and you will probably be more successful on tests.

You will find this manual most useful if you first try to solve the problems on your own. If you get stuck on a particular question, open the manual, consult the solution here, read it carefully, compare it with your approach, and then try to solve the problem again. In the textbook, most of the odd-numbered problems are paired with an even-numbered problem that is very much like it. You can use the solutions in this manual as models to solve those even-numbered problems to further hone your problem-solving approach.

Finally, as you consider the connections to biology, physics, geology, materials science, environmental science, medicine, and astronomy that are presented in the text and used as a basis of many of the end-of-chapter problems, we hope that you will begin to see the many contributions of the science of chemistry to these fields.

CHAPTER 1 | Matter and Energy: An Atomic Perspective

1.1. **Collect and Organize**

Figure P1.1(a) shows "molecules," each consisting of one red sphere and one blue sphere, and Figure P1.1(b) has separate blue spheres and red spheres. For each figure we are to determine whether the substance(s) depicted are a solid, liquid, or gas and whether the figures show pure elements or compounds.

Analyze

A pure substance (whether element or compound) is composed of all the same type of molecule or atom, not a mixture of two kinds. An element is composed of all the same type of atom, and a compound is composed of two or more types of atoms. Solids have a definite volume and a highly ordered arrangement where the particles are close together. Liquids also have a definite volume but have a disordered arrangement of particles that are close together. Gases have disordered particles that fill the volume of the container and are far apart from each other.

Solve

(a) Because each particle in Figure P1.1(a) consists of one red sphere and one blue sphere, all the particles are the same—this is a pure compound. The particles fill the container and are disordered, so these particles are in the gas phase.
(b) Because it shows a mixture of red and blue spheres, Figure P1.1(b) depicts a mixture of blue element atoms and red element atoms. The blue spheres fill the container and are disordered, so these particles are in the gas phase. The red spheres have a definite volume and are slightly disordered, so these particles are in the liquid phase.

Think about It

Remember that both elements and compounds may be either pure or present in a mixture.

1.3. **Collect and Organize**

In this question we are to consider whether the reactants, as depicted, undergo a chemical reaction and/or a phase change.

Analyze

Chemical reactions involve the breaking and making of bonds in which atoms are combined differently in the products than in the reactants. When we consider a possible phase change, remember the following: Solids have a definite volume and a highly ordered arrangement where the particles are close together. Liquids also have a definite volume but have a disordered arrangement of particles that are close together. Gases have disordered particles that fill the volume of the container and are far apart from one another.

Solve

In Figure P1.3, two pure elements (red–red and blue–blue) in the gas phase recombine to form a compound (red–blue) in the solid phase (ordered array of molecules). Therefore, answer b describes the reaction shown.

Think about It

A phase change does not necessarily accompany a chemical reaction. We will learn later that the polarity of the product will determine whether a substance will be in the solid, liquid, or gaseous state at a given temperature.

1.5. **Collect and Organize**

Given a space-filling model of formic acid pictured in Figure P1.5, we are to write the molecular formula of formic acid.

Analyze

To determine the identity of the atoms in the space-filling model, we use the Atomic Color Palette (inside back cover of your textbook): black is carbon, red is oxygen, and white is hydrogen. To determine the formula, we need to count each type of atom in the structure.

Solve

The structure of formic acid includes two hydrogen atoms, two oxygen atoms, and one carbon atom. Therefore, its molecular formula is CH_2O_2.

Think about It

Writing the molecular formula as "2HC2O" is confusing and wrong. We indicate the number of atoms in a molecular formula with a subscript within the molecular formula, not with a coefficient. Also, you will find that it is a convention for organic molecular formulas to list C first, followed by H.

1.7. **Collect and Organize**

We are asked to compare the arrangement of water molecules in water as a solid (ice) and water as a liquid.

Analyze

Figure A1.7 depicts the arrangement of the water molecules in both of these phases.

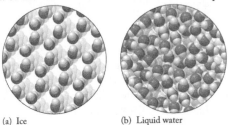

(a) Ice   (b) Liquid water

Figure A1.7

Solve

Water molecules in both the ice and liquid forms contain hydrogen bonds that link individual molecules together closely. In these arrangements, the hydrogen atoms in a water molecule point to an oxygen atom of a neighboring water molecule. The oxygen atom, in turn, points toward a hydrogen atom of a neighboring molecule. The hydrogen bonds in liquid water have no regular structure, whereas they do in ice, which has a hexagonal arrangement of water molecules.

Think about It

The structure of ice is more open than the structure of liquid water. This is why, when water freezes, it expands.

1.9. **Collect and Organize**

We are to determine which phase (solid, liquid, or gas) has the greatest particle motion and which has the least.

Analyze

Gases have particles much separated from each other; these particles, therefore, have a wide range of movement. Particles in solids and liquids are close to one another, and therefore the particle motion in both phases is restricted. Solids hold their particles in rigid arrays.

Solve

Because of their freedom of movement, gases have the greatest particle motion; because of the restriction of their solid lattice, solids have the least particle motion.

Think about It

Heating a solid or liquid can melt or vaporize a substance. During these phase changes with the addition of heat, particle motion increases.

1.11. **Collect and Organize**

We are asked to identify the process that results in snow disappearing, but not melting, on a sunny but cold winter day.

Analyze

The cold air temperature does not allow the snow to melt, but the sunny day does add warmth to the solid snow.

Solve

The snow, instead of melting, sublimes: directly forming water vapor from the solid ice crystals in snow.

Think about It

A more familiar example of sublimation is that of "dry ice," which is solid CO_2 and at ambient temperature and pressure sublimes, rather than melts, to give a "fog" for stage shows.

1.13. **Collect and Organize**

Energy and work must be related because, from our everyday experience, we know that doing work takes energy.

Analyze

In this context, energy is defined as the capacity to do work. Work is defined as moving an object with a force over some distance. Energy is also thought to be a fundamental component of the universe. The Big Bang theory postulates that all matter originated from a burst of energy, and Albert Einstein proposed that $m = E/c^2$ (mass equals energy divided by the speed of light squared).

Solve

Energy is needed to do work, and doing work uses energy.

Think about It

A system with high energy has the potential to do a lot of work.

1.15. **Collect and Organize**

From three statements about heat, we are asked to choose those that are true.

Analyze

Heat is defined as the transfer of energy between objects or regions of different temperature and the thermal energy flows from high thermal energy to low thermal energy. Heat is an extrinsic property; the amount of heat in a substance depends on the quantity of the substance and it is measured by measuring the temperature.

Solve

All these statements (a, b, and c) are true.

Think about It

Later in this course we will be able to quantify the heat in a substance or the heat released or absorbed by a physical change or a chemical reaction.

1.17. **Collect and Organize**

We are asked to compare the kinetic energy of a subcompact car (1400 kg) to that of a dump truck (18,000 kg) when they are traveling at the same speed.

Analyze

We can compare the kinetic energies by using the equation

$$KE = \frac{1}{2}mu^2$$

Solve

For the subcompact car:

$$KE = \frac{1}{2}(1400 \text{ kg})u_1^2$$

For the dump truck:

$$KE = \frac{1}{2}(18,000 \text{ kg})u_2^2$$

Because $u_1 = u_2$, the ratio of the kinetic energies is

$$\frac{KE_2}{KE_1} = \frac{\frac{1}{2}(18,000 \text{ kg})u_2{}^2}{\frac{1}{2}(1400 \text{ kg})u_2{}^2} = \frac{18,000 \text{ kg}}{1400 \text{ kg}} = 13$$

When traveling at the same speed, the dump truck has 13 times more kinetic energy than the subcompact car.

Think about It
The same dump truck has more kinetic energy when traveling at a higher speed because kinetic energy depends on the velocity of an object as well as its mass.

1.19. **Collect and Organize**
For the foods listed, we are to determine which are heterogeneous.

Analyze
A heterogeneous mixture has visible regions of different composition.

Solve
Clear regions of different composition are evident in a Snickers bar (b) and in an uncooked hamburger (d), but not in solid butter (a) or in grape juice (c).

Think about It
When butter melts, you notice milk solids and clear regions that are definitely discernible. Therefore, homogeneous solid butter becomes heterogeneous when heated.

1.21. **Collect and Organize**
For the foods listed, we are to determine which are heterogeneous.

Analyze
A heterogeneous mixture has visible regions of different composition.

Solve
Clear regions of different composition are evident in orange juice (with pulp) (d), but not in apple juice, cooking oil, solid butter, or tomato juice (a–c, e).

Think about It
When butter melts, you notice milk solids and clear regions that are definitely discernible. Therefore, homogeneous solid butter becomes heterogeneous when heated.

1.23. **Collect and Organize**
For this question we are to list some chemical and physical properties of gold.

Analyze
A chemical property is seen when a substance undergoes a chemical reaction, thereby becoming a different substance. A physical property can be seen without any transformation of one substance into another.

Solve
One chemical property of gold is its resistance to corrosion (oxidation). Gold's physical properties include its density, color, melting temperature, and electrical and thermal conductivity.

Think about It
Another metal that does not corrode (or rust) is platinum. Platinum and gold, along with palladium, are often called "noble metals."

1.25. **Collect and Organize**
We are asked in this question to name three properties to distinguish among table sugar, water, and oxygen.

Analyze

We can distinguish among substances by using either physical properties (such as color, melting point, and density) or chemical properties (such as chemical reactions, corrosion, and flammability).

Solve

We can distinguish among table sugar, water, and oxygen by examining their physical states (sugar is a solid, water is a liquid, and oxygen is a gas) and by their densities, melting points, and boiling points.

Think about It

These three substances are also very different at the atomic level. Oxygen is a pure element made up of diatomic molecules, water is a liquid compound made up of discrete molecules of hydrogen and oxygen (H_2O), and table sugar is a solid compound made up of carbon, hydrogen, and oxygen atoms.

1.27. **Collect and Organize**

From the list of properties of sodium, we are to determine which are physical and which are chemical properties.

Analyze

Physical properties are those that can be observed without transforming the substance into another substance. Chemical properties are observed only when one substance reacts with another and therefore is transformed into another substance.

Solve

Density, melting point, thermal and electrical conductivity, and softness (a–d) are all physical properties, whereas tarnishing and reaction with water (e and f) are both chemical properties.

Think about It

Because the density of sodium is less than that of water, a piece of sodium will float on water as it reacts.

1.29. **Collect and Organize**

We are to explain whether an extensive property can be used to identify a substance.

Analyze

An extensive property is one that, like mass, length, and volume, is determined by size or amount.

Solve

Extensive properties will change with the size of the sample and therefore cannot be used to identify a substance.

Think about It

We could, for example, have the same mass of feathers and lead, but their mass alone will not tell us which mass measurement belongs to which—the feathers or the lead.

1.31. **Collect and Organize**

In this question we think about the information needed to formulate a hypothesis.

Analyze

A hypothesis is a tentative explanation for an observation.

Solve

To form a hypothesis, we need at least one observation, experiment, or idea (from examining nature).

Think about It

A hypothesis that is tested and shown to be valid can become a theory.

1.33. **Collect and Organize**

We are to consider whether we can disprove a hypothesis.

Analyze

A hypothesis is a tentative explanation for an observation.

Solve

Disproving a scientific hypothesis is possible. In fact, many experiments are designed to do just that as the best test of the hypothesis's validity.

Think about It

We can even disprove a theory (although doing so is harder) or cause a theory to be modified when new evidence, a new experimental technique, or new data from a new instrument give observations that are counter to the explanation stated by the theory.

1.35. **Collect and Organize**

We are to define *theory* as used in conversation.

Analyze

Theory in everyday conversation has a different meaning from its meaning in science.

Solve

Theory in normal conversation is someone's idea or opinion or speculation that can easily be changed and may not have much evidence or many arguments to support it.

Think about It

A theory in science is a generally accepted and highly tested explanation of observed facts.

1.37. **Collect and Organize**

We are to compare SI units with U.S. Customary units.

Analyze

SI units are based on a decimal system to describe basic units of mass, length, temperature, energy, and so on. U.S. Customary units vary.

Solve

SI units, which were based on the original metric system, can be easily converted into a larger or smaller unit by multiplying or dividing by multiples of 10. U.S. Customary units are more complicated to manipulate. For example, to convert miles to feet you have to know that 5280 feet are in 1 mile, and to convert gallons to quarts you have to know that 4 quarts are in 1 gallon.

Think about It

Once you can visualize a meter, a gram, and a liter, using the SI system is quite convenient.

1.39. **Collect and Organize**

For this problem we need to convert the distance of the Olympic mile (1500 m) in meters to miles and then to feet. Then we need to compare that distance with an actual mile by using a ratio and then converting that into a percentage.

Analyze

To convert the distance, we can use the following conversions:

$$\frac{1 \text{ km}}{1000 \text{ m}}, \frac{0.6214 \text{ mi}}{1 \text{ km}}, \text{ and } \frac{5280 \text{ ft}}{1 \text{ mi}}$$

To determine the percentage the Olympic mile distance is compared with the actual mile, we will use

$$\% \text{ distance} = \frac{\text{Olympic mile distance in feet}}{5280 \text{ ft}} \times 100$$

Solve

$$1500 \text{ m} \times \frac{1 \text{ km}}{1000 \text{ m}} \times \frac{0.6214 \text{ mi}}{1 \text{ km}} \times \frac{5280 \text{ ft}}{1 \text{ mi}} = 4921 \text{ ft}$$

$$\% \text{ distance} = \frac{4921 \text{ ft}}{5280 \text{ ft}} \times 100 = 93.20\%$$

Think about It

This calculation shows that the Olympic mile is just a little bit shorter than the conventional mile.

1.41. **Collect and Organize**

This problem asks for a simple conversion of length: from meters to miles.

Analyze

The conversions that we need include meters to kilometers and kilometers to miles:

$$\frac{1 \text{ km}}{1000 \text{ m}} \quad \text{and} \quad \frac{0.6214 \text{ mi}}{1 \text{ km}}$$

Solve

$$4.0 \times 10^3 \text{ m} \times \frac{1 \text{ km}}{1000 \text{ m}} \times \frac{0.6214 \text{ mi}}{1 \text{ km}} = 2.5 \text{ mi}$$

Think about It

The answer is reasonable because 4000 m would be a little over 2 mi when estimated. For a natural piece of silk to be that long, though, is surprising.

1.43. **Collect and Organize**

To determine the Calories burned by the wheelchair marathoner in a race, we can first find the number of hours the race will be for the marathoner at the pace of 13.1 miles per hour. We can then calculate the Calories burned from that value and the rate at which the marathoner burns Calories.

Analyze

The time for the marathoner to complete the race will be given by

$$\text{time to complete the marathon} = \frac{\text{distance of the marathon}}{\text{pace of the marathoner}}$$

The Calories burned will be computed by

$$\text{Calories burned} = \frac{\text{Calories burned}}{\text{hr}} \times \text{length of the marathon race}$$

Solve

$$\text{time to complete the marathon} = \frac{26.2 \text{ mi}}{13.1 \text{ mi/hr}} = 2.00 \text{ hr}$$

$$\text{Calories burned} = \frac{665 \text{ Cal}}{\text{hr}} \times 2.00 \text{ hr} = 1330 \text{ Cal}$$

Think about It

We could solve this problem without touching a calculator. Because the marathoner takes 2.00 hr to complete the race, the Calories she burns are simply twice the number of Calories she burns in 1 hr.

1.45. **Collect and Organize**

A light-year is the distance light travels in 1 yr. To determine the distance of 4.3 light-years in kilometers, we will first have to convert 4.3 yr into seconds and then use the speed of light to determine the distance the light travels over that amount of time.

Analyze

The length of time of 4.3 yr in seconds can be found by using the following conversions:

$$\frac{1 \text{ yr}}{365.25 \text{ d}}, \frac{1 \text{ d}}{24 \text{ hr}}, \frac{1 \text{ hr}}{60 \text{ min}}, \text{ and } \frac{1 \text{ min}}{60 \text{ s}}$$

The distance of 4.3 light-years in meters can be found from the speed of light:

distance of 4.3 light-years = speed of light (in meters/second) × 4.3 yr (in seconds)

This can be converted into kilometers by using

$$\frac{1 \text{ km}}{1000 \text{ m}}$$

Solve

$$4.3 \text{ yr} \times \frac{365.25 \text{ d}}{1 \text{ yr}} \times \frac{24 \text{ hr}}{1 \text{ d}} \times \frac{60 \text{ min}}{1 \text{ hr}} \times \frac{60 \text{ s}}{1 \text{ min}} = 1.36 \times 10^8 \text{ s}$$

$$\text{distance to Proxima Centauri} = (1.36 \times 10^8 \text{ s}) \times \frac{2.9979 \times 10^8 \text{ m}}{\text{s}} \times \frac{1 \text{ km}}{1000 \text{ m}} = 4.1 \times 10^{13} \text{ km}$$

Think about It

This is a very large distance since light travels so fast. The light-year, being such a large distance, is an ideal unit for expressing astronomical distances.

1.47. **Collect and Organize**

To solve this problem, we need to know the volume of water in liters that is to be removed from the swimming pool. Using that volume and the rate at which the water can be siphoned, we can find how long removing the water will take.

Analyze

The volume of water to be removed in cubic meters can be found from

length of pool (in meters) × width of pool (in meters) × depth of water to be removed (in meters)

This volume will have to be converted to liters through the conversion

$$\frac{1 \text{ L}}{1 \times 10^{-3} \text{ m}^3}$$

The time to siphon the water is determined by the rate at which the siphon pump operates:

$$\text{time to siphon the water} = \frac{\text{volume of water to be siphoned in liters}}{\text{rate at which the water can be siphoned in liters per second}}$$

Solve

The volume of the water to be siphoned out of the pool is (using 6 in = 0.50 ft)

$$50.0 \text{ m} \times 25.0 \text{ m} \times \left(3.0 \text{ cm} \times \frac{1 \text{ m}}{100 \text{ cm}}\right) = 37.5 \text{ m}^3$$

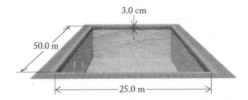

Converting this into gallons,

$$37.5 \text{ m}^3 \times \frac{1 \text{ L}}{1 \times 10^{-3} \text{ m}^3} = 3.75 \times 10^4 \text{ L}$$

The amount of time to siphon this water is

$$\text{time to siphon the water} = \frac{3.75 \times 10^4 \text{ L}}{5.2 \text{ L/s}} = 7210 \text{ s}$$

$$7210 \text{ s} \times \frac{1 \text{ min}}{60 \text{ s}} = 120 \text{ min, or } 2.0 \text{ h}$$

Think about It
This may be a surprisingly long time to siphon only 3.0 cm of water from the pool, but the total volume to be siphoned is quite large because of the pool's size.

1.49. **Collect and Organize**
We can solve this by converting the time for the runner to complete the race into seconds and then converting the distance of the race from kilometers into meters. The runner's speed is the ratio of distance (meters) to time (seconds).

Analyze
Conversions for time that are needed are

$$\frac{1 \text{ min}}{60 \text{ s}} \quad \text{and} \quad \frac{1 \text{ hr}}{60 \text{ min}}$$

For converting kilometers into miles we need

$$\frac{1000 \text{ m}}{1 \text{ km}}$$

Solve
The time for the runner to complete the race is

$$\left(41 \text{ min} \times \frac{60 \text{ s}}{1 \text{ min}} \right) + 23 \text{ s} = 2483 \text{ s}$$

The distance of the race in kilometers is

$$10.0 \text{ km} \times \frac{1000 \text{ m}}{\text{km}} = 1.00 \times 10^4 \text{ m}$$

The runner's average speed then is

$$\frac{1 \times 10^4 \text{ m}}{2483 \text{ s}} = 4.0 \text{ m/s}$$

Think about It
The answer makes sense because a walking speed is around 3 mph, or 1.3 m/s. Running could easily be imagined at 9 mph, or 4.0 m/s.

1.51. **Collect and Organize**
In this problem we need to use the density of magnesium to find the mass of a specific size block of the metal.

Analyze
Density is defined as the mass of a substance per unit volume. Appendix 3 gives the density of magnesium as 1.738 g/cm^3. We have to find the volume of the block of magnesium by multiplying the length by the height by the depth (this will be in cubic centimeters). We can then find mass through the following formula:

$$\text{mass (g)} = \text{density (g/cm}^3) \times \text{volume (cm}^3)$$

Solve
The volume of the block of magnesium is

$$2.5 \text{ cm} \times 3.5 \text{ cm} \times 1.5 \text{ cm} = 13 \text{ cm}^3$$

Therefore, the mass of the block is

$$13 \text{ cm}^3 \times 1.738 \text{ g/cm}^3 = 23 \text{ g}$$

Think about It

The mass of a sample depends on how much there is of a substance. Here we have about 23 g. For a quick estimate, a block of magnesium of about 10 cm^3 would weigh more than 1.7 times that of 1 cm^3, or 17 g. Because we have more than 10 cm^3 of this sample and the density is a little greater than 1.7 g/cm^3, our answer of 23 g is reasonable.

1.53. Collect and Organize

In this problem we use the density to find the volume of sulfuric acid required by the chemist. This situation uses the definition density = mass/volume.

Analyze

We can easily solve this problem by rearranging the density equation:

$$\text{density} = \frac{\text{mass}}{\text{volume}} \quad \text{or} \quad \text{volume} = \frac{\text{mass}}{\text{density}}$$

Solve

$$\text{volume needed} = \frac{35.0 \text{ g}}{1.84 \text{ g/mL}} = 19.0 \text{ mL}$$

Think about It

With a density of about 2 g/cm^3 to get a mass of about 40 g, we might estimate we would need 20 mL. This estimate shows that our answer is reasonable.

1.55. Collect and Organize

This problem asks for the conversion of weights: from ounces to grams and then to kilograms.

Analyze

Conversions for weight (mass) that are needed are

$$\frac{1 \text{ oz}}{28.35 \text{ g}} \quad \text{and} \quad \frac{1 \text{ kg}}{1000 \text{ g}}$$

Solve

$$0.934 \text{ oz} \times \frac{28.35 \text{ g}}{1 \text{ oz}} = 26.5 \text{ g}$$

$$26.5 \text{ g} \times \frac{1 \text{ kg}}{1000 \text{ g}} = 0.0265 \text{ kg}$$

Think about It

Because the silver dollar weighs just under an ounce, its mass will be slightly less than 28.35 g, so our answer of 26.5 g makes sense.

1.57. Collect and Organize

To answer this question we need to use the density of copper to compute the mass of the copper sample that is 125 cm^3 in volume. Next, we use that mass to find out how much volume (in cubic centimeters) that mass of gold would occupy.

Analyze

We need the density both of copper and of gold from Appendix 3 to make the conversions from volume to mass (for copper) and then from mass to volume (for gold). These densities are 8.96 g/mL for copper and 19.3 g/mL for gold. One milliliter is equivalent to 1 cm^3, so the densities are 8.96 g/cm^3 and 19.3 g/cm^3, respectively. The density formulas that we need are

$$\text{mass of copper} = \text{density of copper} \times \text{volume}$$

$$\text{volume of gold} = \frac{\text{mass}}{\text{density of gold}}$$

Solve

$$\text{mass of copper} = 8.96 \text{ g/cm}^3 \times 125 \text{ cm}^3 = 1120 \text{ g}$$

$$\text{volume of gold} = \frac{1120 \text{ g}}{19.3 \text{ g/cm}^3} = 58.0 \text{ cm}^3$$

Think about It
Because gold is more than twice as dense as copper, we would expect the volume of a gold sample to have about half the volume of that of the same mass of copper.

1.59. **Collect and Organize**
Using the density of mercury, we can find the volume of 1.00 kg of mercury.

Analyze
Appendix 3 gives the density of mercury as 13.546 g/mL. Because this property is expressed in grams per milliliter, not kilograms per milliliter, we have to convert kilograms into grams by using the conversion factor

$$\frac{1000 \text{ g}}{1 \text{ kg}}$$

Once we have the mass in grams, we can use the rearranged formula for density to find volume:

$$\text{volume of mercury (mL)} = \frac{\text{mass of mercury (g)}}{\text{density of mercury (g/mL)}}$$

Solve

$$1.00 \text{ kg} \times \frac{1000 \text{ g}}{1 \text{ kg}} = 1.00 \times 10^3 \text{ g}$$

$$\text{volume of mercury} = \frac{1.00 \times 10^3 \text{ g}}{13.546 \text{ g/mL}} = 73.8 \text{ mL}$$

Think about It
This result is a fairly small amount that weighs 1 kg. This value is due to the relatively high density of mercury.

1.61. **Collect and Organize**
Because we are not directly given the mass and volume of the two planets, Earth and Venus, we have to use their relative masses and volumes to find the density of Venus compared with that of Earth.

Analyze
The relative masses and volumes of the two planets can be expressed as

$$\text{volume of Venus} = 0.88 \times \text{volume of Earth}$$

$$\text{mass of Venus} = 0.815 \times \text{mass of Earth}$$

To find the density of Venus, we will have to rearrange these into

$$\frac{\text{mass of Earth}}{\text{volume of Earth}} \times \frac{\text{volume of Earth}}{\text{volume of Venus}} \times \frac{\text{mass of Venus}}{\text{mass of Earth}} = \frac{\text{mass of Venus}}{\text{volume of Venus}}$$

or

$$\text{density of Earth} \times \frac{100}{88} \times \frac{81.5}{100} = \text{density of Venus}$$

Solve

$$\frac{5.5 \text{ g}}{\text{cm}^3} \times \frac{100}{88} \times \frac{81.5}{100} = 5.1 \text{ g/cm}^3$$

Think about It

With Earth being larger than Venus, and more massive, immediately predicting whether Venus would be more or less dense than Earth is hard. However, because the difference in the mass (18.5%) between Earth and Venus is greater than the difference in volume (12%), it makes sense that the density of Venus is lower than that of Earth.

1.63. Collect and Organize

To determine whether the high-density polyethylene (HDPE) will float on water, we need to compare the density of the HDPE with that of water. If its density is less than water's, the HDPE will float.

Analyze

To compare the densities of the two substances (water and HDPE), we need to have them in the same units. We can approach this in either of two ways—convert the seawater density to kilograms per cubic meter or convert the HDPE density to grams per cubic centimeter. Let's do the latter, using the following conversions:

$$\frac{100 \text{ cm}}{1 \text{ m}} \quad \text{and} \quad \frac{1000 \text{ g}}{1 \text{ kg}}$$

To calculate the density of the HDPE sample, we must divide the mass of the cube of HDPE in grams by the volume in cubic centimeters.

Solve

$$\text{volume of the HDPE cube} = \left(1.20 \times 10^{-2} \text{ m}\right)^3 \times \left(\frac{100 \text{ cm}}{1 \text{ m}}\right)^3 = 1.728 \text{ cm}^3$$

$$\text{mass of the HDPE cube in grams} = 1.70 \times 10^{-3} \text{ kg} \times \frac{1000 \text{ g}}{1 \text{ kg}} = 1.70 \text{ g}$$

$$\text{density of the HDPE cube} = \frac{1.70 \text{ g}}{1.728 \text{ cm}^3} = 0.984 \text{ g/cm}^3$$

This density is less than the density of the seawater (1.03 g/cm^3), so the cube of HDPE will float on water.

Think about It

Certainly boats are made of other materials (such as iron) that are denser than water. These boats float because the mass of the water they displace is greater than their mass.

1.65. Collect and Organize

In this problem we use the mass of a carat (the unit of weight for diamonds) to find the mass of a large diamond and then use the density to calculate the volume of that large diamond.

Analyze

We need the fact that 1 carat = 0.200 g and that density is defined as mass per unit volume. To find the volume of the diamond, we can rearrange the density equation to read

$$\text{volume} = \frac{\text{mass}}{\text{density}}$$

Solve

The mass of the 5.0 carat diamond is

$$5.0 \text{ carat} \times \frac{0.200 \text{ g}}{1 \text{ carat}} = 1.0 \text{ g}$$

The volume of the diamond is then

$$\frac{1.0 \text{ g}}{3.51 \text{ g/cm}^3} = 0.28 \text{ cm}^3$$

Think about It
For this relatively large diamond in terms of carats, the mass is fairly small (1 g is about 1/5 of the mass of a nickel), and so even though the density is relatively low, the volume is also quite small.

1.67. Collect and Organize
Given the experimental data for three different techniques to measure the sodium content of a candy bar, we are to determine which techniques were precise and which were accurate.

Analyze
Precise measurements have a narrow numerical range and describe the agreement of repeated measurements. Accurate measurements give an average measurement that is close to the actual value.

Solve
Techniques 1 and 3 are both precise since their values do not vary by more than ±1 mg. Because the true value is 115 mg, Technique 3 is obviously accurate as well as precise. The average of the not-very-precise Technique 2 (115 mg), however, also agrees with the true value, so this technique is also accurate. Techniques 1 and 3 have a range of 2 mg for their measurements, whereas Technique 2 has a range of 10 mg.

Think about It
Remember that you can be accurate without being precise, and you can be precise without being accurate. In making lab measurements, you can calibrate instruments and learn the technique well (with lots of practice) to obtain data that are both accurate and precise.

1.69. Collect and Organize
For each quantity given, we choose those that contain three significant figures.

Analyze
Writing all the quantities in scientific notation will help determine the number of significant figures in each.
(a) 7.02
(b) 6.452
(c) $302 = 3.02 \times 10^2$
(d) 6.02×10^{23}
(e) $12.77 = 1.277 \times 10^1$
(f) 3.43

Solve
The quantities that have three significant figures are (a) 7.02, (c) 302, (d) 6.02×10^{23}, and (f) 3.43.

Think about It
Remember that a zero between two other digits is always significant.

1.71. Collect and Organize
We are to express the result of each calculation to the correct number of significant figures.

Analyze
Section 1.8 in the textbook gives the rules regarding the significant figures that carry over in calculations. Remember to operate on the weak-link principle.

Solve
(a) The least well-known value has three significant figures, so the calculator result of 17.363 is reported as 17.4 with rounding up the tenths place.
(b) The least well-known value has only one significant figure, so the calculator result of 1.044×10^{-13} is reported as 1×10^{-13}.

(c) The least well-known value has three significant figures, so the calculator result of 5.701×10^{-23} is reported as 5.70×10^{-23}.

(d) The least well-known value has three significant figures, so the calculator result of 3.5837×10^{-3} is reported as 3.58×10^{-3} with rounding.

Think about It

Indicating the correct number of significant figures for a calculated value indicates the level of confidence we have in our calculated value. Reporting too many significant figures would indicate a higher level of precision in our number than we actually have.

1.73. Collect and Organize

For this question we are to think about why scientists might prefer the Celsius scale over the Fahrenheit scale.

Analyze

The Celsius scale is based on a 100-degree range between the freezing point and boiling point of water, whereas the Fahrenheit scale is based on the 100-degree range between the freezing point of a concentrated salt solution and the average internal human body temperature.

Solve

Scientists might prefer the Celsius scale because it is based on the phase changes (freezing and boiling) for a pure common solvent (water).

Think about It

Because the difference in the freezing and boiling point of water on the Fahrenheit scale is 180 degrees compared with the Celsius scale of 100 degrees, one degree Fahrenheit is smaller than one degree Celsius. Notice in Figure A1.73 that a 10°C range is much larger than a 10°F range.

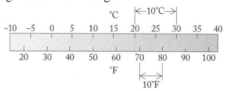

Figure A1.73

1.75. Collect and Organize

In this question we define the *absolute* temperature scale.

Analyze

The Kelvin scale is the absolute temperature scale, and its lowest temperature is 0 K.

Solve

The absolute temperature scale (Kelvin scale) has no negative temperatures, and its zero value is placed at the lowest possible temperature.

Think about It

Because the Kelvin scale has no negative temperatures, it will often be used in equations when using a negative temperature (in Celsius) would result in a nonsensical answer.

1.77. Collect and Organize

We are asked in this problem to convert from kelvins to Celsius degrees.

Analyze

The relationship between the Kelvin temperature scale and the Celsius temperature scale is given by

$$K = {}^\circ C + 273.15$$

Rearranging this gives the equation to convert Kelvin to Celsius temperatures:
$$°C = K - 273.15$$

Solve

$$°C = 4.2 \ K - 273.15 = -269.0\ °C$$

Think about It

Because 4.2 K is very cold, we would expect that the Celsius temperature would be very negative. It should not, however, be lower than –273.15 K, since that is the lowest temperature possible.

1.79. ### Collect and Organize

Given the boiling point of ethyl chloride in degrees Celsius, we are to compute the boiling point in °F and K.

Analyze

The relationship between the Kelvin temperature scale and the Celsius temperature scale is given by
$$K = °C + 273.15$$
The relationship between the Celsius and Fahrenheit temperature scales is given by
$$°C = \frac{5}{9}\left(°F - 32\right)$$
We will have to rearrange this expression to find °F from °C:
$$°F = \frac{9}{5}\left(°C\right) + 32$$

Solve

The boiling point of ethyl chloride in the Fahrenheit and Kelvin scales is
$$K = 12.3\ °C + 273.15 = 285.4 \ K$$
$$°F = \frac{9}{5}\left(12.3\ °C\right) + 32 = 54.1\ °F$$

Think about It

Notice that the answer is reported to four significant figures for the temperature in Kelvin and to two significant figures for the temperature in Fahrenheit because of the addition and multiplication rule.

1.81. ### Collect and Organize

This question asks us to convert the coldest temperature recorded on Earth from Fahrenheit to Celsius degrees and kelvins.

Analyze

Since the Celsius and Kelvin scales are similar (offset by 273.15°), once we convert from Fahrenheit to Celsius, finding the Kelvin temperature will be straightforward. The equations we need are
$$°C = \frac{5}{9}\left(°F - 32\right)$$
$$K = °C + 273.15$$

Solve

$$°C = \frac{5}{9}\left(-128.6\ °F - 32\right) = -89.2\ °C$$
$$K = -89.2\ °C + 273.15 = 183.9 \ K$$

Think about It

This temperature is cold on any scale!

1.83. **Collect and Organize**

We are asked to compare the critical temperature (T_c) of three superconductors. The critical temperatures, however, are given in three different temperature scales, so for the comparison, we will need to convert them to a single scale.

Analyze

Which temperature scale we use as the common one does not matter, but since the critical temperatures are low, expressing all the temperatures in kelvins might be easiest. The equations we will need are

$$K = {}^\circ C + 273.15 \quad \text{and} \quad {}^\circ C = \frac{5}{9}\left({}^\circ F - 32\right)$$

Solve

The T_c for $YBa_2Cu_3O_7$ is already expressed in kelvins, $T_c = 93.0$ K.
The T_c of Nb_3Ge is expressed in degrees Celsius and can be converted to kelvins by

$$K = -250.0\,{}^\circ C + 273.15 = 23.2 \text{ K}$$

The T_c of $HgBa_2CaCu_2O_6$ is expressed in Fahrenheit degrees. To get this temperature in kelvins, first convert to Celsius degrees:

$$ {}^\circ C = \frac{5}{9}\left(-231.1\,{}^\circ F - 32\right) = -146.2\,{}^\circ C$$

$$K = -146.2\,{}^\circ C + 273.15 = 127.0 \text{ K}$$

The superconductor with the highest T_c is $HgBa_2CaCu_2O_6$ with a T_c of 127.0 K.

Think about It

The superconductor with the lowest T_c is Nb_3Ge with a T_c of 23.2 K, more than 100 K lower than the T_c of $HgBa_2CaCu_2O_6$.

1.85. **Collect and Organize**

This question considers the runoff of nitrogen every year into a stream caused by a farmer's application of fertilizer. We must consider that not all the fertilizer contains nitrogen and not all the fertilizer runs off into the stream. We must also account for the flow of the stream in taking up the nitrogen runoff.

Analyze

First, we have to determine the amount of nitrogen in the fertilizer (10% of 1.50 metric tons, or 1500 kg since 1 metric ton = 1000 kg). Then, we need to find how much of that nitrogen gets washed into the stream (15% of the mass of N in the fertilizer). Our final answer must be in milligrams of N, so we can convert the mass of N that gets washed into the stream from kilograms to milligrams.

$$\text{mass of fertilizer in kg} \times 0.10 = \text{mass of N in fertilizer in kg}$$

$$\text{mass of N in fertilizer in kg} \times 0.15 = \text{mass of N washed into the stream in kg}$$

$$\text{mass of N that washes into the stream in kg} \times \frac{1000 \text{ g}}{1 \text{ kg}} \times \frac{1000 \text{ mg}}{1 \text{ g}} = \text{mass of N that washes into the stream in mg}$$

Next, we need to know how much water flows through the farm each year via the stream. To find this, we must convert the rate of flow in cubic meters per minute to liters per year. We can convert this through one line by using dimensional analysis with the following conversions:

$$\frac{1000 \text{ L}}{1 \text{ m}^3}, \quad \frac{1 \text{ hr}}{60 \text{ min}}, \quad \frac{1 \text{ d}}{24 \text{ hr}}, \quad \text{and} \quad \frac{1 \text{ yr}}{365.25 \text{ d}}$$

Solve

The amount of N washed into the stream each year is

$$1500 \text{ kg} \times 0.10 = 150 \text{ kg N in the fertilizer}$$

$$150 \text{ kg} \times 0.15 = 22.5 \text{ kg N washed into the stream in one year}$$

$$22.5 \text{ kg} \times \frac{1000 \text{ g}}{1 \text{ kg}} \times \frac{1000 \text{ mg}}{1 \text{ g}} = 2.25 \times 10^7 \text{ mg of N washed into the stream in one year}$$

The amount of stream water flowing through the field each year is

$$\frac{1.4 \text{ m}^3}{1 \text{ min}} \times \frac{1000 \text{ L}}{1 \text{ m}^3} \times \frac{60 \text{ min}}{1 \text{ hr}} \times \frac{24 \text{ hr}}{1 \text{ d}} \times \frac{365.25 \text{ d}}{1 \text{ yr}} = 7.36 \times 10^8 \text{ L/yr}$$

The additional concentration of N added to the stream by the fertilizer is

$$\frac{2.25 \times 10^7 \text{ mg N/yr}}{7.36 \times 10^8 \text{ L/yr}} = 0.031 \text{ mg/L}$$

Think about It

The calculated amount of nitrogen added to the stream seems reasonable. The concentration is relatively low because the stream is moving fairly swiftly and the total amount of nitrogen that washes into the stream over the year is not too great. The problem, however, does not tell us whether this amount would harm the plant and animal life in the stream.

1.87. **Collect and Organize**

In this problem we need to express each mixture of chlorine and sodium as a ratio. The mixture closest to the ratio for chlorine to sodium will be the one with the desired product, leaving neither sodium nor chlorine left over.

Analyze

First, we must calculate the ratio of chlorine to sodium in sodium chloride. This is a simple ratio of the masses of these two substances:

$$\frac{\text{mass of chlorine}}{\text{mass of sodium}} = \text{ratio of the two components}$$

We can compare the ratios of the other mixtures by making the same calculations.

Solve

In sodium chloride, the mass ratio of chlorine to sodium is

$$\frac{1.54 \text{ g of chlorine}}{1.00 \text{ g of sodium}} = 1.54$$

Repeating this calculation for the four mixtures, we obtain the ratio of chlorine to sodium:

$$\frac{17.0 \text{ g}}{11.0 \text{ g}} = 1.55 \text{ for mixture a} \qquad \frac{12.0 \text{ g}}{6.5 \text{ g}} = 1.8 \text{ for mixture c}$$

$$\frac{10.0 \text{ g}}{6.5 \text{ g}} = 1.5 \text{ for mixture b} \qquad \frac{8.0 \text{ g}}{6.5 \text{ g}} = 1.2 \text{ for mixture d}$$

Both mixtures a and b react so that neither sodium nor chlorine is left over.

Think about It

Mixture c has leftover chlorine and mixture d has leftover sodium after the reaction is complete.

1.89. **Collect and Organize**

This problem asks us to compute the percentages of the two ingredients in trail mix as manufactured on different days.

Analyze

Because we compare each day's percentage of peanuts in the trail mix bags to the ideal range of 65%–69%, we have to compute each day's percentage of peanuts from the data given. Each day has a total of 82 peanuts plus raisins, so the percentage of the mix in peanuts for each day is calculated by the equation

$$\% \text{ peanuts} = \frac{\text{number of peanuts in mix}}{82} \times 100$$

Solve

For each day, the percent peanuts is

$$\frac{50}{82} \times 100 = 61\% \text{ peanuts, Day 1} \qquad \frac{48}{82} \times 100 = 59\% \text{ peanuts, Day 21}$$

$$\frac{56}{82} \times 100 = 68\% \text{ peanuts, Day 11} \qquad \frac{52}{82} \times 100 = 63\% \text{ peanuts, Day 31}$$

The only day that met the specifications for the percentage of peanuts in the trail mix was Day 11.

Think about It

On Days 1, 21, and 31, too few peanuts were in the trail mix.

1.91. **Collect and Organize**

Given the correct dosage of phenobarbital per day and the details of the drug given to a patient over 3 days, we are to determine how many times over the prescribed dose was given to an overdose patient.

Analyze

We can use a common unit of milligrams of the drug to compare the prescribed amount with the overdose amount. To do so we will have to convert 0.5 grains into milligrams and multiply by the 3 days the drug was given. The actual amount given to the patient was four times 130 mg. We can then compare these two dosages in a ratio.

Solve

Amount of phenobarbital prescribed for 3 days in milligrams:

$$\frac{0.5 \text{ grains}}{\text{day}} \times \frac{64.7981 \text{ mg}}{\text{grain}} \times 3 \text{ days} = 97.1984 \text{ mg}$$

Actual amount given to patient in four doses:

$$\frac{130 \text{ mg}}{\text{dose}} \times 4 \text{ doses} = 520 \text{ mg}$$

Ratio of actual dose to prescribed dose for 3 days:

$$\frac{520 \text{ mg}}{97.2 \text{ mg}} = 5 \text{ times too much phenobarbital was given}$$

Think about It

An overdose of such a powerful sedative as phenobarbital can be fatal. Symptoms include shallow breathing, extreme sleepiness, and blurry vision.

1.93. **Collect and Organize**

Given the temperatures for the freezing point and boiling point of water measured using three digital hospital thermometers, we are to determine which ones could detect a 0.1°C increase in temperature and which would give an accurate reading of normal body temperature of 36.8°C.

Analyze

(a) To detect a 0.1°C temperature rise, the scale on the thermometer would not have to be expanded over the range so that the 0.1°C could be detected (the thermometers all read only to the tenth of a degree). However, if the temperature scale for the thermometer is contracted, it will detect the 0.1°C temperature change because its intervals of 0.1°C are smaller.

(b) To determine whether any of the thermometers can accurately measure a temperature of 36.8°C, we need to consider the calibration curves (constructed by comparing the measured freezing and boiling points with the actual—that is, by plotting the correct temperatures vs. the measured temperatures). From the equation for the line, we can solve for the reading on the thermometer when the actual temperature is 36.8°C.

Solve

(a) Both thermometer A, with a total range of 100.2°C, and thermometer C, with a total range of 100.6°C, have expanded ranges and therefore would not be able to detect a 0.1°C temperature change. However, thermometer B, with a total range of 99.6°C, and therefore a compressed range, will be able to detect the 0.1°C temperature change.

(b) The calibration curves for all three thermometers are shown below. In each graph, the slope is derived from the actual range of the freezing point and boiling point of water (100–0°C, Δy) and the range for the particular thermometer for these points (Δx).

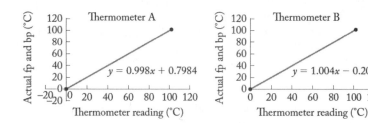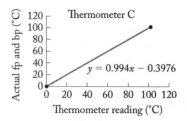

The equation of the line gives the calibration equation for us to use in the calculation of the temperature each thermometer would read (x) for the actual temperature of 36.8°C (y).

For thermometer A:
$$36.8°C = 0.998x + {-}0.8$$
$$x = 37.0°C$$

For thermometer B:
$$36.8°C = 1.004x + 0.2$$
$$x = 35.2°C$$

For thermometer C:
$$36.8°C = 0.994x + 0.4$$
$$x = 36.6°C$$

None of these thermometers can accurately read the patient's temperature as 36.8°C.

Think about It

Thermometer C comes closest in accuracy at body temperature despite appearing to always read high from its range of 0.4 to 101.0°C.

CHAPTER 2 | Atoms, Ions, and Molecules: The Building Blocks of Matter

2.1. Collect and Organize

This question asks us to recall which elements were formed after the Big Bang and before galaxies formed, and to correlate those elements' identities with their position on the periodic table.

Analyze

We read in the chapter that after the Big Bang and initial cooling of the universe, protons and neutrons fused to form ^2H (an isotope of hydrogen), which then could fuse with another ^2H to form ^4He.

Solve

Were other elements produced by fusion from ^4He and ^1H? We read that the next heavier elements (^5Li and ^8Be) were not formed because these particular isotopes are unstable. Elements other than hydrogen and helium weren't produced until galaxies formed. The position of hydrogen on the periodic table is the first element under group 1. This element is shaded purple in the periodic table in Figure P2.1. Helium is the second element on the periodic table and is positioned as the first element in group 18. This is the element shaded dark blue in the periodic table.

Think about It

The heavy elements that make up the universe, and Earth in particular, have to be made in dense stars that support nucleosynthesis through processes such as neutron capture, α particle fusion, and β decay.

2.3. Collect and Organize

We are asked to identify which shaded element in Figure P2.1 is stable and yet has no neutrons in its nucleus.

Analyze

The presence of neutrons in nuclei helps to overcome the repulsive forces of more than one proton in the nucleus.

Solve

The only shaded element that does not have more than one proton in its nucleus and therefore would be stable without neutrons is the element shaded purple, hydrogen.

Think about It

Without the neutrons, the nuclei with more than one proton would fly apart.

2.5. Collect and Organize

For this question we need to correlate properties of the elements with their positions in the periodic table. We need to use the definition of *inert* and know the general regions of the periodic table that have gaseous, metallic, and nonmetallic elements.

Analyze

Inert means that the chemical species does not (or does not readily) combine with other species. Here we are looking for elements that are relatively unreactive as a group; these are the noble gases. On the periodic table, metallic elements tend to be on the left-hand side; nonmetallic elements are on the right-hand side. The gases tend to be in groups 18 (noble gases) and 17 (the halogens: fluorine and chlorine) along with oxygen, nitrogen, and hydrogen. Of these gases, the noble gases are monatomic, but the others are all diatomic (N_2, O_2, H_2, F_2, Cl_2).

Solve

In the periodic table shown in Figure P2.4, elements Na, Ne, Cl, Au, and Lr are highlighted.
(a) Chlorine (Cl_2) is a diatomic gas at room temperature (yellow). It is a nonmetal.
(b) Neon (Ne) is a chemically inert gas (red).
(c) Sodium (Na, dark blue), gold (Au, green), and lawrencium (Lr, orange) are all metals.

Think about It
Gold and lawrencium are different from sodium (which is highly reactive) as metals. Gold can be found as an element in nature and is not very reactive, and lawrencium is radioactive and synthesized in small amounts; therefore, its chemistry is relatively unexplored.

2.7. **Collect and Organize**
Using Figure P2.7 and our knowledge of the charges and the masses of α and β particles, we are to determine which arrow (red, blue, or green) represents each particle's behavior as it moves through an electric field.

Analyze
Alpha particles are much more massive than β particles and they have a positive charge, whereas β particles have a negative charge.

Solve
Alpha particles, with their positive charges, will be deflected toward the negative side of the electric field. Their behavior is represented by the red arrow. Beta particles, however, are deflected toward the positive side of the electric field because they carry a negative charge; they are represented by the green arrow. Notice, too, that the α particles travel farther and with less arc in their deflection than the lighter beta particles. This is because with their heavier mass, their momentum through the electric field is higher and it would take a stronger field to deflect them to the same degree.

Think about It
The blue arrow must represent a particle that is neutral, because it is not deflected by the electric field.

2.9. **Collect and Organize**
This question asks us to correlate the position of an element in the periodic table with typical charges on the ions for the groups (or families) of elements.

Analyze
Figure 2.10 in the textbook shows the common charges on the elements used in forming compounds. That figure will help us to answer which elements in monatomic form give the charges named in the question.

Solve
Highlighted elements in Figure P2.6 are K, Mg, Sc, Ag, O, and I.
(a) Elements in group 1 form 1+ ions, so K will form K^+ (dark blue). Silver (green) also typically forms a 1+ cation.
(b) Elements in group 2 form 2+ ions, so Mg forms Mg^{2+} (gray).
(c) Elements in group 3 form 3+ ions, so Sc forms Sc^{3+} (yellow).
(d) Elements in group 17 (the halogens) form 1– ions, so I forms I^- (purple).
(e) Elements in group 16 form 2– ions, so O forms O^{2-} (red).

Think about It
Elements on the left-hand side of the periodic table form cations, and the ones on the right-hand side tend to form anions.

2.11. **Collect and Organize**
In this question we are asked to explain how Rutherford's gold-foil experiment changed the plum-pudding model of the atom.

Analyze
The plum-pudding model of the atom viewed the electrons as small particles in a diffuse, positively charged "pudding." In Rutherford's experiment, most of the α particles (positively charged particles) directed at the gold foil went straight through, but a few of them bounced back toward the source of the α particles.

Solve

From his experiments, Rutherford concluded that the positive charge in the atom could not be spread out (the pudding) in the atom but instead must result from a concentration of charge in the center of the atom (the nucleus). Most of the α particles were deflected only slightly or passed directly through the gold foil, so he reasoned that the nucleus must be small compared with the size of the entire atom. The negatively charged electrons did not deflect the α particles, and Rutherford reasoned that the electrons took up the rest of the space of the atom outside the nucleus.

Think about It

The nucleus is about 10^{-15} m in diameter, whereas the atom is about 10^{-10} m. This size difference has often been compared to "a fly in a cathedral."

2.13. Collect and Organize

In this question we are to explain how J. J. Thomson discovered that cathode rays were not pure energy but were actually particles.

Analyze

Thomson's experiment directed the cathode ray through a magnetic field, and he discovered that the ray was deflected. A magnetic field would not deflect pure energy "rays."

Solve

When Thomson observed cathode rays being deflected by a magnetic field, he reasoned that the rays were streams of charged particles because only moving charged particles would interact with a magnetic field. Pure energy rays would not.

Think about It

Thomson's discovery of the electron in cathode rays did not eliminate the use of the term *cathode ray*. CRTs (cathode-ray tubes) are the traditional (not LCD) television and computer screens.

2.15. Collect and Organize

Helium is found in pitchblende, an ore found on Earth. We are asked to explain why the helium is present in the ore.

Analyze

Pitchblende contains uranium oxide, and uranium is a naturally occurring radioactive element.

Solve

The helium is present because uranium (and some of its products of further decays) decays by α emission. Alpha particles, composed of two protons and two neutrons, easily pick up electrons from their environment to become helium.

Think about It

All the helium on Earth is generated in this fashion and trapped. Helium, though, once in the atmosphere, escapes into space because it is so light.

2.17. Collect and Organize

This question asks us to consider the ratio of neutrons to protons in an element where we are given the fact that the mass number is more than twice the atomic number.

Analyze

We can find the number of neutrons for an isotope by relating the number of protons to the mass number. From that result we can then determine the neutron-to-proton ratio.

Solve

We are given an isotope in which the mass number is more than twice the number of protons. With m being the mass number and p the number of protons, we can express this relationship as

$$m > 2p$$

The mass number is also equal to the number of protons plus the number of neutrons (n),

$$m = p + n$$

Combining these expressions

$$p + n > 2p$$

and solving for n gives

$$n > 2p - p$$
$$n > p$$

Therefore, the number of neutrons in this isotope is greater than the number of protons, and the neutron-to-proton ratio is greater than 1.

Think about It

We wouldn't have had to express the relationships between the nuclear particles mathematically if the isotope had a mass number equal to twice the number of protons. Then the number of neutrons would have to be the same as the number of protons, giving a neutron-to-proton ratio of 1:1.

2.19. Collect and Organize

Given that most stable nuclides have at least equal numbers of neutrons in their nuclei as protons (and often more), we are to identify the element to which this rule is an exception.

Analyze

Neutrons help stabilize the nucleus by counteracting the repulsive forces between protons.

Solve

Hydrogen, with only one proton, does not need neutrons to be stable and so is the exception.

Think about It

Hydrogen, however, can have one (for deuterium) and even two (for tritium) neutrons in its nucleus.

2.21. Collect and Organize

For each element in this question, we must look at the relationship of the neutrons, protons, and electrons. We need to determine the element's atomic number from the periodic table and, from the mass number given for the isotope, compute the number of neutrons to give that isotope.

Analyze

An isotope is given by the symbol $^A_Z X$, where X is the element symbol from the periodic table, Z is the atomic number (the number of protons in the nucleus), and A is the mass number (the number of protons and neutrons in the nucleus). Often, Z is omitted because the element symbol gives us the same information about the identity of the element. To determine the number of neutrons in the nucleus for each named isotope, we subtract Z (number of protons) from A (mass number). If the elements are neutral (no charge), the number of electrons equals the number of protons in the nucleus.

Solve

	Atom	Mass Number	Atomic Number = Number of Protons	Number of Neutrons = Mass Number – Atomic Number	Number of Electrons = Number of Protons
(a)	^{14}C	14	6	8	6
(b)	^{59}Fe	59	26	33	26
(c)	^{90}Sr	90	38	52	38
(d)	^{210}Pb	210	82	128	82

Think about It
Isotopes of an element contain the same number of protons but a different number of neutrons. Thus, isotopes have different masses.

2.23. Collect and Organize
To fill in the table, we have to consider how the numbers of nuclear particles relate to each other. We also need to recall how the symbols for the isotopes are written. From the table, it is apparent that we have to work backward in some cases from the number of electrons or protons and mass number for the element symbol.

Analyze
An isotope is given by the symbol $_{Z}^{A}X$, where X is the element symbol from the periodic table, Z is the atomic number (the number of protons in the nucleus), and A is the mass number (the number of protons and neutrons in the nucleus). We can determine the number of neutrons in the nucleus for the isotopes by subtracting Z (number of protons) from A (mass number). If the elements are neutral (no charge), the number of electrons equals the number of protons in the nucleus.

Solve

Symbol	^{23}Na	^{89}Y	^{118}Sn	^{197}Au
Number of Protons	11	39	50	79
Number of Neutrons	12	50	68	118
Number of Electrons	11	39	50	79
Mass Number	23	89	118	197

Think about It
Because the nuclear particles are all related to each other, we can either work from the isotope symbol to find the number of protons, neutrons, and electrons for a particular isotope, or we can work from the mass number and the number of electrons or protons to determine the number of neutrons and write the element symbol.

2.25. Collect and Organize
An isotope is given by the symbol $_{Z}^{A}X^{n}$, where X is the element symbol from the periodic table, Z is the atomic number (the number of protons in the nucleus), A is the mass number (the number of protons and neutrons in the nucleus), and n is the charge on the species.

Analyze
If we are given the number of protons in the nucleus, the element can be identified from the periodic table. We can determine the mass number by adding the protons to the neutrons in the nucleus for the isotope. We can determine the number of neutrons or protons in the nucleus for the isotopes by subtracting Z (number of protons) or the number of neutrons from A (mass number), respectively. We can account for the charge on the species by adding electrons (to form a negatively charged ion) or by subtracting electrons (to form a positively charged ion).

Solve

Symbol	$^{37}Cl^{-}$	$^{23}Na^{+}$	$^{81}Br^{-}$	$^{226}Ra^{2+}$
Number of Protons	17	11	35	88
Number of Neutrons	20	12	46	138
Number of Electrons	18	10	36	86
Mass Number	37	23	81	226

Think about It
To form a singly charged ion, there has to be one electron more (for a negative charge) or one electron less (for a positive charge) than the number of protons in the nucleus. For a doubly charged ion, we add or take away two electrons.

2.27. Collect and Organize

Knowing that Mendeleev labeled his groups on the left of the periodic table on the basis of the formulas of the compounds they formed with oxygen, we are to assign his labels to groups 2, 3, and 4 on the modern periodic table.

Analyze

Groups 2, 3, and 4 have cations of 2+, 3+, and 4+, respectively. Oxygen forms an anion of 2– charge. The oxygen compounds that would form would balance the positive cation charge with the negative anion charge by combining the elements in that group with oxygen in whole-number ratios.

Solve

Group 2, with a 2+ charge, would form RO with oxygen; group 3, with a 3+ charge, would form an R_2O_3 compound with oxygen; and group 4, with a 4+ charge, would form an RO_2 compound with oxygen.

Think about It

This classification was based on the chemical behavior of the elements, which was Mendeleev's brilliant insight.

2.29. Collect and Organize

We are asked why Mendeleev did not leave spaces for the noble gases in his periodic system.

Analyze

The noble gases are characterized by their remarkable unreactivity. Unreactive elements can be quite unnoticeable because they do not form compounds with other elements.

Solve

The noble gases were not discovered until after Mendeleev put together his periodic table. He also could not have predicted the existence of the noble gases at the time since (a) none of them was isolated and characterized on the basis of their reactivity (or lack thereof) and (b) he arranged the elements in order of increasing mass, not atomic number. If he had been aware of atomic numbers as characteristic of the elements, he would have noticed that the atomic numbers for the noble gases were missing as a column in his table.

Think about It

The noble gases are monatomic, are colorless and odorless, and have a remarkably narrow liquid range (their boiling points and melting points are close together).

2.31. Collect and Organize

Knowing that the explosive TNT contains second-row elements in groups 14, 15, and 16 as well as hydrogen, we are to name those particular elements.

Analyze

The second-row elements start with lithium and end at neon.

Solve

The elements in TNT besides hydrogen are carbon (group 14), nitrogen (group 15), and oxygen (group 16).

Think about It

Many explosives have the same elements. The powerful C4 explosive is composed mainly of the explosive RDX_2, which has the chemical formula $C_3H_6N_6O_6$.

2.33. Collect and Organize

Given information about the elements (their group numbers and relationship to each other in the periodic table) used in catalytic converters, we are to name the elements.

Analyze

In examining the clues in parts a–c, we can guess that these will all be transition metals.

Solve

(a) The element in the fifth row of the periodic table (Rb–Xe) in group 10 is palladium (Pd).
(b) The element to the left of Pd in group 9 is rhodium (Rh).
(c) The element below Pd in group 10 is platinum (Pt).

Think about It

These metals are generally as expensive as gold. Platinum is about \$1400/oz and gold is about \$1200/oz. Rhodium and palladium are less expensive, at about \$1000/oz and \$700/oz, respectively.

2.35. Collect and Organize

For the elements in the third row of the periodic table, we are to count the metallic elements.

Analyze

The third row in the periodic table begins at sodium and ends at argon. The semimetal elements begin at silicon and move into the nonmetals with phosphorus.

Solve

Three metallic elements are in the third row in the periodic table: sodium (Na), magnesium (Mg), and aluminum (Al).

Think about It

As a semimetal, silicon has some, but not all, the properties of a metal but has a structure more like that of a nonmetal.

2.37. Collect and Organize

We define *weighted average* for this question.

Analyze

An average is a number that expresses the middle of the data (here, for various masses of atoms or isotopes).

Solve

A weighted average takes into account the proportion of each value in the group of values to be averaged. For example, the average of 2, 2, 2, and 5 would be computed as $(2 + 2 + 2 + 5)/4 = 2.75$. This average shows the heavier weighting toward the values of 2.

Think about It

Because isotopes for any element are not equally present but have a range of natural abundances, all the masses in the periodic table for the elements are calculated weighted averages.

2.39. Collect and Organize

Given that the abundance of the two isotopes of an element are both 50%, we are to express the average atomic mass of the element if the mass of isotope X is m_X and the mass of isotope Y is m_Y.

Analyze

Because each isotope is present in exactly 50% abundance, the average atomic mass will be the simple average of the two masses of isotopes X and Y.

Solve

$$\text{average atomic mass} = \frac{m_X + m_Y}{2}$$

Think about It

Some elements in nature have just one naturally occurring isotope. Can you find some examples in Appendix 3?

2.41. **Collect and Organize**

Given the mass numbers (50 and 51) for the two isotopes of vanadium, we are to determine which is most abundant.

Analyze

The atomic mass on the periodic table for vanadium is 50.942 amu. This value is closer to 51 than to 50.

Solve

^{51}V is the more abundant isotope.

Think about It

In Appendix 3 you can see that ^{51}V is actually 99.750% abundant, so ^{50}V is only 0.250% abundant.

2.43. **Collect and Organize**

We have to consider the concept of weighted average atomic mass to answer this question.

Analyze

We are asked to compare two isotopes and their weighted average mass. If the lighter isotope is more abundant, the average atomic mass will be less than the average if both isotopes are equally abundant. If the heavier isotope is more abundant, the average atomic mass will be greater than the simple average of the two isotopes. We are given the mass number for the isotopes as part of the isotope symbol, and we will take that as the mass of that isotope in atomic mass units.

Solve

(a) The simple average atomic mass for ^{10}B and ^{11}B would be 10.5 amu. The actual average mass (10.811 amu) is greater than this; therefore, ^{11}B is more abundant.
(b) The simple average atomic mass for ^{6}Li and ^{7}Li would be 6.5 amu. The actual average mass (6.941 amu) is greater than this; therefore, ^{7}Li is more abundant.
(c) The simple average atomic mass for ^{14}N and ^{15}N would be 14.5 amu. The actual average mass (14.007 amu) is less than this; therefore, ^{14}N is more abundant.

Think about It

This is a quick question to answer for elements such as boron, lithium, and nitrogen that have the dominance of only two isotopes in terms of their abundance. Answering the same question for elements with more than two stable isotopes in relatively high abundances is a little harder.

2.45. **Collect and Organize**

In this question we are given the masses and abundances of the naturally occurring isotopes of copper. From this information, we can calculate the average atomic mass of copper.

Analyze

To calculate the average atomic mass, we have to consider the relative abundances according to the following formula:

$$m_x = a_1 m_1 + a_2 m_2 + a_3 m_3 + \cdots$$

where a_n refers to the abundance of isotope n and m_n refers to the mass of isotope n. If the relative abundances are given as percentages, the value we use for a_n in the formula is the percentage divided by 100.

Solve

For the average atomic mass of copper

$$m_{Cu} = (0.6917 \times 62.9296 \text{ amu}) + (0.3083 \times 64.9278 \text{ amu}) = 63.55 \text{ amu}$$

Think about It

Because copper-63 is more abundant than copper-65, we expect that the average atomic mass for copper would be below the simple average of 64.

2.47. Collect and Organize

Here we are asked to find out whether the mass of magnesium on Mars is the same as here on Earth. We are given the masses of each of the three isotopes of Mg in the Martian sample. Once we calculate the weighted average for Mg for the Martian sample, we can compare it to the average mass for Mg found on Earth.

Analyze

To calculate the average atomic mass, we have to consider the relative abundances according to the following formula:

$$m_x = a_1 m_1 + a_2 m_2 + a_3 m_3 + \cdots$$

where a_n refers to the abundance of isotope n and m_n refers to the mass of isotope n. If the relative abundances are given as percentages, the value we use for a_n in the formula is the percentage divided by 100.

Solve

For the average atomic mass of magnesium in the Martian sample

$$m_{Mg} = (0.7870 \times 23.9850 \text{ amu}) + (0.1013 \times 24.9858 \text{ amu}) + (0.1117 \times 25.9826 \text{ amu})$$
$$= 24.31 \text{ amu}$$

The average mass of Mg on Mars is the same as here on Earth.

Think about It

The mass of Mg on Mars should be close to the same value as on Earth; the magnesium on both planets arrived in the solar system via the same ancient stardust.

2.49. Collect and Organize

In this problem, we again use the concept of weighted average atomic mass, but here we are asked to work backward from the average mass to find the exact mass of the ^{48}Ti isotope.

Analyze

We can use the formula for finding the weighted average atomic mass, but this time our unknown quantity is one of the isotope masses. Here,

$$m_{Ti} = a_{^{46}Ti} m_{^{46}Ti} + a_{^{47}Ti} m_{^{47}Ti} + a_{^{48}Ti} m_{^{48}Ti} + a_{^{49}Ti} m_{^{49}Ti} + a_{^{50}Ti} m_{^{50}Ti}$$

Solve

$$47.867 \text{ amu} = (0.0825 \times 45.9526) + (0.0744 \times 46.9518) + (0.7372 \times m_{^{48}Ti})$$
$$+ (0.0541 \times 48.94787) + (0.0518 \times 49.94479)$$
$$m_{^{48}Ti} = 47.9483 \text{ amu}$$

Think about It

This answer makes sense since the exact mass of ^{48}Ti should be close to 48 amu.

2.51. Collect and Organize

From the formulas for three ionic compounds, CaF_2, Na_2S, and Cr_2O_3, we are to calculate the masses of the formula units.

Analyze

For each formula we will sum the masses of the elements, making sure that we also account for the number of a particular element present in the formula.

Solve

(a) CaF_2: 40.078 amu + 2(18.998 amu) = 78.074 amu

(b) Na_2S: 2(22.990 amu) + 32.065 amu = 78.045 amu

(c) Cr_2O_3: 2(51.996 amu) + 3(15.999 amu) = 151.989 amu

Think about It

In determining the formula mass, use as many significant figures in your calculation as listed on the periodic table. Resist the temptation to round up or down, which would make the calculation for the mass less accurate.

2.53. **Collect and Organize**

For each given molecular formula, we are to determine the number of carbon atoms in each.

Analyze

The subscript in each formula after the C atom is the number of carbons in the molecule.

Solve

(a) 1

(b) 3

(c) 6

(d) 6

Think about It

These molecules are all organic molecules, and writing their formulas as $C_aH_bN_cO_d$ followed by other elements, if present, is customary.

2.55. **Collect and Organize**

For a list of five compounds, we are to determine their molecular masses and then rank them in order of increasing mass.

Analyze

When we use the masses on the periodic table to calculate the molecular masses, we obtain the following:

CO = 28.01 amu

Cl_2 = 70.91 amu

CO_2 = 44.01 amu

NH_3 = 17.03 amu

CH_4 = 16.04 amu

Solve

In order of increasing molecular mass: (e) CH_4 < (d) NH_3 < (a) CO < (c) CO_2 < (b) Cl_2.

Think about It

In this problem fewer significant figures were necessary for the molecular masses because we were going to compare masses, and the masses were not likely to be too close together to warrant more than four significant digits.

2.57. **Collect and Organize**

For describing a collection of atoms or molecules, we are asked why using a *dozen* to express the number of atoms or molecules we have might not be a good idea.

Analyze

A dozen is 12 objects and therefore a relatively small group.

Solve

Although a dozen is a convenient and recognizable unit for donuts and eggs, it is too small a unit to express the very large number of atoms, ions, or molecules present in a mole.

$$\frac{6.022 \times 10^{23} \text{ atoms}}{\text{mole}} \times \frac{1 \text{ dozen}}{12 \text{ atoms}} = 5.02 \times 10^{22} \text{ dozen/mole}$$

Think about It

The mole (6.022×10^{23}) is a much more convenient unit to express the number of atoms or molecules in a sample.

2.59. Collect and Organize

In this exercise, we convert the given number of atoms or molecules of each gas to moles.

Analyze

To convert the number of atoms or molecules to moles, we divide by Avogadro's number.

Solve

(a) $\dfrac{4.4 \times 10^{14} \text{ atoms of Ne}}{6.022 \times 10^{23} \text{ atoms/mol}} = 7.3 \times 10^{-10} \text{ mol Ne}$

(c) $\dfrac{2.5 \times 10^{12} \text{ molecules of O}_3}{6.022 \times 10^{23} \text{ molecules/mol}} = 4.2 \times 10^{-12} \text{ mol O}_3$

(b) $\dfrac{4.2 \times 10^{13} \text{ molecules of CH}_4}{6.022 \times 10^{23} \text{ molecules/mol}} = 7.0 \times 10^{-11} \text{ mol CH}_4$

(d) $\dfrac{4.9 \times 10^{9} \text{ molecules of NO}_2}{6.022 \times 10^{23} \text{ molecules/mol}} = 8.1 \times 10^{-15} \text{ mol NO}_2$

Think about It

The trace gas that has the largest number of atoms or molecules present also has the largest number of moles present. In this sample of air, the amount of the trace gases decreases in the order $Ne > CH_4 > O_3 > NO_2$.

2.61. Collect and Organize

From the chemical formulas for various iron compounds with oxygen, we are asked to determine how many moles of iron are in 1 mol of each substance.

Analyze

The chemical formula reflects the molar ratios of the elements in the compound. If one atom of iron is in the compound's chemical formula, then 1 mol of iron is in 1 mol of the compound. Likewise, if three atoms of iron are in the chemical formula, 3 mol of iron is present in 1 mol of the substance.

Solve

(a) One atom of iron is in FeO; therefore, 1 mol of FeO contains 1 mol of iron.
(b) Two atoms of iron are in Fe_2O_3; therefore, 1 mol of Fe_2O_3 contains 2 mol of iron.
(c) One atom of iron is in $Fe(OH)_3$; therefore, 1 mol of $Fe(OH)_3$ contains 1 mol of iron.
(d) Three atoms of iron are in Fe_3O_4; therefore, 1 mol of Fe_3O_4 contains 3 mol of iron.

Think about It

The parentheses used in $Fe(OH)_3$ show that three OH units are in this compound. If the question had asked how many moles of oxygen were present in 1 mol of this substance, the answer would be 3 mol of oxygen.

2.63. Collect and Organize

We are to calculate the mass of a given number of moles of magnesium carbonate.

Analyze

To convert from moles to mass, multiply the number of moles by the molar mass of the substance. The molar mass of $MgCO_3$ is $24.30 + 12.01 + 3(16.00) = 84.31$ g/mol.

Solve

$$0.122 \text{ mol MgCO}_3 \times \frac{84.31 \text{ g}}{\text{mol}} = 10.3 \text{ g}$$

Think about It

Moles in chemistry are like a common currency in exchanging money. From moles we can calculate mass; from mass we can calculate moles.

2.65. **Collect and Organize**

In this exercise we convert from the moles of titanium contained in a substance to the number of atoms present.

Analyze

For each substance, we need to take into account the number of moles of titanium *atoms* present in *1 mol* of the substance. For 0.125 mol of substance, then, a substance that contains two atoms of titanium in its formula contains $0.125 \times 2 = 0.250$ mol of titanium. We can then use Avogadro's number to convert the moles of titanium to the number of atoms present in the sample.

Solve

(a) Ilmenite, $FeTiO_3$, contains one atom of Ti per formula unit, so 0.125 mol of ilmenite contains 0.125 mol of Ti.

$$0.125 \text{ mol Ti} \times \frac{6.022 \times 10^{23} \text{ Ti atoms}}{1 \text{ mol}} = 7.53 \times 10^{22} \text{ Ti atoms}$$

(b) The formula for titanium(IV) chloride is $TiCl_4$. This formula contains only one Ti atom per formula unit as well, so the answer is identical to that calculated in (a).

$$0.125 \text{ mol Ti} \times \frac{6.022 \times 10^{23} \text{ Ti atoms}}{1 \text{ mol}} = 7.53 \times 10^{22} \text{ Ti atoms}$$

(c) Ti_2O_3 contains two titanium atoms in its formula, so 0.125 mol of Ti_2O_3 contains $0.125 \times 2 = 0.250$ mol of titanium.

$$0.250 \text{ mol Ti} \times \frac{6.022 \times 10^{23} \text{ Ti atoms}}{1 \text{ mol}} = 1.51 \times 10^{23} \text{ Ti atoms}$$

(d) Ti_3O_5 contains three titanium atoms in its formula, so 0.125 mol of Ti_2O_3 contains $0.125 \times 3 = 0.375$ mol of titanium.

$$0.375 \text{ mol Ti} \times \frac{6.022 \times 10^{23} \text{ Ti atoms}}{1 \text{ mol}} = 2.26 \times 10^{23} \text{ Ti atoms}$$

Think about It

The number of atoms of titanium in 0.125 mol of each compound reflects the number of atoms of Ti in the chemical formula. Ti_2O_3 has twice the number of Ti atoms, and Ti_3O_5 has three times the number of Ti atoms, compared to the number of Ti atoms in the same number of moles of $FeTiO_3$ and $TiCl_4$.

2.67. **Collect and Organize**

Given the formulas and the moles of each substance in a pair, we are asked to decide which compound contains more moles of oxygen.

Analyze

To answer this question, we have to take into account the moles of oxygen present in the substance formulas as well as the initial number of moles specified for each substance.

Solve

(a) One mole of Al_2O_3 contains 3 mol of oxygen, and 1 mol of Fe_2O_3 also contains 3 mol of oxygen. These compounds contain the same number of moles of oxygen.
(b) One mole of SiO_2 contains 2 mol of oxygen, and 1 mol of N_2O_4 contains 4 mol of oxygen. Therefore, N_2O_4 contains more moles of oxygen (twice as much).
(c) Three moles of CO contains 3 mol of oxygen, and 2 mol of CO_2 contains 4 mol of oxygen. Therefore, the 2 mol of CO_2 contains more oxygen.

Think about It
We cannot decide which substance has more moles of oxygen by comparing only the amounts of the substances present. If that were the case, we would have concluded wrongly that 3 mol of CO contains more moles of oxygen than 2 mol of CO_2.

2.69. Collect and Organize
For each aluminosilicate, we are given the chemical formula. From that formula we are asked to deduce the number of moles of aluminum in 1.50 mol of each substance.

Analyze
The number of moles of aluminum in 1 mol of each substance is reflected in its chemical formula. We need next to take into account that we are starting with 1.50 mol of each substance.

Solve
(a) Each mole of pyrophyllite, $Al_2Si_4O_{10}(OH)_2$, contains 2 mol of Al atoms. Therefore, 1.50 mol of pyrophyllite contains 1.50 mol × 2 = 3.00 mol of Al.
(b) Each mole of mica, $KAl_3Si_3O_{10}(OH)_2$, contains 3 mol of Al. Therefore, 1.50 mol of mica contains 1.50 mol × 3 = 4.50 mol of Al.
(c) Each mole of albite, $NaAlSi_3O_8$, contains 1 mol of Al. Therefore, 1.50 mol of albite contains 1.50 mol of Al.

Think about It
These minerals could all be distinguished by analyzing the amount of aluminum present in the same number of moles of each substance.

2.71. Collect and Organize
This exercise has us compute the molar mass of various molecular compounds of oxygen.

Analyze
We can find the molar mass of each compound by adding the molar mass of each element from the periodic table, taking into account the number of moles of each atom present in 1 mol of the substance.

Solve
(a) SO_2: 32.065 + 2(15.999) = 64.063 g/mol
(b) O_3: 3(15.999) = 48.997 g/mol
(c) CO_2: 12.011 + 2(15.999) = 44.009 g/mol
(d) N_2O_5: 2(14.007) + 5(15.999) = 108.009 g/mol

Think about It
The three compounds SO_2, O_3, and CO_2 have three atoms in their chemical formula, but each has a different molar mass.

2.73. Collect and Organize
This exercise has us compute the molar mass of various flavorings.

Analyze
We can find the molar mass of each flavoring by adding the molar mass of each element from the periodic table, taking into account the number of moles of each atom present in 1 mol of the flavoring. Each flavoring contains only carbon (12.01 g/mol), hydrogen (1.01 g/mol), and oxygen (16.00 g/mol).

Solve
(a) Vanillin, $C_8H_8O_3$: 8(12.011) + 8(1.0079) + 3(15.999) = 152.148 g/mol
(b) Oil of cloves, $C_{10}H_{12}O_2$: 10(12.011) + 12(1.0079) + 2(15.999) = 164.203 g/mol
(c) Anise oil, $C_{10}H_{12}O$: 10(12.011) + 12(1.0079) + 15.999 = 148.204 g/mol
(d) Oil of cinnamon, C_9H_8O: 9(12.011) + 8(1.0079) + 15.999 = 132.161 g/mol

Think about It

Each flavoring has a distinctive odor and flavor due in part to its different chemical formula. Another factor, however, in differentiating these flavorings is their chemical structure, or the arrangement in which the atoms are attached, as shown by the structures of these flavorings:

| Vanillin | Oil of cloves | Anise oil | Oil of cinnamon |

2.75. Collect and Organize

We are asked to convert a mass of carbon in grams to moles.

Analyze

We need the mass of 1 mol of carbon to compute the number of moles of carbon in the 500.0 g sample. From the periodic table, we see that the molar mass of carbon is 12.011 g/mol.

Solve

$$500.0 \text{ g C} \times \frac{1 \text{ mol}}{12.011 \text{ g}} = 41.63 \text{ mol C}$$

Think about It

Because carbon's molar mass is relatively low at 12 g/mol, 500 g of this substance contains a fairly substantial number of moles.

2.77. Collect and Organize

Given a molar amount of calcium titanate, we are asked to determine the number of moles and mass of Ca^{2+} ions in the substance.

Analyze

The formula for calcium titanate gives us the number of moles of Ca in the compound. Because the mass of the two missing electrons in the Ca^{2+} cation is negligible, the molar mass of the Ca^{2+} ion is taken as the same as the molar mass of Ca. We can use this to determine the mass of Ca^{2+} in the 0.25 mol of calcium titanate.

Solve

Because calcium titanate contains one atom of Ca in its formula, 0.25 mol of $CaTiO_3$ contains 0.25 mol of Ca^{2+} ions. The mass of Ca^{2+} ions in the sample, therefore, is

$$0.25 \text{ mol Ca}^{2+} \times \frac{40.078 \text{ g}}{1 \text{ mol}} = 10 \text{ g Ca}^{2+}$$

Think about It

Our answer makes sense. One-quarter of a mole of Ca^{2+} should give us 40/4, or about 10 g, of Ca in the 0.25 mol of calcium titanate.

2.79. Collect and Organize

Between two balloons filled with 10.0 g of different gases, we are to choose which balloon has the greater number of particles.

Analyze

The balloon with the greater number of particles has the greater number of moles. The greater number of moles contained in 10.0 g of a gas is for the gas with the lowest molar mass. A gas with a lower molar mass contains more moles in 10.0 g mass and, therefore, has a greater number of moles than a 10.0 g mass of a higher molar mass gas.

Solve

(a) The molar mass of CO_2 is 44 g/mol, and the molar mass of NO is 30 g/mol. Therefore, the balloon containing NO has the greater number of particles.

(b) The molar mass of CO_2 is 44 g/mol, and the molar mass of SO_2 is 64 g/mol. Therefore, the balloon containing CO_2 has the greater number of particles.

(c) The molar mass of O_2 is 32 g/mol, and the molar mass of Ar is 40 g/mol. Therefore, the balloon containing O_2 has the greater number of particles.

Think about It

We could numerically determine the number of moles of gas in each balloon to make the comparisons in this problem, but doing so is unnecessary because we know the relationship between moles and molar mass.

2.81. **Collect and Organize**

Given a mass of quartz, we are to determine the moles of SiO_2 present.

Analyze

To convert from mass to moles, we divide the mass given by the molar mass of SiO_2 [28.086 + 2(15.999) = 60.084g/mol].

Solve

$$\frac{45.2 \text{ g } SiO_2}{60.084 \text{ g/mol}} = 0.752 \text{ mol } SiO_2$$

Think about It

Because the initial mass is less than the molar mass, we would expect less than 1 mol of SiO_2 to be in the quartz sample.

2.83. **Collect and Organize**

This exercise asks us to compute the moles of uranium and carbon (diamond) atoms in a 1 cm^3 block of each element and then to compare them.

Analyze

Starting with the 1 cm^3 block of each element, we can obtain the mass of the block by multiplying by the density of the element. Dividing that result by the molar mass of the element gives us the moles of atoms in that block. The element block with the larger number of moles of atoms must have the larger number of atoms. We can compute the actual number of atoms by multiplying the moles of atoms for each element by Avogadro's number.

Solve

$$1 \text{ cm}^3 \text{ C} \times \frac{3.514 \text{ g}}{\text{cm}^3} \times \frac{1 \text{ mol}}{12.011 \text{ g}} \times \frac{6.022 \times 10^{23} \text{ C atoms}}{\text{mol}} = 1.762 \times 10^{23} \text{ atoms of C}$$

$$1 \text{ cm}^3 \text{ U} \times \frac{19.05 \text{ g}}{\text{cm}^3} \times \frac{1 \text{ mol}}{238.03 \text{ g}} \times \frac{6.022 \times 10^{23} \text{ U atoms}}{\text{mol}} = 4.820 \times 10^{22} \text{ atoms of U}$$

Therefore, the 1 cm^3 block of diamond contains more atoms.

Think about It

We might expect that, because the block of uranium weighs so much more than the diamond block (more than five times as much), the uranium block would contain more atoms. However, we also have to take into account the very large molar mass of uranium. The result is that the diamond block has about 3.7 times more atoms in it than the same-sized block of uranium.

2.85. **Collect and Organize**

Of the particles listed, we are asked which formed first and which formed last in the universe's history.

Analyze

We expect the smaller, least complex particles to have formed first and the larger, more complicated particles to form later from them. In rough order of size: quark < neutron = proton < deuteron (^{2}H nucleus).

Solve

The first particles formed in the universe were quarks (d), the smallest elementary particles; the last particle from the list formed would be the deuteron (a), which would have had to result from the fusing of a proton with a neutron.

Think about It

The early universe was too hot to allow anything but the smallest fundamental particles to exist.

2.87. **Collect and Organize**

We consider why energy is released in the fusion process in the synthesis of the elements that precede iron in the periodic table.

Analyze

The binding energy as a function of the mass number is shown in Figure 2.21.

Solve

The mass of the nucleus for elements before iron in the periodic table is less than the sum of the masses of the nucleons that make up the nucleus of these elements. This means that a mass defect exists for these nuclei that is released as energy when these elements undergo fusion reactions.

Think about It

The binding energy of the nucleus per nucleon is highest with iron, so it is the most stable element.

2.89. **Collect and Organize**

We consider why helium requires higher temperatures to undergo fusion than hydrogen.

Analyze

For nuclei to fuse, the strong repulsive forces between the nuclei must be overcome.

Solve

Helium fusion would require higher temperatures than hydrogen fusion because we must force nuclei with 2+ charges (two protons) together rather than nuclei with 1+ charges. The higher the charge (the number of protons) is, the more repulsion the nuclei feel for each other.

Think about It

"Burning" higher elements, such as carbon, in fusion reactions would require even higher temperatures.

2.91. **Collect and Organize**

We are asked to explain why elements other than H, He, and Li were not formed early in the history of the universe.

Analyze

The early universe (within minutes) cooled significantly after the Big Bang.

Solve

Elements other than H, He, and Li were not formed in the primordial nucleosynthesis because the expanding universe was cooling and therefore could not support the high temperatures needed for fusion. Also, the expanding universe was not dense enough for nuclei to fuse.

Think about It

The heavier elements all were produced later in stars.

2.93. **Collect and Organize**

We consider here what happens to the neutron-to-proton ratio when a nucleus undergoes β decay.

Analyze

Beta decay converts a neutron into a proton.

Solve

In a nucleus that undergoes β decay, a neutron is "lost" and a proton is "gained." The neutron-to-proton ratio will decrease.

Think about It

Remember that, although the β particle is an electron, it is emitted from the nucleus of an atom. It is not simply lost by the atom in the ionization process to become a cation.

2.95. **Collect and Organize**

We are asked to predict the products of fusion reactions in a giant star.

Analyze

To answer this, we fuse the two isotopes, determining the identity of the element and its mass number by balancing the nuclear reaction.

Solve

(a) $^{12}_{6}\text{C} + {}^{4}_{2}\text{He} \rightarrow {}^{16}_{8}\text{O}$

(b) $^{20}_{10}\text{Ne} + {}^{4}_{2}\text{He} \rightarrow {}^{24}_{12}\text{Mg}$

(c) $^{32}_{16}\text{S} + {}^{4}_{2}\text{He} \rightarrow {}^{36}_{18}\text{Ar}$

Think about It

When helium nuclei (α particles) are added to the nucleus, the mass number increases by 4 and the atomic number increases by 2.

2.97. **Collect and Organize**

We are asked to predict the products of neutron capture reactions in the core of a collapsing giant star.

Analyze

To solve this problem, we balance the reactions for mass number and atomic number between the reactants and products. We have to take into account that multiple neutrons can be added under these conditions.

Solve

(a) $^{96}_{42}\text{Mo} + 3\,^{1}_{0}\text{n} \rightarrow {}^{99}_{43}\text{Tc} + {}^{0}_{-1}\beta$

(b) $^{118}_{50}\text{Sn} + 3\,^{1}_{0}\text{n} \rightarrow {}^{121}_{51}\text{Sb} + {}^{0}_{-1}\beta$

(c) $^{108}_{47}\text{Ag} + {}^{1}_{0}\text{n} \rightarrow {}^{109}_{48}\text{Cd} + {}^{0}_{-1}\beta$

Think about It
Adding neutrons to the nucleus does not itself change the atomic number. Subsequent β emission, however, does, and the result is the building up of heavier elements in the periodic table.

2.99. Collect and Organize
We are asked to consider whether the transmutations of ^{137}I to ^{137}Xe to ^{137}Cs involve β decay. We have to write balanced nuclear equations to determine the type of decay for each nuclear reaction.

Analyze
Two nuclear processes are under consideration here: the transformation of ^{137}I to ^{137}Xe and the transformation of ^{137}Xe to ^{137}Cs. Therefore, we write two nuclear reactions. To balance the reactions, we must balance the superscripts (mass numbers) and subscripts (atomic numbers or numbers of protons) for the reactants and the products. If a β particle, $_{-1}^{0}\beta$, is used to balance the equations on the product side, then the process involves β emission.

Solve
The transformation of ^{137}I to ^{137}Xe can be balanced as

$$_{53}^{137}\text{I} \rightarrow {}_{54}^{137}\text{Xe} + {}_{-1}^{0}\beta$$

The transformation of ^{137}Xe to ^{137}Cs can be balanced as

$$_{54}^{137}\text{Xe} \rightarrow {}_{55}^{137}\text{Cs} + {}_{-1}^{0}\beta$$

Both nuclear reactions involve β emission.

Think about It
When a nucleus undergoes β emission, a neutron becomes a proton. This means that the atomic number increases by 1, but the mass number (the total number of protons and neutrons) remains the same.

2.101. Collect and Organize
We are asked to write balanced nuclear equations to describe the bombardment of ^{209}Bi to form ^{211}At.

Analyze
Bismuth and astatine differ in atomic number by 2. The mass numbers for the two isotopes for this problem differ only by 2. Therefore, an appropriate particle with which to bombard ^{209}Bi is the α particle with the emission of two neutrons.

Solve

$$_{83}^{209}\text{Bi} + {}_{2}^{4}\alpha \rightarrow {}_{85}^{211}\text{At} + 2\,{}_{0}^{1}\text{n}$$

Think about It
The emission of neutrons does not change the atomic number, only the mass number.

2.103. Collect and Organize
For the nuclear reactions to prepare some isotopes used in medicine, we are to complete them by supplying the missing nuclide or nuclear particle.

Analyze
For these reactions to balance, the sum of the mass numbers of the reactants must equal that of the products. Likewise, the sum of the atomic numbers of the reactants must equal that of the products.

Solve
(a) $_{16}^{32}\text{S} + {}_{0}^{1}\text{n} \rightarrow {}_{15}^{32}\text{P} + {}_{1}^{1}\text{H}$

(b) $_{25}^{55}\text{Mn} + {}_{1}^{1}\text{H} \rightarrow {}_{26}^{52}\text{Fe} + 4\,\underline{{}_{0}^{1}\text{n}}$

(c) $^{75}_{33}\text{As} + \underline{2\,^{1}_{1}\text{H}} \rightarrow \,^{77}_{35}\text{Br}$

(d) $^{124}_{54}\text{Xe} + \,^{1}_{0}\text{n} \rightarrow \,^{125}_{\underline{54}}\text{Xe} \rightarrow \,^{125}_{53}\text{I} + \,^{0}_{\underline{1}}\beta$

Think about It
All these nuclides are produced through the collision of light particles (neutron or hydrogen) with nuclides of larger mass.

2.105. Collect and Organize
For the nuclear reactions given, we are to complete them by supplying the missing nuclide or nuclear particle.

Analyze
For these reactions to balance, the sum of the mass numbers of the reactants must equal that of the products. Likewise, the sum of the atomic numbers of the reactants must equal that of the products.

Solve
(a) $^{131}_{52}\text{Te} \rightarrow \,^{131}_{53}\text{I} + \,^{0}_{-1}\beta$

(b) $^{122}_{53}\text{I} \rightarrow \,^{122}_{54}\text{I} + \,^{0}_{-1}\beta$

(c) $^{10}_{5}\text{B} + \,^{4}_{2}\text{He} \rightarrow \,^{13}_{7}\text{N} + \,^{1}_{0}\text{n}$

(d) $^{68}_{30}\text{Zn} + \,^{1}_{1}\text{H} \rightarrow \,^{67}_{31}\text{Ga} + 2\,^{1}_{0}\text{n}$

Think about It
Adding a neutron to a nucleus, as in reaction c, does not change the atomic number, only the mass number.

2.107. Collect and Organize
J. J. Thomson's experiment revealed the electron and its behavior in magnetic and electric fields. In this question, we look closely at his experiment.

Analyze
Thomson showed that a cathode ray was deflected by a magnetic field in one direction and by an electric field in the other direction. He saw the deflection of the cathode ray when the ray hit a fluorescent plate at the end of his experimental apparatus, as shown in the textbook in Figure 2.2. The cathode ray was deflected by the electrically charged plates as shown. We can imagine the experiment proceeding from no voltage across the charged plates to low voltages and then to higher voltages. From this thought experiment, the ray must be deflected more by an increase in the voltage across the charged plates. Thomson reasoned that the cathode ray was composed of tiny charged particles, which were later called electrons.

Solve
(a) Today we call cathode rays electrons.
(b) The beam of electrons was deflected between the charged plates because they were attracted to the oppositely charged plate as the beam passed through the electric field. Indeed, in Figure 2.2 we see the beam deflected up toward the (+) plate.
(c) If the polarities of the plates were switched, the electron would still be deflected toward the positively charged plate, which would now be at the bottom of the tube.
(d) If we reduced the voltage by half, the light spot would be deflected half as much, so the position of the light spot on the fluorescent screen would be halfway between the position where it was before the voltage was reduced and the 0 spot position when no voltage exists between the plates.

Think about It
This experiment was key to the discovery of subatomic particles, which until then in the atomic theory were not known to exist. It was believed before that time that the atom was the smallest indivisible component of matter.

2.109. Collect and Organize

In this problem we are given the masses of the three isotopes of magnesium (^{24}Mg = 23.9850 amu, ^{25}Mg = 24.9858 amu, and ^{26}Mg = 25.9826 amu) and given that the abundance of ^{24}Mg is 78.99%. From this information and the average (weighted) atomic mass units of magnesium (24.3050 amu), we must calculate the abundances of the other two isotopes, ^{25}Mg and ^{26}Mg.

Analyze

The average atomic mass is derived from a weighted average of the isotopes' atomic masses. If x = abundance of ^{25}Mg and y = abundance of ^{26}Mg, the weighted average of magnesium is

$$(0.7899 \times 23.9850) + 24.9858x + 25.9826y = 24.3050$$

Because the sum of the abundances of the isotopes must add up to 1.00,

$$0.7899 + x + y = 1.00$$

So

$$x = 1.00 - 0.7899 - y = 0.2101 - y$$

Substituting this expression for x in the weighted average mass equation gives

$$(0.7899 \times 23.9850) + 24.9858(0.2101 - y) + 25.9826y = 24.3050$$

Solve

$$18.94575 + 5.249517 - 24.9858y + 25.9826y = 24.3050$$
$$0.9968y = 0.1097$$
$$y = 0.1101$$

So

$$x = 0.2101 - 0.1101 = 0.1000$$

The abundance of ^{25}Mg is $x \times 100 = 10.00\%$, and the abundance of ^{26}Mg is $y \times 100 = 11.01\%$.

Think about It

Although the abundances of ^{25}Mg and ^{26}Mg are nearly equal to each other at the end of this calculation, we cannot assume that in setting up the equation. We have to solve this problem algebraically by setting up two equations with two unknowns.

2.111. Collect and Organize

For the absorption of a neutron by ^{11}B and the subsequent α or β decay of the product ^{12}B, we are to write balanced equations for these two processes.

Analyze

We can use the usual method to balance the nuclear reactions. For each we must make sure that the sum of the atomic numbers for the reactants equals the sum of the atomic numbers of the products. Likewise, the sum of the mass numbers of the reactants must equal the sum of the mass numbers of the products.

Solve

$$^{11}_{5}B + ^{1}_{0}n \rightarrow ^{12}_{5}B$$
$$^{12}_{5}B \rightarrow ^{12}_{6}C + ^{0}_{-1}\beta$$
$$^{12}_{5}B \rightarrow ^{8}_{3}Li + ^{4}_{2}He$$

Think about It

We expect that ^{8}Li would decay by β decay because it is neutron rich, but ^{12}C is a stable element.

2.113. Collect and Organize

For the synthesis of one atom of ^{269}Ds, we are to write the balanced nuclear reaction when ^{208}Pb is bombarded with ^{62}Ni.

Analyze

For this reaction to balance, the sum of the mass numbers of the reactants must equal that of the products. Likewise, the sum of the atomic numbers of the reactants must equal that of the products.

Solve

$$^{208}_{82}\text{Pb} + {}^{62}_{28}\text{Ni} \rightarrow {}^{269}_{110}\text{Ds} + {}^{1}_{0}\text{n}$$

Think about It

This fusion reaction also produces a mole of neutrons for every 1 mol of ^{269}Ds produced.

2.115. Collect and Organize

To determine the number of moles and atoms of carbon in the Hope Diamond, we have to first convert its given mass of 45.52 carats to mass in grams.

Analyze

To convert the mass of the diamond to grams, we use the relationship 1 carat = 200 mg. The moles of carbon atoms is equal to the mass of the diamond divided by the molar mass of carbon (12.011 g/mol); the number of carbon atoms in the diamond is the number of moles of carbon multiplied by Avogadro's number.

Solve

(a) The mass of the diamond in grams is

$$45.52 \text{ carats} \times \frac{200 \text{ mg}}{1 \text{ carat}} \times \frac{1 \text{ g}}{1000 \text{ mg}} = 9.104 \text{ g}$$

The number of moles of carbon atoms in the diamond is

$$9.104 \text{ g} \times \frac{1 \text{ mol}}{12.011 \text{ g}} = 0.7580 \text{ mol of C}$$

(b) The number of carbon atoms in the diamond is

$$0.7580 \text{ mol} \times \frac{6.022 \times 10^{23} \text{ atoms}}{1 \text{ mol}} = 4.565 \times 10^{23} \text{ atoms of C}$$

Think about It

Diamond is the hardest natural substance and is an electrical insulator while being an excellent conductor of heat.

CHAPTER 3 | Atomic Structure: Explaining the Properties of Elements

3.1. Collect and Organize

From the highlighted elements in Figure P3.1, we can correlate position on the periodic table with orbital (s, p, d) filling.

Analyze

The periodic table consists of the s-block elements, which are the first two columns (groups 1–2); the d-block elements, which are the next 10 columns (groups 3–12); and the p-block elements, which are the rightmost six columns (groups 13–18). The f-block elements are in the two rows at the bottom of the table. From their positions in these blocks, we can ascertain the elements' electron configurations.

Solve

(a) Group 1 elements have an ns^1 configuration, including the element shaded purple (Na). Because half-filled and filled d orbitals are predicted for transition metals, the red-shaded ($3d^5 4s^1$, Cr) and orange-shaded ($5d^{10}6s^1$, Au) elements also have a single s electron in their outermost shells.

(b) Filled sets of s and p orbitals (ns^2np^6 configuration) occur for the noble gases (group 18 elements), including the element shaded blue (Ne).

(c) Filled sets of d orbitals would occur for elements in period 4 and below, having in their electron configuration nd^{10}. Because a filled d orbital is stable for transition elements, the orange-shaded element (Au) is predicted to have a $5d^{10}6s^1$ configuration.

(d) A half-filled d-orbital set would be predicted for the element shaded red (Cr); its electron configuration would be $3d^5 4s^1$.

(e) Filled s orbitals would occur in the outermost shells of the blue element ($2s^2 2p^6$, Ne) and the green-shaded element ($3s^2 3p^5$, Cl).

Think about It

Remember that the outermost shell of an atom includes all those electrons above the previous noble gas core.

3.3. Collect and Organize

Of the highlighted elements in Figure P3.1, we are to find the elements that form common monatomic ions (cations or anions) that are larger and smaller than the element itself.

Analyze

Nonmetals tend to form anions and metals tend to form cations. Anions are larger than the parent atom, so for part a we are looking for elements that will probably form an anion (X^{n-}) and we are looking for an element located on the right-hand side of the periodic table. Cations are smaller than the parent atom, and so for part b we are looking for elements that will form Y^{n+} and for an element on the left-hand side of the periodic table.

Solve

(a) Both the green and blue elements are nonmetals and potentially form anions. Green (Cl) would form Cl^-, picking up an electron to fill its outermost shell. Blue (Ne), however, would not form an anion; its outermost shell is already full.

(b) Any of the metals—purple (Na), red (Cr), and orange (Au)—will form cations smaller than their parent ions.

Think about It

Most elements in the periodic table are classified as metals, so most elements tend to form cations, not anions.

3.5. Collect and Organize

Of the highlighted elements in Figure P3.4, we are to find the elements that form cations or anions that are smaller than the parent atom.

Analyze

Cations are always smaller than the parent atom, so we look for elements that are likely to form cations (X^{n+}). Metals tend to form cations, so we look for elements on the left side of the periodic table.

Solve

Blue, green, and orange are all metals and potentially lose electrons to form cations that are smaller than their corresponding atoms.

Think about It

As an atom loses more electrons, the size continues to decrease. Therefore, $X^+ > X^{2+} > X^{3+}$ in size.

3.7. **Collect and Organize**

Pictured in Figure P3.7 are three waves. Wave A is shone on a metal surface and from it an electron is emitted. We are to choose the statement that reflects the effect that waves B and C would have when they are shone on the metal surface in place of wave A.

Analyze

Wave B has a longer wavelength and thus lower energy than wave A. This wave might be as energetic as wave A in emitting electrons, but we can't be sure because we do not know the threshold value for the photoemission for this metal. Wave C has shorter wavelength and thus higher energy than wave A, and so it will definitely also emit electrons from the metal surface.

Solve

Statement (c) is correct.

Think about It

The difference in the effect of wave A and wave C will be in the speed of the electron emitted from the metal. Electrons ejected from the metal by wave C, with a greater energy, will have greater kinetic energy than those of wave A, with a lower energy.

3.9. **Collect and Organize**

Of the four choices of the group 2 cation and the group 17 anion from Problem 3.8, we are to choose the one that best reflects their relative ion sizes.

Analyze

The M (alkaline earth) atom would decrease its size significantly upon forming the M^{2+} cation, and the X (halogen) atom would increase greatly in size upon forming the X^- anion.

Solve

Representation (a) best shows their relative sizes. The metal will form a 2+ cation, which will very much decrease its size, whereas the halogen will form a 1– anion, which will increase the size, albeit not substantially (by adding only one electron).

Think about It

Periodic trends apply to ions as well, but we have to be careful to consider the number of electrons lost or gained. In order of increasing cation size: $Al^{3+} < Mg^{2+} < Na^+$. In order of increasing anion size: $Cl^- < S^{2-} < P^{3-}$.

3.11. **Collect and Organize / Analyze**

All forms of radiant energy (light) from gamma rays to low-energy radio waves are called *electromagnetic radiation*. Why?

Solve

All these forms of light have perpendicular, oscillating electric and magnetic fields that travel together through space, as described by Maxwell.

Think about It
All forms of electromagnetic radiation travel at the speed of light (3.00×10^8 m/s in a vacuum).

3.13. Collect and Organize
We are asked why a lead shield is used at the dentist's office when X-ray images are taken.

Analyze
Light interacts with matter and X-rays are high-energy light, which can damage living cells.

Solve
The lead shield must protect the part of our bodies that might be exposed to X-rays but are not being imaged. Lead is a very high-density metal with many electrons, which interact with X-rays and absorb nearly all the X-rays before they can reach our bodies.

Think about It
Exposure to high-energy radiation (γ rays and X-rays in particular) may cause genetic damage in cells, which may lead to cancers.

3.15. Collect and Organize
We consider whether as molten lava cools and no longer glows, it still emits radiation.

Analyze
The electromagnetic spectrum covers a wide range of wavelengths, from low-energy radio waves to high-energy γ rays. The visible part of the spectrum is confined to 400–700 nm and is only a small portion.

Solve
As the lava cools the energy given off does not cease, but it no longer gives off energy in the visible range (so it is no longer glowing). The lava is still hot and it radiates heat, which is in the infrared region of the electromagnetic spectrum.

Think about It
Night-vision goggles detect infrared radiation from objects warmer than ambient temperature and convert it into visible (usually green) light.

3.17. Collect and Organize
We are to calculate the frequency of light of a wavelength given in nanometers ($\lambda = 616$ nm).

Analyze
The wavelength of light is related to the frequency through the equation $v = c/\lambda$. Wavelength must be expressed in meters for this calculation (1 nm = 1×10^{-9} m).

Solve
$$v = \frac{2.998 \times 10^8 \text{ m/s}}{\left(616 \text{ nm} \times \dfrac{1 \times 10^{-9} \text{ m}}{1 \text{ nm}}\right)} = 4.87 \times 10^{14} \text{ s}^{-1}$$

Think about It
Be sure to convert nanometers to meters when using this equation.

3.19. Collect and Organize
Given the frequencies of several radio stations, we are to calculate the corresponding wavelengths.

Analyze

The equation to calculate wavelength from frequency is

$$\lambda = c/\nu$$

where λ is in meters, $c = 2.998 \times 10^8$ m/s, and ν is in hertz (per second). We need to convert megahertz to hertz for our calculation (1×10^6 Hz = 1 MHz).

Solve

(a) $\lambda_{KRNU} = \dfrac{2.998 \times 10^8 \text{ m/s}}{90.3 \times 10^6 \text{ s}^{-1}} = 3.32$ m

(b) $\lambda_{WBRU} = \dfrac{2.998 \times 10^8 \text{ m/s}}{95.5 \times 10^6 \text{ s}^{-1}} = 3.14$ m

(c) $\lambda_{WYLD} = \dfrac{2.998 \times 10^8 \text{ m/s}}{98.5 \times 10^6 \text{ s}^{-1}} = 3.04$ m

(d) $\lambda_{WAAF} = \dfrac{2.998 \times 10^8 \text{ m/s}}{107.3 \times 10^6 \text{ s}^{-1}} = 2.79$ m

Think about It

Remember that the speed of electromagnetic radiation in air is approximately the same as in a vacuum (2.998×10^8 m/s).

3.21. Collect and Organize

We are to compare the frequency of 1090 kHz radio waves versus that of the green light emitted from an LED.

Analyze

We can convert the wavelength of light (550 nm) to frequency by using $\nu = c/\lambda$. Wavelength has to be expressed in meters for this calculation (1 nm = 1×10^{-9} m).

Solve

The frequency of the LED light (b) is

$$\nu = \frac{2.998 \times 10^8 \text{ m/s}}{550 \times 10^{-9} \text{ m}} = 5.45 \times 10^{14} \text{ s}^{-1}$$

This frequency is much higher than 1090 kHz (1.090×10^6 Hz) from the radio station. Therefore, the radio station (a) has the lower frequency.

Think about It

The radio station has the longer wavelength since wavelength and frequency are inversely related.

3.23. Collect and Organize

Earth is 149.6 million km from the sun. We are to calculate how long the sun's light takes to reach Earth.

Analyze

We can find the time light takes to travel from the sun to Earth by dividing the distance (149.6 million km) by the speed at which light travels (2.998×10^8 m/s).

Solve

$$\text{time} = \frac{\left(149.6 \times 10^6 \text{ km} \times \dfrac{1000 \text{ m}}{\text{km}}\right)}{2.998 \times 10^8 \text{ m/s}} = 499 \text{ s, or } 8.32 \text{ min}$$

Think about It

Even though light travels very fast, the large distance between Earth and the sun means that events (for example, solar flares) we witness on the sun actually happened 8 min ago.

3.25. **Collect and Organize**

We are asked to compare the atomic emission and absorption spectra of an element.

Analyze

Emission of light from an atom occurs when the atoms are heated to a high temperature and an electron at a high energy level falls to a lower energy level. Absorption of light occurs when the atoms absorb energy from an external source of energy to promote an electron from a lower energy level to a higher energy level. We are asked to compare the two resulting spectra for an atomic element.

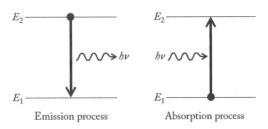

Solve

The atomic absorption spectrum consists of dark lines at wavelengths specific to the element where it absorbs energy to enter an excited state. The emission spectrum has bright lines on a dark background with the lines appearing at the same wavelengths as the dark lines in the absorption spectrum. The bright lines are where an excited-state electron falls to a lower energy state.

Think about It

The atom absorbs only certain amounts of energy (as seen in the absorption spectrum) and, once excited to those higher energy states, emits that same energy back (in the emission spectrum) to go back to its ground (lowest) energy state.

3.27. **Collect and Organize**

We are asked how study of the emission spectra of the elements led to identification of the dark Fraunhofer lines in the sun's spectrum.

Analyze

The emission lines for elements match the absorption lines exactly in energy because these processes are the exact reverse of each other.

Solve

Because each element shows distinctive and unique absorption and emission lines, the bright emission lines observed for the pure elements could be matched to the many dark absorption lines in the spectrum of sunlight. This approach can be used to deduce the sun's elemental composition.

Think about It

The elemental composition of distant stars can be determined in this way as well.

3.29. **Collect and Organize / Analyze**

We are to define the term *quantum*.

Solve

Named by Max Planck, the quantum is the smallest indivisible amount of radiant energy that an atom can absorb or emit.

Think about It

Planck also defined the relationship between the energy of a quantum particle and its frequency ($E = h\nu$).

3.31. **Collect and Organize**
We are to determine whether and what color a piece of tungsten would glow if heated to 1000 K.

Analyze
We can treat the tungsten wire as a blackbody emitter. Figure 3.11 shows the dependence of intensity of emitted radiation as a function of wavelength for different temperatures of a blackbody.

Solve
No, the tungsten wire would not glow, as no intensity of light exists in the visible spectrum at 1000 K.

Think about It
At 2000 K, however, the tungsten wire would give off visible light. The red region of the visible spectrum has a higher intensity, so we might expect it to appear reddish at that temperature.

3.33. **Collect and Organize**
We are asked to calculate the energy of one UV photon of wavelength 3.00×10^{-7} m.

Analyze
The pertinent equation to consider here is $E = hc/\lambda$, where h is Planck's constant, c is the speed of light, and λ is the wavelength of the UV light.

Solve
$$E = \frac{(6.626 \times 10^{-34}\,\text{J}\cdot\text{s}) \times (2.998 \times 10^{8}\,\text{m/s})}{3.00 \times 10^{-7}\,\text{m}} = 6.62 \times 10^{-19}\,\text{J}$$

Think about It
This is the energy for only one photon. For an entire mole of photons, the energy would be 6.62 $\times\ 10^{-19}$ J multiplied by Avogadro's number to give 3.99×10^{5} J, or 399 kJ.

3.35. **Collect and Organize**
From a list, we are to choose which have quantized values.

Analyze
Something is quantized if it is present only in discrete amounts and can have only whole-number multiples of the smallest amount.

Solve
(a) The elevation of a step on a moving escalator continuously changes, so this is not a quantized value.
(b) Because the doors open only *at* the floors and not *between* the floors, this value is quantized.
(c) The speed of an automobile can change smoothly, so this is not a quantized value.

Think about It
Any quantity that is quantized has to have changes occurring in discrete steps.

3.37. **Collect and Organize**
The kinetic energy of an ejected photon is given by the equation
$$KE_{electron} = h\nu - \Phi$$
where Φ is the work function or the energy threshold required to eject the electron from the metal.

Analyze

In this problem, we solve for Φ:

$$\Phi = h\nu - KE_{electron}$$

where $h = 6.626 \times 10^{-34}$ J · s, ν = frequency of the light used to eject the electron, and $KE_{electron} = 5.34 \times 10^{-19}$ J. We can find ν of the irradiating light from $\nu = c/\lambda$, where $c = 2.998 \times 10^8$ m/s and we are given $\lambda = 162$ nm $(1.62 \times 10^{-7}$ m).

Solve

$$\Phi = \left(6.626 \times 10^{-34} \text{ J} \cdot \text{s} \times \frac{2.998 \times 10^8 \text{ m/s}}{1.62 \times 10^{-7} \text{ m}} \right) - 5.34 \times 10^{-19} \text{ J} = 6.92 \times 10^{-19} \text{ J}$$

Think about It

This does not seem to be a large amount of energy to emit one electron, but remember if we were to consider a mole of electrons to be ejected, we would need $(6.92 \times 10^{-19}$ J$) \times (6.0221 \times 10^{23}$/mol$) = 4.17 \times 10^5$ J/mol, or 417 kJ per mol. This is the ionization energy in kilojoules per mole for this metal.

3.39. Collect and Organize

We can use the equation for the photovoltaic effect to determine whether electrons could be ejected from tantalum by using light with a wavelength of 500 nm.

Analyze

As long as the energy of the light that shines on the metal is greater than the work function for tantalum ($\Phi = 6.81 \times 10^{-19}$ J), the light will eject electrons and tantalum would therefore be useful in a voltaic cell. The energy of the light can be calculated from $E = hc/\lambda$.

Solve

The energy of light of 500 nm wavelength can be found as

$$E = \frac{6.626 \times 10^{-34} \text{ J} \cdot \text{s} \times 2.998 \times 10^8 \text{ m/s}}{5.00 \times 10^{-7} \text{ m}} = 3.97 \times 10^{-19} \text{ J}$$

This energy is less than the work function for tantalum ($\Phi = 6.81 \times 10^{-19}$ J), so tantalum could not be used to convert solar energy at 500 nm to electricity.

Think about It

The wavelength of light that would be needed to eject electrons from tantalum would be

$$\lambda = \frac{hc}{\Phi} = \frac{6.626 \times 10^{-34} \text{ J} \cdot \text{s} \times 2.998 \times 10^8 \text{ m/s}}{6.81 \times 10^{-19} \text{ J}} = 2.92 \times 10^{-7} \text{ m, or 292 nm}$$

3.41. Collect and Organize

We are to calculate the velocity (speed) of electrons ejected from Na and K when irradiated by a 300 nm light source to determine which has the higher speed. Because the work function for potassium is lower than that of sodium, we expect that an electron ejected from potassium has a higher kinetic energy.

Analyze

For each metal, $KE_{electron} = h\nu - \Phi$, where the frequency of the light irradiating the metals would be found from $\nu = c/\lambda$, where $\lambda = 300$ nm $(3.00 \times 10^{-7}$ m). The speed of the electron can then be found as

$$KE = \frac{1}{2} m_e u^2, \text{ or } u = \sqrt{\frac{2KE}{m_e}}$$

where m_e is the mass of an electron, 9.11×10^{-31} kg.

Solve

Potassium:

$$KE = \left(6.626 \times 10^{-34} \text{ J} \cdot \text{s} \times \frac{2.998 \times 10^{8} \text{ m/s}}{3.00 \times 10^{-7} \text{ m}}\right) - 3.68 \times 10^{-19} \text{ J} = 2.942 \times 10^{-19} \text{ J}$$

$$u = \sqrt{\frac{2 \times 2.942 \times 10^{-19} \text{ kg} \cdot \text{m}^2/\text{s}^2}{9.11 \times 10^{-31} \text{ kg}}} = 8.04 \times 10^{5} \text{ m/s}$$

Sodium:

$$KE = \left(6.626 \times 10^{-34} \text{ J} \cdot \text{s} \times \frac{2.998 \times 10^{8} \text{ m/s}}{3.00 \times 10^{-7} \text{ m}}\right) - 4.41 \times 10^{-19} \text{ J} = 2.212 \times 10^{-19} \text{ J}$$

$$u = \sqrt{\frac{2 \times 2.212 \times 10^{-19} \text{ kg} \cdot \text{m}^2/\text{s}^2}{9.11 \times 10^{-31} \text{ kg}}} = 6.97 \times 10^{5} \text{ m/s}$$

Potassium's ejected electrons have a greater speed.

Think about It

The units of $1 \text{ J} = 1 \text{ kg} \cdot \text{m}^2/\text{s}^2$ are useful in ensuring that the speeds are in meters per second.

3.43. **Collect and Organize**

Using the information that a red laser's power is 1 J/s (1 W), we are to calculate the number of photons emitted by the laser per second.

Analyze

The energy of the photons of red laser light ($\lambda = 630$ nm) is given by

$$E = hc/\lambda$$

This corresponds to the number of photons in a second by

$$\text{number of photons} = \left(1 \text{ J}\right) \times \left(\frac{1 \text{ photon}}{\text{energy of photon}}\right)$$

Solve

Energy of one photon with $\lambda = 630$ nm:

$$E = \frac{6.626 \times 10^{-34} \text{ J} \cdot \text{s} \times 2.998 \times 10^{8} \text{ m/s}}{6.30 \times 10^{-7} \text{ m}} = 3.153 \times 10^{-19} \text{ J/photon}$$

Number of photons per second:

$$1.00 \text{ watt} \times \frac{1 \text{ J/s}}{\text{watt}} \times \frac{1 \text{ photon}}{3.153 \times 10^{-19} \text{ J}} = 3.17 \times 10^{18} \text{ photons/s}$$

Think about It

Greater power (watts) leads to more photons being emitted each second. Also, the shorter the wavelength, the greater the energy per photon and the higher the power (watts) for the same number of photons emitted.

3.45. **Collect and Organize**

We are asked to explain how the Balmer equation is just a special case of the Rydberg equation.

Analyze

The Balmer equation, where $m > 2$ and $n = 2$, is

$$\lambda \text{ (in nm)} = \left(\frac{364.56 m^2}{m^2 - n^2}\right)$$

The Rydberg equation, where $n_2 > n_1$ (and they may be any integers), is

$$\frac{1}{\lambda} = R_{\text{H}}\left(\frac{1}{n_1^2} - \frac{1}{n_2^2}\right)$$

Solve

Although their forms appear fairly different, both predict the spectrum of the hydrogen atom. The Rydberg equation is more general, with variable integers for n_1 and n_2, and so could predict lines outside the visible spectrum.

Think about It

The Balmer equation is equivalent to the Rydberg equation when $n_1 = 2$ with $n_2 = 1$ and $m = 3$.

3.47. **Collect and Organize**

We consider here the process of emission of light from a hydrogen atom in an excited state. Does the energy emitted depend on the values of n_1 and n_2 or only on the difference between them $(n_1 - n_2)$?

Analyze

The emission of light from an H atom in the excited state is the result of the electron dropping from a higher energy orbit to a lower-lying orbit.

Solve

Because the difference in the orbits' energy correlates with the light energy emitted by the hydrogen atom in the excited state, the difference between n levels determines emission energy as the excited H atom relaxes to its ground state.

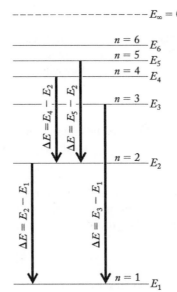

Think about It

The n levels get closer in energy as n increases so that $n_2 - n_1 > n_3 - n_2 > n_4 - n_3$, etc.

3.49. **Collect and Organize**

In considering the absorption of energy for an electron to be promoted from a lower energy orbit to a higher energy orbit $(n_1 < n_2)$, we can predict which transition requires the shortest wavelength of light.

Analyze

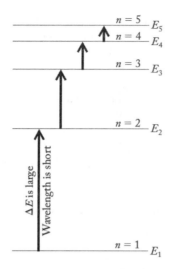

The transition with the shortest wavelength has the highest change in energy. The energy levels (*n*) in hydrogen are not evenly spaced; as *n* increases, the differences in energy between adjacent energy levels decrease.

Solve

All the transitions given involve changes between adjacent levels ($\Delta n = 1$). Because the energy levels become more closely spaced as *n* increases, ΔE values for energy levels for lower *n* values are greater and therefore have shorter wavelengths associated with them. Therefore, choice a, where the electron is "promoted" from *n* = 1 to *n* = 2, has the shortest wavelength.

Think about It

The transitions will have the following order (from longest to shortest wavelength):

(d) *n* = 4 to *n* = 5 > (c) *n* = 3 to *n* = 4 > (b) *n* = 2 to *n* = 3 > (a) *n* = 1 to *n* = 2

3.51. Collect and Organize / Analyze

The lines of the Fraunhofer series from hydrogen in the sun's spectrum are observed in the visible region of the electromagnetic spectrum. These arise from transitions from *n* = 2 to higher energy levels (*n* = 3 to 6). We are asked whether any transitions from *n* = 1 (the ground state) to higher energy levels would be observed among the Fraunhofer lines.

Solve

From Figure 3.17 (which shows emission, not absorption, but the two are complementary) we see that the *n* = 1 to *n* = 2, 3, 4, 5, and 6 energy states have generally larger energies associated with them than transitions from *n* = 2, so no Fraunhofer lines are associated with absorption from the ground state.

Think about It

Absorptions from the ground state are associated with the Lyman series.

3.53. Collect and Organize

We are asked to explain why Balmer observed the *n* = 6 to *n* = 2 transition in hydrogen but not that for *n* = 7 to *n* = 2.

Analyze

As seen in Figure 3.17 the energy levels become more closely spaced as the value of *n* increases. We can use the equation below to calculate the wavelength of the transition.

$$\frac{1}{\lambda} = [1.097 \times 10^{-2} \ (\text{nm})^{-1}] \left(\frac{1}{n_1^2} - \frac{1}{n_2^2} \right)$$

Solve

At $n = 7$, the electron energy wavelength has moved out of the visible region:

$$\frac{1}{\lambda} = [1.097 \times 10^{-2} \ (nm)^{-1}]\left(\frac{1}{2^2} - \frac{1}{7^2}\right)$$

$$\lambda = 397.0 \ nm$$

At $n = 7$, the wavelength of the electron's transition ($n = 7$ to $n = 2$) has moved out of the visible region.

Think about It

The transition from the $n = 7$ energy level can be detected in the UV region of the electromagnetic spectrum.

3.55. **Collect and Organize**

To calculate the wavelength emitted when an electron in hydrogen undergoes a transition from $n = 4$ to $n = 3$, we can use the Rydberg equation. The region of the electromagnetic spectrum corresponding to that wavelength can be found from Figure 3.1 in the textbook.

Analyze

In the Rydberg equation, $n_1 = 3$ and $n_2 = 4$.

$$\frac{1}{\lambda} = [1.097 \times 10^{-2} \ (nm)^{-1}]\left(\frac{1}{n_1^2} - \frac{1}{n_2^2}\right)$$

Solve

$$\frac{1}{\lambda} = [1.097 \times 10^{-2} \ (nm)^{-1}]\left(\frac{1}{3^2} - \frac{1}{4^2}\right) = 5.333 \times 10^{-4} (nm)^{-1}$$

$$\lambda = 1875 \ nm$$

This wavelength occurs in the infrared region of the electromagnetic spectrum.

Think about It

In the Rydberg equation, n_2 is a higher orbit number (n) than n_1. In this way we don't get the nonsensical result of a negative wavelength.

3.57. **Collect and Organize**

The equation given relates the photon's energy to atomic number and the energy-level transition.

Analyze

The equation shows a direct relationship between the energy and the atomic number and between the energy and the transition of the electron between n_1 and n_2 as

$$\frac{1}{n_1^2} - \frac{1}{n_2^2}$$

Solve

(a) Because the energy of the photons is directly related to the atomic number in the equation, as Z increases, the energy increases. Because energy is inversely related to wavelength, the wavelength decreases as Z increases.

(b) The energy of the photon for $Z = 1$ (hydrogen) is

$$E = (2.18 \times 10^{-18} \ J)(1)^2\left(\frac{1}{1^2} - \frac{1}{2^2}\right) = 1.635 \times 10^{-18} \ J$$

The wavelength of this photon is

$$\lambda = \frac{6.626 \times 10^{-34} \ J \cdot s \times 2.998 \times 10^8 \ m/s}{1.635 \times 10^{-18} \ J} = 1.21 \times 10^{-7} \ m, \ or \ 121 \ nm$$

This wavelength is in the UV range. As Z increases, the energy of the photon increases and the wavelength decreases, so the transition will never be observed in the visible range.

Think about It
The $n = 1$ and $n = 2$ energy levels are too far apart in energy to give an emitted photon in the visible range.

3.59. Collect and Organize
The difference between the hydrogen atom and the Li^{2+} ion is the charge on the nucleus. Both are one-electron species, so we can use the Bohr equation to calculate the energy (and then the wavelength) of the $n = 3$ to $n = 2$ transition in Li^{2+}.

Analyze
In the equation

$$E = \left(2.18 \times 10^{-18} \text{ J}\right) Z^2 \left(\frac{1}{n_f^2} - \frac{1}{n_i^2}\right)$$

for Li^{2+}, $Z = 3$, $n_i = 3$, and $n_f = 2$ for this problem. To convert energy into wavelength, use $\lambda = hc/E$.

Solve

$$E = \left(2.18 \times 10^{-18} \text{ J}\right)(3)^2 \left(\frac{1}{2^2} - \frac{1}{3^2}\right) = 2.725 \times 10^{-18} \text{ J}$$

$$\lambda = \frac{6.626 \times 10^{-34} \text{ J} \cdot \text{s} \times 2.998 \times 10^8 \text{ m/s}}{2.725 \times 10^{-18} \text{ J}} = 7.29 \times 10^{-8} \text{ m, or } 72.9 \text{ nm}$$

This wavelength is much shorter than the wavelength associated with the same transition in an H atom.

Think about It
This answer would be the energy and wavelength of the photon *emitted* from the Li^{2+} ion.

3.61. Collect and Organize / Analyze

The de Broglie equation is

$$\lambda = \frac{h}{mu}$$

We are to define the symbols in the equation and explain how this equation shows the wavelike properties of a particle.

Solve

In the de Broglie equation, λ is the wavelength that the particle of mass m exhibits as it travels at speed u, with h being Planck's constant. This equation states that any moving particle has wavelike properties because a wavelength can be calculated through the equation and that the wavelength of the particle is inversely related to its momentum (mass × velocity).

Think about It

From the equation, we see that as mass and/or speed increases, the wavelength of a particle decreases.

3.63. Collect and Organize / Analyze

We consider whether the shape or density of an object affects its de Broglie wavelength.

Solve

The de Broglie equation relates only the mass and the speed to the wavelength, so neither the shape nor the density would affect the de Broglie wavelength.

Think about It

From the de Broglie equation we see that as the mass or the speed of a particle increases, the wavelength associated with that particle decreases.

3.65. Collect and Organize

When two objects of different masses move at the same speed, we can use the de Broglie relationship to compare their wavelengths and determine whether the given statements are true.

Analyze

From the de Broglie equation,

$$\lambda = \frac{h}{mu}$$

we see that wavelength is inversely proportional to the mass of the particle.

Solve

(a) False. Heavier particles have a *shorter* wavelength than lighter particles.
(b) True. When $m_2 = 2m_1$, then

$$\frac{\lambda_2}{\lambda_1} = \frac{h/2m_1u}{h/m_1u} = \frac{1}{2}$$

(c) True. Doubling the speed gives $u_2 = 2u_1$:

$$\frac{\lambda_2}{\lambda_1} = \frac{h/m2u_1}{h/mu_1} = \frac{1}{2}$$

This is the same as doubling the mass in (b).

Think about It

Small, fast-moving particles exhibit the longest wavelengths.

3.67. Collect and Organize

Given the mass of objects (from a muon to Earth), we are to use the de Broglie equation to calculate the wavelength of the objects moving at given speeds.

Analyze

The de Broglie equation is

$$\lambda = \frac{h}{mu}$$

where Planck's constant is $h = 6.626 \times 10^{-34}$ J·s, m is the mass of the particle in kilograms, and u is the speed of the particle in meters per second. Recall that $1\ \text{J} = 1\ \text{kg}\cdot\text{m}^2/\text{s}^2$.

Solve

(a) Muon:

$$\lambda = \frac{6.626 \times 10^{-34}\ \text{kg}\cdot\text{m}^2/\text{s}}{1.884 \times 10^{-28}\ \text{kg} \times 325\ \text{m/s}} = 1.08 \times 10^{-8}\ \text{m, or } 10.8\ \text{nm}$$

(b) Electron:

$$\lambda = \frac{6.626 \times 10^{-34}\ \text{kg}\cdot\text{m}^2/\text{s}}{9.10939 \times 10^{-31}\ \text{kg} \times 4.05 \times 10^6\ \text{m/s}} = 1.80 \times 10^{-10}\ \text{m, or } 0.180\ \text{nm}$$

(c) Sprinter:

$$\lambda = \frac{6.626 \times 10^{-34}\ \text{kg}\cdot\text{m}^2/\text{s}}{82\ \text{kg} \times 9.9\ \text{m/s}} = 8.2 \times 10^{-37}\ \text{m, or } 8.2 \times 10^{-28}\ \text{nm}$$

(d) Earth:

$$\lambda = \frac{6.626 \times 10^{-34}\ \text{kg}\cdot\text{m}^2/\text{s}}{6.0 \times 10^{24}\ \text{kg} \times 3.0 \times 10^4\ \text{m/s}} = 3.68 \times 10^{-63}\ \text{m, or } 3.68 \times 10^{-54}\ \text{nm}$$

Think about It

Only small particles with low mass generally show wavelike behavior. We can detect λ only on the order of the size of atoms, or 10^{-10} m. We therefore do not observe the sprinter's or Earth's waves.

3.69. Collect and Organize

Heisenberg's uncertainty principle states that the uncertainty in the position (Δx) multiplied by $m\Delta u$, where m is the particle's mass and Δu is the uncertainty in the particle's speed, must be equal to or greater than $h/4\pi$; that is,

$$\Delta x \cdot m\Delta u \geq \frac{h}{4\pi}$$

Analyze

For the H_2^+ particle in the cyclotron, the 3% uncertainty in velocity would be

$$\Delta u = 4 \times 10^6\ \text{m/s} \times 0.03 = 1.2 \times 10^5\ \text{m/s}$$

The mass of the H_2^+ particle would be

$$\frac{2.016\ \text{g}}{1\ \text{mol}} \times \frac{1\ \text{mol}}{6.022 \times 10^{23}\ \text{particles}} \times \frac{1\ \text{kg}}{1000\ \text{g}} = 3.35 \times 10^{-27}\ \text{kg}$$

Solve

Rearranging Heisenberg's equation to solve for Δx:

$$\Delta x \geq \frac{h}{4\pi m\Delta u} = \frac{6.626 \times 10^{-34}\ \text{kg}\cdot\text{m}^2/\text{s}}{4\pi \times 3.35 \times 10^{-27}\ \text{kg} \times 1.2 \times 10^5\ \text{m/s}} = 1.3 \times 10^{-13}\ \text{m}$$

Think about It

The minimum uncertainty in position is very small, smaller than what we can measure, so in principle we can accurately determine the position of the H_2^+ particle moving at this speed.

3.71. Collect and Organize / Analyze

We are to differentiate between a Bohr orbit and a quantum theory orbital.

Solve

The Bohr model orbit showed the quantized nature of the electron in the atom as a particle moving around the nucleus in concentric orbits, much like planets moving around the sun.

In quantum theory, an orbital is a region of space where the probability of finding the electron is high. The electron is not viewed as a particle but as a wave, and it is not confined to a clearly defined orbit; rather, we refer to the probability of the electron being at various locations around the nucleus.

Think about It

Bohr's model helped explain atomic spectra. The quantum theory of the atom helped to explain much more, including how atoms bond and the probability of an electronic transition in an atom.

3.73. Collect and Organize / Analyze

To identify the orbital for an electron, we are asked how many quantum numbers we would need.

Solve

We need to describe the shell, the subshell, and the orbital's orientation to define a particular orbital. Therefore, we need three quantum numbers: n, ℓ, and m_ℓ.

Think about It

We could not use fewer quantum numbers to describe a particular orbital because confusion would arise as to what shell or subshell an electron belonged to, or what its orientation was.

3.75. Collect and Organize

As the principal quantum number, n, increases, so does the number of orbitals available at the n level.

Analyze

The number of orbitals at each level n is n^2.

Solve

(a) For $n = 1$, there is only 1 orbital (an s orbital).
(b) For $n = 2$, there are 4 orbitals (one s and three p orbitals).
(c) For $n = 3$, there are 9 orbitals (one s, three p, and five d orbitals).
(d) For $n = 4$, there are 16 orbitals (one s, three p, five d, and seven f orbitals).
(e) For $n = 5$, there are 25 orbitals (one s, three p, five d, seven f, and nine g orbitals). This totals 55 orbitals in the atom.

Think about It

Each subshell has an odd number of orbitals, and the number of orbitals in a particular subshell is $2\ell + 1$, where $\ell = 0$ for s orbitals, 1 for p orbitals, 2 for d orbitals, and 3 for f orbitals.

3.77. Collect and Organize

We are to list all the possible ℓ values when $n = 4$.

Analyze

The angular momentum quantum number is related to n as $\ell = n - 1, n - 2, n - 3, \ldots, 0$.

Solve

When $n = 4$, $\ell = 3, 2, 1, 0$.

Think about It

These ℓ values correspond to the f, d, p, and s subshells, respectively.

3.79. Collect and Organize
For each set of quantum numbers of n and ℓ, we are to write the orbital designation.

Analyze
The principal quantum number gives the shell number, which is just expressed as the number. The angular momentum quantum number, however, is given a letter designation ($\ell = 0$ is an s orbital, $\ell = 1$ is a p orbital, $\ell = 2$ is a d orbital, and $\ell = 3$ is an f orbital).

Solve
(a) $n = 2$, $\ell = 0$ represents $2s$.
(b) $n = 3$, $\ell = 1$ represents $3p$.
(c) $n = 4$, $\ell = 2$ represents $4d$.
(d) $n = 1$, $\ell = 0$ represents $1s$.

Think about It
The letter designation for the shape of the orbital provides a shorthand designation of the orbital as a number plus a letter. This system is easier than describing the orbital with two numbers (n and ℓ).

3.81. Collect and Organize
Given values for the quantum numbers n, ℓ, and m_ℓ, we are to determine the number of electrons that could occupy the orbitals described by these quantum numbers.

Analyze
The principal quantum number gives us the shell of the orbitals. This then gives the allowed values of ℓ ($n - 1$), which in turn describes the type of orbital (s, p, d, or f). The m_ℓ quantum number gives us the orientation of the orbital and its allowed values ($-\ell, -\ell + 1, \ldots, \ell - 1, \ell$), which gives us the number of orbitals available for that subshell. Each orbital can accommodate two electrons.

Solve
(a) The set of quantum numbers $n = 2$, $\ell = 0$ describes a $2s$ orbital that can be occupied by two electrons.
(b) The set of quantum numbers $n = 3$, $\ell = 1$, $m_\ell = 0$ describes one of the $3p$ orbitals that can be occupied by two electrons.
(c) The set of quantum numbers $n = 4$, $\ell = 2$ describes the set of $4d$ orbitals. Five d orbitals are in the subshell, so 10 electrons can occupy this orbital set.
(d) The set of quantum numbers $n = 1$, $\ell = 0$, $m_\ell = 0$ describes the $1s$ orbital that can be occupied by two electrons.

Think about It
Remember that one s, three p, five d, seven f, and nine g orbitals exist in shells for which these are allowed.

3.83. Collect and Organize
Given values for the quantum numbers n, ℓ, m_ℓ, and m_s we are to determine which combinations are allowed.

Analyze
The principal quantum number (n) can take on whole numbers starting with 1 ($n = 1, 2, 3, 4, \ldots$). The angular momentum quantum numbers (ℓ) possible for a given n value are $n - 1, n - 2, \ldots, 0$. The magnetic quantum numbers (m_ℓ) allowed for a given ℓ are $-\ell, -\ell + 1, \ldots, \ell - 1, \ell$. Allowed values for m_s are $+\frac{1}{2}$ and $-\frac{1}{2}$.

Solve
(a) For $n = 1$, the only allowed value of ℓ and m_ℓ is 0; the combination $n = 1$, $\ell = 1$, $m_\ell = 0$, $m_s = +\frac{1}{2}$ is not allowed because $\ell \neq 1$ when $n = 1$.
(b) For $n = 3$, the allowed values of ℓ are 0, 1, and 2 and when $\ell = 0$ the allowed value of m_ℓ is 0; this combination of $n = 3$, $\ell = 0$, $m_\ell = 0$, $m_s = -\frac{1}{2}$ is allowed.

(c) For $n = 1$, the only allowed value for ℓ and m_ℓ is 0; the combination $n = 1$, $\ell = 0$, $m_\ell = 1$, $m_s = -\frac{1}{2}$ is not allowed because $m_\ell \neq 1$ when $\ell = 0$.

(d) For $n = 2$, the allowed values of ℓ are 0 and 1 and when $\ell = 1$ the allowed value of $m_\ell = -1, 0, 1$; this combination of $n = 2$, $\ell = 1$, $m_\ell = 2$, $m_s = +\frac{1}{2}$ is not allowed because $m_\ell \neq 2$ when $\ell = 1$.

Think about It
For the allowed combination of quantum numbers, part b describes a $3s$ orbital.

3.85. Collect and Organize / Analyze
We are asked what is meant by *degenerate orbitals*.

Solve
Degenerate orbitals have the same energy and are indistinguishable from each other.

Think about It
In the hydrogen atom, all the orbitals in a given n level are degenerate. This means that in hydrogen the $3s$, $3p$, and $3d$ orbitals, for example, all have the same energy. In multielectron atoms, however, these orbitals split in energy and are no longer degenerate.

3.87. Collect and Organize
In the filling of atomic orbitals, the $4s$ level fills before the $3d$. We are asked how this is evident in the periodic table.

Analyze
The two leftmost columns in the periodic table correspond to the s block, whereas columns 3–12 starting in period 4 correspond to the d block.

Solve
As we start from an argon core of electrons, we move to potassium and calcium, which are located in the s block on the periodic table. It is not until Sc, Ti, V, etc., that we begin to fill electrons into the $3d$ shell.

Think about It
The $6s$ orbitals fill (Cs and Ba), followed by the $4f$ orbitals (Ce–Yb) and then the $5d$ orbitals (La–Hg).

3.89. Collect and Organize
For multielectron atoms, we are to identify the subshells defined by their n and ℓ quantum numbers and then arrange them in order of increasing energy.

Analyze
The higher the energy of an orbital, the farther the electron is from the nucleus. This means that for different n values the order of energies is $1 < 2 < 3$, etc. For orbitals in the same n shell, the orbitals increase in energy; that is, $s < p < d < f$ for multielectron atoms.

Solve
The orbitals described are (a) $3d$, for $n = 3$, $\ell = 2$; (b) $7f$, for $n = 7$, $\ell = 3$; (c) $3s$, for $n = 3$, $\ell = 0$; and (d) $4p$ for $n = 4$, $\ell = 1$, $m_\ell = 1$.
In increasing order of energy: (c) $3s <$ (a) $3d <$ (d) $4p <$ (b) $7f$.

Think about It
To determine the energy of an orbital, first look to the n quantum number and then to the ℓ.

3.91. Collect and Organize
We can use the periodic table and Figure 3.32 to write the electron configurations for several elemental species, including anions and cations.

Analyze

When a cation is formed, electrons are removed from the highest energy orbital. None of the species are transition metals, so we remove the electrons from the orbitals last filled in building the electron configuration of the element. To form an anion, we need to add electrons to the highest energy orbital or the next orbital up in energy. We use the previous noble gas configuration as the "core" to write the condensed form of the configurations.

Solve

Li^+: [He] or $1s^2$ Mg^{2+}: $[He]2s^22p^6$ or [Ne]

Ca: $[Ar]4s^2$ Al^{3+}: $He]2s^22p^6$ or [Ne]

F^-: $[He]2s^22p^6$ or [Ne]

Think about It

Because F^-, Mg^{2+}, and Al^{3+} all have the same electron configurations and thus the same number of electrons, they are isoelectronic with each other.

3.93. Collect and Organize

We are to write the condensed electron configurations (using the noble gas core configuration in brackets) for several species, including cationic and anionic species.

Analyze

When a cation is formed, electrons are removed from the highest energy orbital. To form an anion, we need to add electrons to the highest energy orbital or the next orbital up in energy.

Solve

K: $[Ar]4s^1$ Ti^{4+}: [Ar] or $[Ne]3s^23p^6$

K^+: [Ar]   Ni: $[Ar]4s^23d^8$

Ba: $[Xe]6s^2$

Think about It

K^+ and Ti^{4+} are isoelectronic with each other and with Ar.

3.95. Collect and Organize

We can use the periodic table and Figure 3.32 to write the electron configurations for several elemental species.

Analyze

When a cation is formed, electrons are removed from the highest energy orbital. Mn is a transition metal, so we have to remember to remove electrons from its *s* orbital in forming the 2+ cation. We use the previous noble gas configuration as the "core" to write the condensed form of the configurations.

Solve

Ra: $[Rn]7s^2$ Mn: $[Ar]4s^23d^5$

I: $[Kr]5s^24d^{10}5p^5$ Mn^{2+}: $[Ar]4s^03d^5$

In: $[Kr]5s^24d^{10}5p^1$

Think about it

Indium and iodine are both considered *p*-block elements.

3.97. Collect and Organize

To determine the number of unpaired electrons in the ground-state atoms and ions, we have to first write the electron configuration for each species and then detail how the electrons are distributed among the highest energy orbitals.

Analyze
If the highest energy orbital (*s*, *p*, *d*, or *f*) is either empty or full, the species have no unpaired electrons. If the highest energy orbital is partially full, electrons singly occupy the degenerate orbitals at that level before pairing up in those orbitals (by Hund's rule).

Solve
(a) N: $[\text{He}]2s^2 2p^3$ 3 unpaired e^-
(b) O: $[\text{He}]2s^2 2p^4$ 2 unpaired e^-
(c) P^{3-}: $[\text{Ne}]3s^2 3p^6$ 0 unpaired e^-
(d) Na^+: $[\text{Ne}]$ or $[\text{He}]2s^2 2p^6$ 0 unpaired e^-

Think about It
The ground-state configuration of these elements fills the *s* orbital first and then places electrons into the *p* orbitals. This is because for a multielectron atom, $s < p$ in terms of energy for a given principal quantum level.

3.99. Collect and Organize
An atom with the electron configuration $[\text{Ar}]3d^2 4s^2$ is in the fourth period in the periodic table and is among the transition metals.

Analyze
This atom has no charge, so we do not have to account for additional or lost electrons.

Solve
The 4*s* orbital is filled for the element Ca. Two additional electrons are present in the 3*d* orbitals for the second transition metal of the fourth period: titanium, Ti. The electron-filling orbital box diagram shows two unpaired electrons.

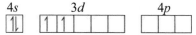

Think about It
Although we write the electron configuration so that 3*d* comes before 4*s*, remember that the 4*s* orbital fills before the 3*d* in building up electron configurations.

3.101. Collect and Organize
We are to name the monatomic anion that has a filled-shell configuration of $[\text{Ne}]3s^2 3p^6$ or $[\text{Ar}]$ and determine the number of unpaired electrons in the ion in its ground state.

Analyze
Because the atom has an extra electron, to form the monatomic anion, the neutral atom would have an electron configuration of one fewer electron.

Solve
Ion's electron configuration: $[\text{Ne}]3s^2 3p^6 = X^-$
Atom's electron configuration: $[\text{Ne}]3s^2 3p^5 = X$
This atom is chlorine and the monatomic anion is chloride, Cl^-. Because electrons fill the *s* and *p* orbitals, Cl^- has no unpaired electrons in its ground state.

Think about It
When identifying elements with the electron configurations of anions, remove the electrons associated with the anionic charge to obtain the electron configuration of the neutral atom.

3.103. Collect and Organize
An electronic excited state exists when an electron has been placed into a higher energy orbital than would be predicted by using the filling rules shown by the periodic table.

Analyze

The order of filling for the orbitals is as follows:

$1s < 2s < 2p < 3s < 3p < 4s < 3d < 4p < 5s < 4d < 5p < 6s < 4f < 5d < 6p < 7s < 5f < 6d < 7p$

Solve

(a) Because the $2s$ orbital is lower in energy than the $2p$ orbital, the lowest energy configuration for this atom is $[\text{He}]2s^2 2p^4$, so the configuration $[\text{He}]2s^1 2p^5$ represents an excited state.

(b) The order of filling of orbitals for atoms after krypton is $5s < 4d < 5p$. This atom has 13 electrons in its outer shell: two fill the $5s$ orbital, 10 fill the $4d$ orbitals, and one is placed in a $5p$ orbital. This configuration, $[\text{Kr}]4d^{10}5s^2 5p^1$, does not represent an excited state.

(c) The order of filling of orbitals for atoms after argon is $4s < 3d < 4p$. This atom has 17 electrons in its outer shell: two fill the $4s$ orbital, 10 fill the $3d$ orbitals, and five are placed in the $4p$ orbitals. This configuration, $[\text{Ar}]3d^{10}4s^2 4p^5$, does not represent an excited state.

(d) Because the $3p$ orbital is lower in energy than the $4s$ orbital, the lowest energy configuration for this atom is $[\text{Ne}]3s^2 3p^3$, so the configuration $[\text{Ne}]3s^2 3p^2 4s^1$ represents an excited state.

Think about It

If each of these configurations is for neutral atoms, we can assign the elements as follows: (a) excited-state O, (b) ground-state In, (c) ground-state Br, and (d) excited-state P.

3.105. Collect and Organize

Iodine-131 has 53 protons, 78 neutrons, and 53 electrons as a neutral atom. We are to identify the subshell containing the highest energy electrons and compare the electron configurations of ^{131}I and ^{127}I.

Analyze

The electron configuration for iodine is $[\text{Kr}]4d^{10}5s^2 5p^5$. The difference between ^{131}I and ^{127}I is that ^{131}I has four additional neutrons in its nucleus.

Solve

The electron configuration of iodine shows that the highest energy electrons are in the $5p$ subshell. Because the difference in isotopes is the number of neutrons present, the electron configurations of ^{131}I and ^{127}I (which are based on total number of electrons in the atom) are the same.

Think about It

Electron configurations, however, do change if the atom gains or loses electrons to become either anionic or cationic, respectively.

3.107. Collect and Organize

Sodium and chlorine atoms are neutral in charge, but the sodium atom in NaCl has a charge of 1+ and the chlorine atom has a charge of 1–. These changes in charge also come with a change in size. Why?

Analyze

When we remove an electron from an atom, we reduce the repulsion for the remaining electrons in the atom. When we add electrons, we increase e^--e^- repulsion.

Solve

If electrons do not repel each other as much in Na^+ as they do in Na, they will have lower energy and be, on average, closer to the nucleus, resulting in a smaller size. When electrons are added to an atom (Cl), the e^--e^- repulsion increases, so the electrons have higher energy and they will be, on average, farther from the nucleus, thereby creating a larger species (Cl^-).

Think about It

The change in size upon forming a cation or anion can be dramatic, as seen in Figure 3.35.

3.109. Collect and Organize

Of the group 1 elements (Li, Na, K, Rb) we are to predict the largest and explain our selection.

Analyze
The sizes of atoms increase down a group because electrons have been added to higher n levels.

Solve
Rb is the largest atom because as we descend a group the atoms get larger because of the addition of electrons to shells farther from the nucleus.

Think about It
The largest atoms are those situated to the lower left in the periodic table.

3.111. Collect and Organize
Ionization energy is the energy required to remove an electron from a gaseous atom.

$$X(g) \rightarrow X^+(g) + e^-$$

We are to state the trends in ionization energies down and across the periodic table.

Analyze
The ionization energy will change with effective nuclear charge (the higher the Z_{eff}, the greater the ionization energy) and with size (an electron farther away from the nucleus requires less energy to remove).

Solve
(a) As the atomic number increases down a group, electrons are added to higher n levels, leading to a decrease in ionization energy.
(b) As the atomic number increases across a period, the effective nuclear charge increases. This means that the ionization energy increases across a period of elements.

Think about It
Ionization energy trends follow atomic size trends; smaller atoms require more energy to ionize than larger atoms.

3.113. Collect and Organize
Fluorine and boron are located in the same period of the periodic table (period 2). Fluorine has nine protons in its nucleus, whereas boron has five. We are to explain why F is harder to ionize than B.

Analyze
Both fluorine and boron have $2s^2 2p^n$ configurations, and the ionized electron is removed from the $2p$ orbital.

Solve
Fluorine, with a higher nuclear charge, exerts a higher Z_{eff} on the $2p$ electrons than boron, resulting in higher ionization energy.

Think about It
The general trend across a period for ionization energies follows the trend for effective nuclear charge. As effective nuclear charge increases, so does ionization energy.

3.115. Collect and Organize
We have to consider the electron configurations of the cations of Br, Kr, Rb, Sr, and Y to determine which of the neutral atoms would have the smallest second ionization energy (IE_2).

Analyze

Element	Number of Protons in Nucleus	Electron Configuration	Cation (X^+) Electron Configuration
Br	35	$[Ar]3d^{10}4s^24p^5$	$[Ar]3d^{10}4s^24p^4$
Kr	36	$[Kr]$	$[Ar]3d^{10}4s^24p^5$
Rb	37	$[Kr]5s^1$	$[Kr]$
Sr	38	$[Kr]5s^2$	$[Kr]5s^1$
Y	39	$[Kr]4d^15s^2$	$[Kr]4d^15s^1$

Solve

Rb^+, with the noble gas configuration of Kr as Rb^+, has the highest IE_2. Both Br^+ and Kr^+ lose the second electron from a $4p$ orbital, which is lower in energy (harder to remove) than the removal of a $5s$ electron (higher in energy, easier to remove). Therefore, the IE_2 for Br^+ and Kr^+ is expected to be higher than that for Sr^+ or Y^+. Sr^+, with fewer protons in the nucleus, holds the $5s$ electron less tightly than Y^+. Therefore, Sr is expected to have the smallest IE_2.

Think about It

In determining relative orders for second, third, etc., IEs, we have to be sure to consider the electron configuration of the cation that will lose the electron for that particular ionization step.

3.117. Collect and Organize

For some elements, the electron affinity is negative and favorable to form the ions compared with that of the neutral atom. We are to decide whether this means that these elements all are present in nature as anions.

Analyze

Figure 3.37 shows electron affinity values for the representative elements. Nearly all these elements have a negative electron affinity, which indicates that the anion is lower in energy than the neutral atom.

Solve

No, a negative electron affinity does not mean that the element is present in nature as an anion. For example, sodium has an electron affinity of –52.9 kJ/mol, but it is always present in nature as Na^+, not even as Na metal. This is also true of the other metals in the table.

Think about It

However, the nonmetals such as the halogens often do have negative charges in their compounds found in nature, such as NaCl and KI.

3.119. Collect and Organize

As we descend the halogens (group 17), the electron affinity values increase (become more positive or less negative). We are to explain this trend.

Analyze

Less negative (or more positive) values of electron affinity mean that the anion formed is getting less stable than the neutral atom as the atoms in a group get larger.

Solve

As the atom gets larger descending a group, the added electron is placed into an orbital that is farther from the nucleus and is therefore less tightly held, resulting in decreased stability of the anion over that of the neutral atom.

Think about It

The trend in descending a group often shows discrepancies for the first element in the group in period 2. The values of the electron affinity for these elements (Be, B, C, N, O, and F) are lower than expected because the electron is being added to a small atom where electron–electron repulsions are more noticeable.

3.121. Collect and Organize

We consider an electron dropping from $n = 732$ to $n = 731$ in a hydrogen atom. We are to calculate the energy of this transition along with its wavelength and say what kind of telescope could detect such radiation.

Analyze

The energy difference between two n levels in the hydrogen atom is given by the equation

$$\Delta E = -2.18 \times 10^{-18} \text{ J} \left(\frac{1}{n_f^2} - \frac{1}{n_i^2} \right)$$

The wavelength of light associated with a particular energy is
$$\lambda = hc/E$$

Solve

(a) $\Delta E = -2.18 \times 10^{-18} \text{ J} \left(\dfrac{1}{731^2} - \dfrac{1}{732^2} \right) = -1.11 \times 10^{-26} \text{ J}$

Because this energy represents a loss of energy as the electron drops from a higher energy level to a lower energy level, this process is exothermic, so the sign of ΔE is negative.

(b) $\lambda = \dfrac{6.626 \times 10^{-34} \text{ J} \cdot \text{s} \times 2.998 \times 10^8 \text{ m/s}}{1.11 \times 10^{-26} \text{ J}} = 17.9 \text{ m}$

(c) This long wavelength occurs in the radio portion of the electromagnetic spectrum, so we would need a radio telescope to detect this transition.

Think about It

Our result makes sense. As n increases in the hydrogen atom, the energy levels get closer and closer together in energy, and a transition between any two adjacent n levels where n is high would emit very little energy (long wavelength).

3.123. Collect and Organize

We consider the emission of energy from an He^+ ion from $n = 3$ to $n = 1$ compared with a stepwise relaxation of an He^+ ion to the ground state ($n = 3$ to $n = 2$ and then $n = 2$ to $n = 1$). We are to determine which of the statements given are true.

Analyze

Both He^+ ions have the same nuclear charge (2+) and the same energies for $n = 3$, $n = 2$, and $n = 1$.

Solve

(a) True. Because the energies of $n = 1$, 2, and 3 do not depend on how the electron relaxes to the ground state, the total energy of $n = 3$ to $n = 1$ is equal to the sum of the energy of $n = 3$ to $n = 2$ and the energy of $n = 2$ to $n = 1$.

(b) False. Although the energies are additive, the wavelengths are not:
$$E_{3\to1} = hc/\lambda_{3\to1}$$
$$E_{3\to1,\,2\to1} = hc/\lambda_{3\to2} + hc/\lambda_{2\to1}$$

These energies are equal, so
$$\frac{hc}{\lambda_{3\to1}} = \frac{hc}{\lambda_{3\to2}} + \frac{hc}{\lambda_{2\to1}}$$
$$\frac{1}{\lambda_{3\to1}} = \frac{1}{\lambda_{3\to2}} + \frac{1}{\lambda_{2\to1}} = \frac{\lambda_{2\to1}}{\lambda_{3\to2}\lambda_{2\to1}} + \frac{\lambda_{3\to2}}{\lambda_{2\to1}\lambda_{3\to2}}$$

Multiplying both sides by $\lambda_{3\to1}$ gives

$$1 = \frac{\lambda_{2\to1}\lambda_{3\to1}}{\lambda_{3\to2}\lambda_{2\to1}} + \frac{\lambda_{3\to2}\lambda_{3\to1}}{\lambda_{2\to1}\lambda_{3\to2}} = \frac{\lambda_{2\to1}\lambda_{3\to1} + \lambda_{3\to2}\lambda_{3\to1}}{\lambda_{3\to2}\lambda_{2\to1}}$$

$$\lambda_{3\to2}\lambda_{2\to1} = \lambda_{2\to1}\lambda_{3\to1} + \lambda_{3\to2}\lambda_{3\to1} = \lambda_{3\to1}\left(\lambda_{2\to1} + \lambda_{3\to2}\right)$$

$$\frac{\lambda_{3\to2}\lambda_{2\to1}}{\lambda_{2\to1} + \lambda_{3\to2}} = \lambda_{3\to1}$$

(c) True. Because the energies are additive, the frequencies are also additive:

$$E_{3\to1} = h\nu_{3\to1}$$
$$E_{3\to2,\,2\to1} = h\nu_{3\to2} + h\nu_{2\to1}$$

Because these energies are equal,

$$h\nu_{3\to1} = h\nu_{3\to2} + h\nu_{2\to1}$$
$$\nu_{3\to1} = \nu_{3\to2} + \nu_{2\to1}$$

(d) True. Using Equation 3.11 in the textbook,

For He^{+}: $\Delta E = -(2.178\times10^{-18}\text{ J})(2)^2\left(\dfrac{1}{1^2} - \dfrac{1}{3^2}\right) = -7.744\times10^{-18}$ J

$$\lambda = \frac{hc}{E} = \frac{6.626\times10^{-34}\text{ J}\cdot\text{s}\times2.998\times10^{8}\text{ m/s}}{7.744\times10^{-18}\text{ J}} = 2.565\times10^{-8}\text{ m, or }25.65\text{ nm}$$

For H^{+}: $\Delta E = -(2.178\times10^{-18}\text{ J})(1)^2\left(\dfrac{1}{1^2} - \dfrac{1}{3^2}\right) = -1.936\times10^{-18}$ J

$$\lambda = \frac{hc}{E} = \frac{6.626\times10^{-34}\text{ J}\cdot\text{s}\times2.998\times10^{8}\text{ m/s}}{1.936\times10^{-18}\text{ J}} = 1.026\times10^{-7}\text{ m, or }102.6\text{ nm}$$

Think about It
Be careful in abruptly concluding that the wavelengths of transitions are additive. Only their energies and frequencies can be added in steps to get to the overall energy.

3.125. **Collect and Organize**
Ionization energy (IE_1) is correlated with electronic structure. In this problem we examine the trends in first and second ionization energies for elements 31–36 (Ga–Kr).

Analyze
The general trend is for increasing IE_1 as atomic number (Z) increases across a period. However, electronic structure (configuration) plays a role. In particular, the IE_1 and IE_2 for Ga–Kr depend on whether the electron is being removed from an s or a p orbital.

Solve
The electron configurations for Ga–Kr for both neutral atoms (X) and singly charged cations (X^+) are as follows:

Element	Electron Configuration X	Electron Configuration X^+
Ga	$[Ar]3d^{10}4s^24p^1$	$[Ar]3d^{10}4s^2$
Ge	$[Ar]3d^{10}4s^24p^2$	$[Ar]3d^{10}4s^24p^1$
As	$[Ar]3d^{10}4s^24p^3$	$[Ar]3d^{10}4s^24p^2$
Se	$[Ar]3d^{10}4s^24p^4$	$[Ar]3d^{10}4s^24p^3$
Br	$[Ar]3d^{10}4s^24p^5$	$[Ar]3d^{10}4s^24p^4$
Kr	$[Ar]3d^{10}4s^24p^6$	$[Ar]3d^{10}4s^24p^5$

For the first ionization energy, the IEs increase in the following order:

$$Ga < Ge < Se < As < Br < Kr$$

In this series, as Z increases, IE_1 generally increases. The IE_1 of Se is less than that of As because the electron pairing ($4p^4$) in one of the p orbitals for Se lowers Se's IE_1 slightly.

For the second ionization, the IE_2 values increase in the following order:

$$Ge < Ga < As < Br < Se < Kr$$

Again, it is generally observed that as Z increases, so does the IE_2. However, Ge's second IE_2 is lower than Ga's because to ionize the second electron in Ga, we need to remove an electron from a lower energy $4s$ orbital. Also, Br's IE_2 is lower than Se's because the electron pairing ($4p^4$) in one of the p orbitals for the Br^+ ion lowers its IE_2 slightly.

Think about It

In comparing the first and second ionization energies for Ga–Kr, notice that the reversal of the general trend at As–Se in IE_1 occurs one pair to the right (Se–Br) in IE_2.

3.127. Collect and Organize

We are to determine which neutral atoms are isoelectronic with Sn^{2+} and Mg^{2+} and which 2+ ion is isoelectronic with Sn^{4+}.

Analyze

(a) The ground-state electron configurations for the neutral atoms Sn and Mg are Sn = $[Kr]4d^{10}5s^25p^2$ and Mg = $[Ne]3s^2$. To form Sn^{2+}, remove the two $5p$ electrons; to form Sn^{4+}, remove the two $5p$ electrons and the two $5s$ electrons. To form Mg^{2+}, remove the two $3s$ electrons.

(b) The neutral atom that has the same electron configuration as Sn^{2+} would have to have two $5s$ electrons and a filled $4d$ shell. The neutral atom that has the same electron configuration as Mg^{2+} would have to have a filled $n = 2$ shell (two $2s$ electrons and six $2p$ electrons).

(c) Isoelectronic species have the same number of electrons. The 2+ cation that would be isoelectronic with Sn^{4+} would have to have no $5s$ or $5p$ electrons but would have a filled $4d$ shell.

Solve

(a) Sn^{2+}: $[Kr]4d^{10}5s^2$
Sn^{4+}: $[Kr]4d^{10}$
Mg^{2+}: $[Ne]$ or $[He]2s^22p^6$

(b) Cadmium has the same electron configuration as Sn^{2+}, and neon has the same electron configuration as Mg^{2+}.

(c) Cd^{2+} is isoelectronic with Sn^{4+}.

Think about It

When writing electron configurations for ionic species, start with the neutral atom and add or remove electrons to form the ions.

3.129. Collect and Organize

Using the equation $Z_{eff} = Z - \sigma$, where Z is the atomic number and σ is the shielding parameter, we are to compare the Z_{eff} (effective nuclear charge) for the outermost electron in neon and argon.

Analyze

(a) In the effective nuclear charge equation given, use $Z = 10$ and $\sigma = 4.24$ for Ne and $Z = 18$ and $\sigma = 11.24$ for Ar.

(b) Shielding depends on the number of electrons lower in energy than the electron of interest.

Solve

(a) Ne: $Z_{eff} = 10 - 4.24 = 5.76$
Ar: $Z_{eff} = 18 - 11.24 = 6.76$

(b) The outermost electron in argon is a $3p$ electron, which is mostly shielded by the electrons in the $n = 2$ level (10 electrons) and the $n = 1$ level (two electrons), whereas the outermost electron in neon is a $2p$ electron, which is shielded only by the electrons in the $n = 1$ level (two electrons).

Think about It

Z_{eff} is greater for the outermost electron in Ar than for Ne. The ionization energy of Ar, however, is lower than the ionization energy for Ne. The effective nuclear charge equation, therefore, doesn't seem to predict the trend in decreasing ionization energy as we descend a group in the periodic table. The effective nuclear charge equation here does not take into account the *n* level from which the electron is removed (ionized) to form the cation. Remember that the farther away the electron is from the nucleus, the lower the energy required to remove it.

3.131. **Collect and Organize**

The *p* orbital has two lobes of different phase with a node between the lobes. We are asked how an electron gets from one lobe to the other without going through the node between them.

Analyze

When we think of an orbital, we should think of the electron not as a particle (which here would have to move through the node, a region of zero probability) but as a wave.

Solve

When we think of the electron as a wave, we can envision the node between the two lobes as a wave of zero amplitude, and the *p* orbital as a standing wave.

Think about It

Remember that an orbital describes the wave function for the electron and does not specifically locate the electron as a particle.

CHAPTER 4 | Chemical Bonding: Understanding Climate Change

4.1. Collect and Organize

In the periodic table shown in Figure P4.1, groups 1, 14, 16, and 18 are highlighted. We are to determine which groups have 1, 4, and 6 valence electrons.

Analyze

The number of valence electrons in an element is equal to the number of electrons in the outermost shell. For the groups highlighted, the electron configurations for the valence electrons are

Group 1	ns^1
Group 14	ns^2np^2
Group 16	ns^2np^4
Group 18	ns^2np^6

Solve

(a) Group 1 (red) elements have 1 valence electron.
(b) Group 14 (blue) elements have 4 valence electrons.
(c) Group 16 (purple) elements have 6 valence electrons.

Think about It

The number of valence electrons for neutral atoms is related to the group number. For groups 1 and 2, the number of valence electrons equals the group number. For the other representative (main group) elements, groups 13–18, the number of valence electrons is 10 fewer than the group number ($13 - 10 = 3$ valence electrons for group 13 elements).

4.3. Collect and Organize

Magnesium is in group 2 of the periodic table, and the neutral atom has an electron configuration of $[Ne]3s^2$.

Analyze

Magnesium loses its two outermost electrons to form the Mg^{2+} cation with an electron configuration of $[Ne]$, which leaves no electrons in the valence shell of Mg^{2+}.

Solve

The Lewis symbol must correctly show both the charge and the number of valence electrons on the species. Here the charge is +2 and no valence electrons are present, so the correct Lewis structure is

$$Mg^{2+}$$

Think about It

The only other correct charge–valence electron choice in this problem for Mg is

$$[Mg\cdot]^+$$

but a charge of +1 is not the most stable for the Mg cation. The other Lewis structures either have too few or too many valence electrons for the Mg^{n+} ion shown.

4.5. Collect and Organize

Bonding capacity is the number of bonds that an atom forms with other atoms in stable compounds. For the metallic elements, ionic compounds are usually formed and the bonding capacity depends on the charge associated with the cation (Na^+ "bonds" with 1 Cl^- to form NaCl, so Na has a bonding capacity of 1). For the nonmetallic elements, the bonding capacity depends on the number of covalent bonds the atom forms to fill its octet (C forms bonds with four other atoms).

Analyze

Applying the definition of bonding capacity gives

Group 1 (red) = bonding capacity of 1
Group 2 (yellow) = bonding capacity of 2

Group 13 (green) = bonding capacity of 3
Group 14 (blue) = bonding capacity of 4
Group 15 (purple) = bonding capacity of 3

Solve

The element highlighted in group 14 in Figure P4.5 (blue, carbon) has the highest bonding capacity.

Think about It

Bonding capacity varies with group number in the periodic table.

4.7. Collect and Organize

Ionic bonds are formed between elements of very different (>2.0) values of electronegativity. All the elements highlighted in Figure P4.6 are in period 2 of the periodic table.

Analyze

As we go across a row in the periodic table, electronegativity increases.

Solve

According to the periodic trend in electronegativity, the element on the far left (Li, red) is the least electronegative and the element on the far right (Ne, peach) would be the most electronegative. However, because neon's shell is full, it does not form a compound with Li. Fluorine (lilac), the element to the left of Ne, is also very electronegative. Therefore, the most ionic bond (greatest electronegativity difference) will be for LiF (red and lilac).

Think about It

Bonds formed between the low electronegative metals (on the left-hand side of the periodic table) and high electronegative nonmetals (on the right-hand side) tend to be ionic.

4.9. Collect and Organize

From the three drawings given in Figure P4.9, we are to determine which best describes the electron density in lithium fluoride.

Analyze

The distribution of electron density in LiF depends on the electronegativities of the atoms in the bond. Lithium has an electronegativity of 1.0 and fluorine has an electronegativity of 4.0. The higher the negative charge, the more red the atom; the higher the positive charge, the more blue the atom, as shown in Figure 4.7.

Solve

The difference in electronegativity between lithium and fluorine is very large. Because fluorine has the highest electronegativity, most of the electron density (carrying a negative charge) resides on the fluorine atom in LiF. Because the difference in electronegativity is greater than 2.0, the bond between Li and F is ionic and best written as Li^+F^-. This is best shown by drawing (b) in Figure P4.9.

Think about It

For this problem, we need not know the exact values for the electronegativities of Li and F. From the periodic trends for electronegativity (which increases as we go across a period), we know that the electronegativity of F is much greater than that of Li.

4.11. Collect and Organize

Given possible structures for S_2O, we are to explain why they are not all resonance forms.

Analyze

Resonance structures show more than one valid Lewis structure for a compound. They have the same arrangement of atoms but different arrangements of electrons.

Solve

The arrangement of the atoms in two of the structures is S—O—S and in the other two structures it is S—S—O. Because the arrangement of atoms differs, they are not resonance structures. Also, for each arrangement, the structures do not show a different arrangement of electrons on the atoms, only that the bonds are drawn bent, not straight. The "bent form" and "linear form" are not resonance forms of each other if the numbers of lone pairs and bonding pairs of electrons on each atom are the same.

Think about It

Valid resonance structures of the atoms arranged as SSO are

$$:\overset{..}{S}=\overset{..}{S}-\overset{..}{\overset{..}{O}}: \longleftrightarrow :\overset{..}{\overset{..}{S}}-\overset{..}{S}=\overset{..}{\overset{..}{O}}:$$

4.13. Collect and Organize

Of the two drawings of bent triatomic molecules in Figure P4.13, we are to choose the one that represents the electron density distribution in sulfur dioxide, SO_2, and explain our choice.

Analyze

Differences in electron density within a molecule depend on the different pulling powers of the atoms in the molecule for electrons (electronegativity). Because sulfur is first in the molecular formula, we can assume that it is the central atom in the molecule. In the drawings, the higher the negative charge, the more red the atom; the higher the positive charge, the more blue the atom, as shown in Figure 4.7.

Solve

Sulfur has a lower electronegativity than oxygen because as we descend a group in the periodic table, electronegativity decreases. The oxygen atoms have the higher electron density, so drawing (a) best represents SO_2.

Think about It

Drawing (b) shows the reverse polarity in which a higher electron density is on the sulfur atom. This implies that the electronegativity of sulfur is greater than that of oxygen, which we know not to be the case.

4.15. Collect and Organize

The elements highlighted in Figure P4.15 are lithium (red), carbon (green), oxygen (light blue), fluorine (purple), phosphorus (dark blue), and gallium (yellow). We are asked which of these elements is reactive enough to form compounds with argon, krypton, and xenon.

Analyze

Only the most electronegative elements form compounds with Ar, Kr, and Xe. Electronegativity is highest for elements at the top of a group and at the end of a period.

Solve

The most reactive (most electronegative) element highlighted is fluorine (purple). Oxygen is also quite reactive. These two elements would be expected to form compounds with Ar, Kr, and Xe.

Think about It

To form a bond with a noble gas, the other atom must force the noble gas atom to share an electron in a covalent bond. Only the most electronegative elements can force the noble gas atom to share electrons.

4.17. Collect and Organize

Elements in groups 1 (red), 2 (green), and 17 (blue) are highlighted in Figure P4.17. We are asked which groups are likely to have a negative partial charge in diatomic HX.

Analyze

Partial negative charge for an atom in a molecule is a result of a difference in electronegativities of the elements. The greater the electronegativity, the greater pull the atom has for the electrons in the molecule and that atom will have a partial negative charge. Group 1 elements have electronegativities of 0.7–1.0. Group 2 elements have electronegativities of 0.9–1.5, and group 17 elements have electronegativities of 2.0–3.5. The electronegativity of H is 2.1.

Solve
The electronegativities of group 17 elements are nearly all greater than that of hydrogen, so these elements would have partial negative charge when bonded to hydrogen.

Think about It
Because the electronegativities of group 1 and 2 elements are all lower than that of H, the hydrogen in these compounds carries a partial negative charge. These compounds are often named *hydrides*.

4.19. Collect and Organize
We are to determine how the number of valence electrons within the elements of a group are related.

Analyze
The number of valence electrons is determined by an atom's electron configuration. Elements in the same group have the same electron configuration.

Solve
Yes, because the elements in a group have the same valence electron configuration, they have the same number of valence electrons.

Think about It
Having the same number of valence electrons means that the elements in a group display very similar reactivities.

4.21. Collect and Organize
We are asked to determine whether the number of valence electrons is ever the same as the atomic number.

Analyze
The atomic number of an element is the number of protons in the nucleus. For a neutral atom, the number of electrons equals the number of protons. The number of valence electrons is the number of electrons in the highest n shell.

Solve
For the first- and second-row elements:

Element	Atomic Number	Number of Valence e$^-$
H	1	1
He	2	2
Li	3	1
Be	4	2
B	5	3
C	6	4
N	7	5
O	8	6
F	9	7
Ne	10	8

Only the atomic numbers of hydrogen and helium equal the number of valence electrons.

Think about It
For the second-row elements,
$$\text{number of valence electrons} = \text{atomic number} - 2$$
For the third-row elements,
$$\text{number of valence electrons} = \text{atomic number} - 10$$
Try to write a similar formula for the fourth-row elements (you will have to distinguish between the main group elements and the transition metals).

4.23. **Collect and Organize**

In this question we consider whether the strength of the ion–ion bond depends on the number of ions in the compound.

Analyze

The strength of the ion–ion bond is described in the proportionality

$$E_{el} \propto \frac{Q_1 \times Q_2}{d}$$

where Q is the charge on the ions and d is their internuclear distance.

Solve

No, the strength (energy) of the electrostatic attraction between two ions does not depend on the number of ions in the compound, but it does depend on the charge on the ions and the distance between them.

Think about It

From the proportionality we see that the higher the charges on the ions and the shorter the distance between the ions, the stronger the ion–ion interaction.

4.25. **Collect and Organize**

We are asked to calculate the energy of the electrostatic attraction, the strength of the ionic bond, between K^+ and Br^-.

Analyze

The equation to determine the electrostatic energy between ions is

$$E_{el} = 2.31 \times 10^{-19} \, \text{J} \cdot \text{nm} \left(\frac{Q_1 \times Q_2}{d} \right)$$

To use this equation, we need the charges on the ions (1+ and 1–) for Q_1 and Q_2 and the sum of the radii of the ions (from Figure 3.35), which is 138 + 195 = 333 pm for d.

Solve

$$E_{el} = 2.31 \times 10^{-19} \, \text{J} \cdot \text{nm} \left(\frac{+1 \times -1}{333 \, \text{pm} \times \dfrac{1 \, \text{nm}}{1000 \, \text{pm}}} \right) = -6.94 \times 10^{-18} \, \text{J}$$

Think about It

The energy is negative, showing that bringing the two ions together gives a lower energy than if the ions were separated.

4.27. **Collect and Organize**

From among KCl, TiO_2, $BaCl_2$, and KI we are to determine which has the most negative lattice energy.

Analyze

We could do these calculations by using the equation

$$E_{el} = 2.31 \times 10^{-19} \, \text{J} \cdot \text{nm} \left(\frac{Q_1 \times Q_2}{d} \right)$$

but we can first see whether obvious differences exist that will make the correct prediction. The charges on the ions have a very big effect on the strength of the electrostatic interaction, more so than the sizes, so we will look there for substantial differences. KCl and KI both have 1+/1– ions, but $BaCl_2$ has a 2+/1– pairing, which will be substantially stronger, and TiO_2 has a 4+/2– pairing, which is stronger yet again. Lattice energy is more negative the stronger the electrostatic interaction between ions.

Solve

TiO_2 will have the most negative lattice energy because of the high charges on titanium and oxygen ions compared with the other ionic compounds on the list.

Think about It

Of the two salts, KCl and KI, potassium chloride will have the most negative lattice energy because Cl^- is smaller than I^-.

4.29. Collect and Organize

We can use Coulomb's law to rank KBr, $SrBr_2$, and CsBr in order of increasing electrostatic potential energy.

Analyze

Coulomb's law states that the attraction between oppositely charged ions is directly proportional to the product of their charges and is inversely proportional to their separation distance:

$$E \propto \frac{Q_1 \times Q_2}{d}$$

The distance between the ions is taken as the sum of the ions' radii. The ionic radii for K^+ and Br^- are shown in Figure 3.35. You can look up the radii of Sr^{2+} and Cs^+ on the internet or other resource. The values used in this calculation are 118 pm for Sr^{2+} and 170 pm for Cs^+.

Solve

For KBr, $E \propto \dfrac{(+1)(-1)}{(138+196)} = -0.00299$

For $SrBr_2$, $E \propto \dfrac{(+2)(-1)}{(118+196)} = -0.00637$

For CsBr, $E \propto \dfrac{(+1)(-1)}{(170+196)} = -0.00273$

In order of increasing ionic attraction: $CsBr < KBr < SrBr_2$.

Think about It

Because the ions in CsBr are large compared with KBr, CsBr has a lower ion–ion attraction. $SrBr_2$ has the highest ion–ion attraction because of the +2 charge on Sr.

4.31. Collect and Organize

When writing names for transition metal compounds, we include Roman numerals in the name. We are asked in this question what purpose these Roman numerals serve.

Analyze

Transition metals often take on more than one oxidation state (or charge).

Solve

Roman numerals are used in the names of compounds of transition elements to indicate the charge on the transition metal cation.

Think about It

The indication of charge on the transition metal cation in the name of the compounds makes writing the formula for a compound easy. For example, without the *(III)* in iron(III) chloride, we would not be sure whether to write $FeCl_3$ or $FeCl_2$ because both compounds exist and exhibit different chemical and physical properties.

4.33. Collect and Organize

For the oxoanions of element X, XO_2^{2-} and XO_3^{2-}, we are to assign one as *-ite*.

Analyze

Compound names that end in *-ite* represent oxoanions that have one fewer oxygen atom than compounds ending in *-ate*.

Solve

Between XO_2^{2-} and XO_3^{2-}, the oxoanion XO_2^{2-} would have a name ending in *-ite*.

Think about It

In Table 4.5, we can see this pattern for oxoanions of chlorine. ClO_3^- is *chlorate* and ClO_2^- is *chlorite*.

4.35. **Collect and Organize**

All the compounds here are oxides of nitrogen. These are all molecular compounds composed of two nonmetallic elements. We name these by using the rules for binary compounds.

Analyze

We will use prefixes (Table 4.4) to indicate the number of oxygen atoms in these compounds. The nitrogen atom is always first in the formula, so it is named first. If only one nitrogen atom is in the formula, we do not need to use the prefix *mono-* for the nitrogen. If more than one nitrogen atom is present, however, we will indicate the number with the appropriate prefix. Also, since *oxide* begins with a vowel, it would be awkward to say *pentaoxide*, so we shorten the double vowel in this part of the chemical name to *pentoxide*.

Solve

(a) NO_3, nitrogen trioxide

(b) N_2O_5, dinitrogen pentoxide

(c) N_2O_4, dinitrogen tetroxide

(d) NO_2, nitrogen dioxide

(e) N_2O_3, dinitrogen trioxide

(f) NO, nitrogen monoxide

(g) N_2O, dinitrogen monoxide

(h) N_4O, tetranitrogen monoxide

Think about It

All these binary compounds of nitrogen and oxygen are uniquely named.

4.37. **Collect and Organize**

To predict the formula for the binary ionic compounds formed from the elements listed in the problem, we first have to decide what charges the metal and nonmetal typically have in ionic compounds. To name the compounds, we use the naming rules for ionic compounds.

Analyze

Metallic elements in group 1 of the periodic table (Na and Li) have a 1+ charge in ionic compounds, those in group 2 (Sr) have a 2+ charge, and those in group 13 (Al) have a 3+ charge. Nonmetals in group 16 (S and O) have a 2– charge, and those in group 17 (Cl) have a 1– charge. Hydrogen here has a 1– charge because it is combining with a metal and is thus a hydride. To write the formulas of the neutral salts, the charges of the anion must be balanced with the charges of the cation. When we name binary ionic compounds, the cation is named first as the element, and the anion is named second with the ending *-ide* added.

Solve

(a) sodium (Na^+) and sulfur (S^{2-}): Na_2S, sodium sulfide

(b) strontium (Sr^{2+}) and chlorine (Cl^-): $SrCl_2$, strontium chloride

(c) aluminum (Al^{3+}) and oxygen (O^{2-}): Al_2O_3, aluminum oxide

(d) lithium (Li^+) and hydrogen (H^-): LiH, lithium hydride

Think about It

In naming binary ionic salts of the main group elements, we do not need to indicate the numbers of anions or cations in the formula with prefixes, making the naming of these compounds very direct.

4.39. Collect and Organize

These compounds are all binary ionic compounds of cobalt and oxygen. Because cobalt is a transition metal and thus has more than one available oxidation state, we use the naming rules that incorporate Roman numerals to indicate the charge on the cobalt in the compound.

Analyze

In these compounds oxygen has a charge of 2–. The charge on the cobalt atoms must balance the charge on the oxygen atoms to give the neutral species listed. When we name these compounds, the metal is named first, followed by the charge in Roman numerals in parentheses. The anion is named as a separate word with the ending *-ide*.

Solve

(a) CoO: cobalt has a 2+ charge, cobalt(II) oxide.
(b) Co_2O_3: cobalt has a 3+ charge, cobalt(III) oxide.
(c) CoO_2: cobalt has a 4+ charge, cobalt(IV) oxide.

Think about It

Because the charges of the cations and anions must balance to give a neutral species, we do not have to indicate the number of oxide anions in these compounds; the cation charge dictates the number of oxides that must be present in the formula.

4.41. Collect and Organize

We are asked to identify the oxoanion from the name of a salt and write its formula with associated charge.

Analyze

The oxoanions are polyatomic ions. The element other than oxygen appears first in the name, and the ending depends on the number of oxygen atoms in the anion. Oxoanions with *-ate* as an ending have one more oxygen in their structure than those ending in *-ite*. Prefixes such as *per-* and *hypo-* can indicate the largest and smallest number of oxygens, respectively. We can use these rules and the examples in the text for chlorine (Table 4.5) as well as the polyatomic ions listed in Table 4.3 to help us write the formulas for the oxoanions in this question.

Solve

(a) hypobromite, BrO^- in analogy with hypochlorite
(b) sulfate, SO_4^{2-}
(c) iodate, IO_3^-
(d) nitrite, NO_2^-

Think about It

The names here do not really help us write the formulas; we have to just remember them. Learning them well for chlorine can help because we can name the other halogen oxoanions by analogy with chlorine oxoanions.

4.43. Collect and Organize

Each of these compounds contains a metal in combination with a polyatomic anion. These compounds are ionic and follow the naming rules for ionic compounds.

Analyze

For these compounds, we name the metal cation first as the element name, then the anion.

Solve

(a) $NiCO_3$, nickel(II) carbonate
(b) $NaCN$, sodium cyanide
(c) $LiHCO_3$, lithium bicarbonate or lithium hydrogen carbonate
(d) $Ca(ClO)_2$, calcium hypochlorite

Think about It
These are named much like the binary ionic compounds. The anion name often ends in *-ide* but can end in *-ate* or *-ite*, depending on the name of the polyatomic anion.

4.45. **Collect and Organize**
We need to name or write the formula for each of the compounds according to the rules for naming acids.

Analyze
Binary acids are named by placing *hydro-* in front of the element name other than hydrogen along with replacing the last syllable with *-ic* and adding *acid*. For acids containing oxoanions that end in *-ate*, the acid name becomes *-ic acid*. For acids containing oxoanions that end in *-ite*, the acid name becomes *-ous acid*.

Solve
(a) HF, a binary acid, hydrofluoric acid
(b) $HBrO_3$, an acid of the bromate anion, bromic acid
(c) phosphoric acid, acid of the phosphate anion, H_3PO_4
(d) nitrous acid, acid of the nitrite anion, HNO_2

Think about It
The rules are somewhat systematic but have to be learned and practiced.

4.47. **Collect and Organize**
All the compounds listed are salts of sodium. Some are composed of polyatomic ions, and others are binary salts.

Analyze
For ionic compounds, name the cation as the element first, and then name the anion. If the anion is an element, the suffix *-ide* is used; if the anion is a polyatomic oxoanion, we simply add the name of that anion.

Solve
(a) Na_2O, sodium oxide
(b) Na_2S, sodium sulfide
(c) Na_2SO_4, sodium sulfate
(d) $NaNO_3$, sodium nitrate
(e) $NaNO_2$, sodium nitrite

Think about It
All these names uniquely describe the compounds. Once we are familiar with the names of the polyatomic anions, we can unambiguously identify the compound by name.

4.49. **Collect and Organize**
We are asked to write the formula of an ionic salt from the name given.

Analyze
We use the rules for naming ionic salts. The first element in the name is the cation in the formula. In binary ionic salts, the anion is the element name with the ending *-ide*. If the ion is a polyatomic ion, the name of that polyatomic anion follows the name of the metal. When writing the formula, we must always balance the charges of the anion and the cation to give a neutral salt.

Solve
(a) potassium sulfide, K^+ with S^{2-} gives K_2S
(b) potassium selenide, K^+ with Se^{2-} gives K_2Se
(c) rubidium sulfate, Rb^+ with SO_4^{2-} gives Rb_2SO_4
(d) rubidium nitrite, Rb^+ with NO_2^- gives $RbNO_2$
(e) magnesium sulfate, Mg^{2+} with SO_4^{2-} gives $MgSO_4$

Think about It

Most of the anions in these salts are dianions with a 2– charge. When combining with 1+ cations, we have to balance the charge by having two cations for every anion in the formula.

4.51. **Collect and Organize**

The formulas for the compounds to be named all contain transition metals with variable charges. In the name, therefore, we must be sure to indicate the charge of the cation.

Analyze

The naming of these compounds is the same as naming other ionic compounds. We need only add Roman numerals to indicate the charge on the transition metal cation.

Solve

(a) MnS, manganese(II) sulfide
(b) V_3N_2, vanadium(II) nitride
(c) $Cr_2(SO_4)_3$, chromium(III) sulfate
(d) $Co(NO_3)_2$, cobalt(II) nitrate
(e) Fe_2O_3, iron(III) oxide

Think about It

Adding Roman numerals to these names clearly indicates the charge of the cation. If the charges were not indicated, the way to write formulas from the names of these compounds would not be clear.

4.53. **Collect and Organize**

We are asked to identify a compound by name from a list of formulas.

Analyze

Sodium sulfite would have the sodium cation (Na^+) and the sulfite anion (SO_3^{2-}) in its formula. To balance the charge, two Na^+ cations would be present for every SO_3^{2-} anion.

Solve

The answer is (b), Na_2SO_3.

Think about It

To write a formula, we have to be very familiar with the names of the cations and anions. Confusing sulfite with sulfate (SO_4^{2-}) or sulfide (S^{2-}) would be easy here.

4.55. **Collect and Organize**

We are asked to consider how Lewis electron counting might be considered double counting.

Analyze

Lewis counts all electrons surrounding the atom in a bond, including all the electrons in shared pairs as well as electrons in lone pairs on the atom.

Solve

In the diatomic molecule XY shown here

Lewis counts 6 e⁻ in three lone pairs on both X and Y. He also counts the two electrons shared between X and Y separately (2 e⁻ for X and 2 e⁻ for Y). However, 4 e⁻ are not being shared, only 2 e⁻. The Lewis counting scheme seems to count the shared electrons twice.

Think about It

The octet rule uses double counting to surround each non-hydrogen atom in a Lewis structure with eight electrons.

4.57. Collect and Organize

We are to consider why water has a bonding pattern of H—O—H instead of H—H—O.

Analyze

We consider the Lewis structures of each compound. For both structures, the total number of valence electrons is 1 e^- (H) + 1 e^- (H) + 6 e^- (O) = 8 e^-. Each oxygen atom wants 8 e^- and each hydrogen atom wants 2 e^-, for a total of 12 e^-. The difference in the number of valence electrons and the number the molecule wants is 12 – 8 e^- = 4 e^-. This means that water has two covalent bonds.

Solve

For the H—O—H bonding pattern, the oxygen of the central atom forms bonds to the two hydrogen atoms. This uses 4 of the 8 e^-, leaving 4 e^- for the two lone pairs. Each hydrogen atom has a duet of electrons, so the lone pairs reside on oxygen and form an octet on oxygen.

$$H-\overset{..}{\underset{..}{O}}-H$$

For H—H—O bonding, the two covalent bonds again use 4 of the 8 e^-, leaving 4 e^- for two lone pairs. If these are placed on the oxygen atom as shown here,

$$H-H-\overset{..}{\underset{..}{O}}$$

oxygen does not complete its octet and the central hydrogen atom has 4 e^-, not a duet. This structure would violate the Lewis structure formalism.

Think about It

Because hydrogen does not expand its duet in covalent bonding, the H atom is always terminal and never a central atom in a Lewis structure.

4.59. Collect and Organize

We are to draw the Lewis symbols for the neutral atoms Cs, Ba, and Al.

Analyze

Lewis symbols show the number of valence electrons as dots around the element symbol. Cs has one valence electron, Ba has two valence electrons, and Al has three valence electrons.

Solve

$$Cs\cdot \quad \cdot Ba\cdot \quad \cdot\overset{\cdot}{Al}\cdot$$

Think about It

The particular placement of the electrons around the element symbol is not crucial to correct Lewis symbols. The electron dots are placed around the four sides of the element symbol and, generally, the electrons are not paired up on a side until each of the other sides also has an electron dot.

4.61. Collect and Organize

We are to draw the Lewis symbols for the ions Na^+, In^+, Ca^{2+}, and S^{2-}.

Analyze

To form the ions, we have to remove or add the appropriate number of electrons on the basis of each neutral element atom.

Element/Ion	Number of Valence e^- in Neutral Atom	Number of e^- in Ion
Na/Na$^+$	1	0
In/In$^+$	3	2
Ca/Ca^{2+}	2	0
S/S^{2-}	6	8

Solve

$$Na^+ \quad [\cdot In \cdot]^+ \quad Ca^{2+} \quad [:\ddot{S}:]^{2-}$$

Think about It

The metals sodium and calcium lose electrons to form cations with a noble gas configuration, whereas the nonmetal sulfur gains electrons to form an anion with a noble gas configuration. The metal indium can exist in either the +3 oxidation state (to have a noble gas configuration) or the +1 oxidation state (in which two electrons remain in the $5s$ orbital).

4.63. Collect and Organize

Of B^{3+}, I^-, Ca^{2+}, and Pb^{2+} we are to identify which have a complete valence-shell octet.

Analyze

A valence-shell octet is also a noble gas configuration.

Ion	Electron Configuration	Number of e⁻ in Valence Shell
B^{3+}	[He]	0
I^-	$[Kr]4d^{10}5s^25p^6$	8
Ca^{2+}	[Ar]	0
Pb^{2+}	$[Xe]4f^{14}5d^{10}6s^2$	2

Solve

The ions I^- and Ca^{2+} have complete valence-shell octets. B^{3+} does not have an octet but rather the duet of the He atom.

Think about It

Cations are formed by loss of electrons to achieve a core noble gas configuration, which leaves no electrons in the valence shell, and anions are formed by gain of electrons to give eight electrons in the valence shell.

4.65. Collect and Organize

For the diatomic species BN, HF, OH⁻, and CN⁻, we are to determine the total number of valence electrons.

Analyze

For each species we need to add the valence electrons for each atom. If the species is charged, we need to reduce or increase the number of electrons as necessary to form cations or anions, respectively.

Solve

(a) 3 valence e⁻ (B) + 5 valence e⁻ (N) = 8 valence e⁻
(b) 1 valence e⁻ (H) + 7 valence e⁻ (F) = 8 valence e⁻
(c) 6 valence e⁻ (O) + 1 valence e⁻ (H) + 1 e⁻ (negative charge) = 8 valence e⁻
(d) 4 valence e⁻ (C) + 5 valence e⁻ (N) + 1 e⁻ (negative charge) = 10 valence e⁻

Think about It

For each of these, we can predict the number of covalent bonds between the atoms by finding the difference between what each species needs (to fill a duet for H and an octet for all other atoms) and the number of valence electrons for the molecule.

Molecule or Ion	Number of e⁻ Species Needs	Number of Valence e⁻	Number of Covalent Bonds
(a) BN	16	8	4
(b) HF	10	8	1
(c) OH⁻	10	8	1
(d) CN⁻	16	10	3

4.67. Collect and Organize

We are to draw correct Lewis structures satisfying the octet rule for all atoms in the diatomic molecules and ions CO, O_2, ClO^-, and CN^-.

Analyze

To draw the Lewis structures, we first must determine the number of valence electrons in each of the structures. Then, we arrange the atoms to show the bonding in the molecule by connecting the atoms with single covalent bonds. Finally, we complete the octets of the atoms bonded to the central atoms and then complete the octet of the central atom.

Solve

(a) For CO

(Step 1) The number of valence electrons in CO is

Element	C		O		
Valence electrons per atom	4	+	6	=	10

(Step 2) Only two atoms are bonded, so neither is the central atom.

$$C\text{---}O$$

(Step 3) We complete the octet on the oxygen atom by adding three lone pairs.

$$C\text{---}\ddot{\underset{\cdot\cdot}{O}}\colon$$

(Step 4) This structure has eight electrons from three lone pairs and one bond pair. We need two more electrons (one pair) to match the valence electrons determined in step 1. We add the lone pair to the carbon atom.

$$\colon C\text{---}\ddot{\underset{\cdot\cdot}{O}}\colon$$

(Step 5) To complete the octet on the carbon atom we convert two lone pairs on the O atom to give a triple bond between the oxygen atom and the carbon atom.

$$\colon C \equiv O \colon$$

The Lewis structure is now complete.

(b) For O_2

(Step 1) The number of valence electrons in O_2 is

Element	2O	
Valence electrons per atom	$(2 \times 6) = 12$	

(Step 2) Only two atoms are bonded, so neither is the central atom.

$$O\text{---}O$$

(Step 3) We complete the octet on one of the oxygen atoms by adding three lone pairs.

$$O\text{---}\ddot{\underset{\cdot\cdot}{O}}\colon$$

(Step 4) This structure has eight electrons from three lone pairs and one bond pair. We need four more electrons (two pairs) to match the valence electrons determined in step 1. We add the lone pairs to the other oxygen atom.

$$\colon\!\ddot{O}\text{---}\ddot{\underset{\cdot\cdot}{O}}\colon$$

(Step 5) To complete the octet on the left oxygen atom in the structure we convert a lone pair on the right O atom to give a double bond between the oxygen atoms.

$$\colon\!\ddot{O}\text{---}\ddot{\underset{\cdot\cdot}{O}}\colon$$

$$\colon\!\ddot{O} = \ddot{O}\colon$$

The Lewis structure is now complete.

(c) For ClO⁻
(Step 1) The number of valence electrons in ClO⁻ is

Element	Cl		O	
Valence electrons per atom	7	+	6	= 13
Gain of electron due to charge				+1
Total valence electrons				14

(Step 2) Only two atoms are bonded, so neither is the central atom.

$$Cl—O$$

(Step 3) We complete the octet on the oxygen atoms by adding three lone pairs.

$$Cl—\ddot{\underset{..}{O}}:$$

(Step 4) This structure has eight electrons from three lone pairs and one bond pair. We need six more electrons (three pairs) to match the valence electrons determined in step 1. We add the lone pairs to the chlorine atom.

$$:\ddot{\underset{..}{Cl}}—\ddot{\underset{..}{O}}:$$

(Step 5) This Lewis structure is complete. To indicate the charge on this ion we add brackets for the structure and the charge.

$$\left[:\ddot{\underset{..}{Cl}}—\ddot{\underset{..}{O}}:\right]^-$$

(d) For CN⁻
(Step 1) The number of valence electrons in CN⁻ is

Element	C		N	
Valence electrons per atom	4	+	5	= 9
Gain of electron due to charge				+1
Total valence electrons				10

(Step 2) Only two atoms are bonded, so neither is the central atom.

$$C—N$$

(Step 3) We complete the octet on the nitrogen atom by adding three lone pairs.

$$C—\ddot{\underset{..}{N}}:$$

(Step 4) This structure has eight electrons from three lone pairs and one bond pair. We need two more electrons (one pair) to match the valence electrons determined in step 1. We add the lone pair to the carbon atom.

$$:C—\ddot{\underset{..}{N}}:$$

(Step 5) To complete the octet on the carbon atom we convert two lone pairs on the N atom to give a triple bond between the nitrogen atom and the carbon atom. Finally, we add brackets to the structure and indicate the charge on this anion.

$$:C—\ddot{\underset{..}{N}}:$$

$$\left[:C≡N:\right]^-$$

The Lewis structure is now complete.

Think about It
When writing Lewis structures for ionic species, don't forget to enclose the structure in brackets and indicate the charge on the ion, as shown in this problem for ClO⁻ and CN⁻.

4.69. Collect and Organize
We are to draw correct Lewis structures satisfying the octet rule for all atoms in the molecules and ions CCl_4, BH_3, SiF_4, BH_4^-, and PH_4^+.

Analyze

To draw the Lewis structures, we first must determine the number of valence electrons in each of the structures. Then we arrange the atoms to show the bonding in the molecule by connecting the atoms with single covalent bonds. Finally, we complete the octets of the atoms bonded to the central atoms and then complete the octet of the central atom.

Solve

(a) For CCl_4

(Step 1) The number of valence electrons in CCl_4 is

Element	C	4Cl	
Valence electrons per atom	4 +	(4×7)	= 28
Total valence electrons			32

(Step 2) Carbon is the atom with the fewest valence electrons (and therefore the greatest bonding capacity), so it is the central atom with the four Cl atoms bonded to it.

$$Cl - \underset{\underset{\displaystyle Cl}{|}}{\overset{\overset{\displaystyle Cl}{|}}{C}} - Cl$$

(Step 3) We complete the octet on the chlorine atoms by adding three lone pairs.

$$:\ddot{Cl} - \underset{\underset{\displaystyle :\ddot{Cl}:}{|}}{\overset{\overset{\displaystyle :\ddot{Cl}:}{|}}{C}} - \ddot{Cl}:$$

(Step 4) This structure has 32 electrons from 12 lone pairs and four bond pairs. This uses all the valence electrons we calculated in step 1.

(Step 5) All octets are satisfied for C and Cl, and so the structure in step 3 is the complete Lewis structure.

(b) For BH_3

(Step 1) The number of valence electrons in BH_3 is

Element	B	3H	
Valence electrons per atom	3 +	$(3 \times 1) = 3$	
Total valence electrons		6	

(Step 2) The central atom is boron with the three hydrogen atoms attached to it.

$$\overset{\displaystyle H}{\underset{\displaystyle H}{\diagdown \diagup}} B - H$$

(Step 3) The duplet on all the H atoms is satisfied.

(Step 4) This structure has six electrons from three bond pairs. We cannot add more electrons to the structure because this matches the valence electron count determined in step 1.

(Step 5) Because we have no lone pairs on hydrogen to complete the octet for boron, this Lewis structure is complete as shown in step 2.

(c) For SiF_4

(Step 1) The number of valence electrons in SiF_4 is

Element	Si	4F	
Valence electrons per atom	4 +	(4×7)	= 28
Total valence electrons			32

(Step 2) Silicon is the atom with the fewest valence electrons and the greatest bonding capacity, so it is the central atom with the four Cl atoms bonded to it.

$$F—Si—F$$

with F above and F below Si.

(Step 3) We complete the octet on the fluorine atoms by adding three lone pairs.

$$:\ddot{F}—Si—\ddot{F}:$$

(Step 4) This structure has 32 electrons from 12 lone pairs and four bond pairs. This uses all the valence electrons we calculated in step 1.

(Step 5) All octets are satisfied for Si and F, and so the structure in step 3 is the complete Lewis structure.

(d) For BH_4^-

(Step 1) The number of valence electrons in BH_4^- is

Element	B		4H
Valence electrons per atom	3	+	$(4 \times 1) = 4$
Gain of electron due to charge			+1
Total valence electrons			8

(Step 2) The central atom is boron with the four hydrogen atoms attached to it because B has the greatest bonding capacity.

$$H—B—H$$

with H above and H below B.

(Step 3) The duplet on all the H atoms is satisfied.

(Step 4) This structure has eight electrons from four bond pairs. We cannot add more electrons to the structure because this matches the valence electron count determined in step 1.

(Step 5) This Lewis structure is complete since the octet is satisfied for boron. Because this species has a charge, we add brackets and indicate the charge.

$$\left[H—B—H \right]^-$$

with H above and H below B.

(e) For PH_4^+

(Step 1) The number of valence electrons in PH_4^+ is

Element	P		4H
Valence electrons per atom	5	+	$(4 \times 1) = 4$
Loss of electron due to charge			−1
Total valence electrons			8

(Step 2) The central atom is phosphorus because it has the greatest bonding capacity with the four hydrogen atoms attached.

$$H—P—H$$

with H above and H below P.

(Step 3) The duplet on all the H atoms is satisfied.

(Step 4) This structure has eight electrons from four bond pairs. We cannot add more electrons to the structure because this matches the valence electron count determined in step 1.

(Step 5) This Lewis structure is complete since the octet is satisfied for phosphorus. Because this species has a charge, we add brackets and indicate the charge.

$$\left[\begin{array}{c} H \\ | \\ H - P - H \\ | \\ H \end{array}\right]^{+}$$

Think about It

In this problem, SiF_4 and CCl_4 are isoelectronic (have the same number of valence electrons), as are BH_4^- and PH_4^+.

4.71. **Collect and Organize**

Using the method described in the textbook, we are to draw Lewis structures for five chlorofluorocarbon greenhouse gases.

Analyze

To draw the Lewis structures, we first must determine the number of valence electrons in each of the structures. Then we arrange the atoms to show the bonding in the molecule by connecting the atoms with single covalent bonds. Finally, we complete the octets of the atoms bonded to the central atoms and then complete the octet of the central atom.

Solve

(a) CCl_3F

(Step 1) The number of valence electrons in CCl_3F is

Element	C	F	3Cl
Valence electrons per atom	4 +	(1×7) +	(3×7) = 32

(Step 2) Carbon has the most unpaired electrons (four) in its Lewis symbol and therefore has the highest bonding capacity and will be the central atom in the structure. The fluorine and chlorine atoms will each be bonded to the carbon.

$$\begin{array}{c} Cl \\ | \\ Cl - C - Cl \\ | \\ F \end{array}$$

(Step 3) We complete the octets on the chlorine and fluorine atoms by adding three lone pairs to each.

$$\begin{array}{c} :\ddot{C}l: \\ | \\ :\ddot{C}l - C - \ddot{C}l: \\ | \\ :\ddot{F}: \end{array}$$

(Step 4) This structure has 32 electrons from 12 lone pairs and four bond pairs. We do not need any more valence electrons in this structure.

(Step 5) With carbon satisfied with its octet, the Lewis structure is complete.

(b) CCl_2F_2

(Step 1) The number of valence electrons in CCl_2F_2 is

Element	C	2Cl	2F
Valence electrons per atom	4 +	(2×7) +	(2×7) = 32

(Step 2) Carbon has the most unpaired electrons (four) in its Lewis symbol and therefore has the highest bonding capacity and will be the central atom in the structure. The fluorine and chlorine atoms will each be bonded to the carbon.

$$
\begin{array}{c}
\text{Cl} \\
| \\
\text{F---C---Cl} \\
| \\
\text{F}
\end{array}
$$

(Step 3) We complete the octets on the chlorine and fluorine atoms by adding three lone pairs to each.

$$
\begin{array}{c}
:\ddot{\text{Cl}}: \\
| \\
:\ddot{\text{F}}\text{---C---}\ddot{\text{Cl}}: \\
| \\
:\ddot{\text{F}}:
\end{array}
$$

(Step 4) This structure has 32 electrons from 12 lone pairs and four bond pairs. We do not need any more valence electrons in this structure.
(Step 5) With carbon satisfied with its octet, the Lewis structure is complete.

(c) $CClF_3$
(Step 1) The number of valence electrons in $CClF_3$ is

Element	C	Cl	3F
Valence electrons per atom	4 +	7 +	(3×7) = 32

(Step 2) Carbon has the most unpaired electrons (four) in its Lewis symbol and therefore has the highest bonding capacity and will be the central atom in the structure. The fluorine and chlorine atoms will each be bonded to the carbon.

$$
\begin{array}{c}
\text{Cl} \\
| \\
\text{F---C---F} \\
| \\
\text{F}
\end{array}
$$

(Step 3) We complete the octets on the chlorine and fluorine atoms by adding three lone pairs to each.

$$
\begin{array}{c}
:\ddot{\text{Cl}}: \\
| \\
:\ddot{\text{F}}\text{---C---}\ddot{\text{F}}: \\
| \\
:\ddot{\text{F}}:
\end{array}
$$

(Step 4) This structure has 32 electrons from 12 lone pairs and four bond pairs. We do not need any more valence electrons in this structure.
(Step 5) With carbon satisfied with its octet, the Lewis structure is complete.

(d) $Cl_2FC\text{---}CClF_2$
(Step 1) The number of valence electrons in $Cl_2FC\text{---}CClF_2$ is

Element	2C	3Cl	3F
Valence electrons per atom	(2×4) +	(3×7) +	(3×7) = 50

(Step 2) The carbon atoms have the most unpaired electrons (four) in their Lewis symbols and therefore have the highest bonding capacity and will be the central atoms in the structure. We are given that a C—C bond is present. The fluorine and chlorine atoms will each be bonded to the carbon atoms.

$$
\begin{array}{cc}
\text{Cl} & \text{Cl} \\
| & | \\
\text{Cl---C---C---F} \\
| & | \\
\text{F} & \text{F}
\end{array}
$$

(Step 3) We complete the octets on the chlorine and fluorine atoms by adding three lone pairs to each.

$$:\overset{\displaystyle ..}{\underset{\displaystyle ..}{Cl}}:\ :\overset{\displaystyle ..}{\underset{\displaystyle ..}{Cl}}:$$

$$:\overset{\displaystyle ..}{\underset{\displaystyle ..}{Cl}}\!-\!C\!-\!C\!-\!\overset{\displaystyle ..}{\underset{\displaystyle ..}{F}}:$$

$$:\overset{\displaystyle ..}{\underset{\displaystyle ..}{F}}:\ :\overset{\displaystyle ..}{\underset{\displaystyle ..}{F}}:$$

(Step 4) This structure has 50 electrons from 18 lone pairs and seven bond pairs. We do not need any more valence electrons in this structure.

(Step 5) With the carbon atoms satisfied with their octets, the Lewis structure is complete.

(e) $ClF_2C-CClF_2$

(Step 1) The number of valence electrons in $ClF_2C-CClF_2$ is

Element	2C	2Cl	2F	
Valence electrons per atom	(2×4) +	(2×7) +	(4×7) =	50

(Step 2) The carbon atoms have the most unpaired electrons (four) in their Lewis symbols and therefore have the highest bonding capacity and will be the central atoms in the structure. We are given that a C—C bond is present. The fluorine and chlorine atoms will each be bonded to the carbon atoms.

$$\begin{array}{ccc} & Cl & Cl \\ & | & | \\ F\!-\!&C\!-\!C&\!-\!F \\ & | & | \\ & F & F \end{array}$$

(Step 3) We complete the octets on the chlorine and fluorine atoms by adding three lone pairs to each.

$$:\overset{\displaystyle ..}{\underset{\displaystyle ..}{Cl}}:\ :\overset{\displaystyle ..}{\underset{\displaystyle ..}{Cl}}:$$

$$:\overset{\displaystyle ..}{\underset{\displaystyle ..}{F}}\!-\!C\!-\!C\!-\!\overset{\displaystyle ..}{\underset{\displaystyle ..}{F}}:$$

$$:\overset{\displaystyle ..}{\underset{\displaystyle ..}{F}}:\ :\overset{\displaystyle ..}{\underset{\displaystyle ..}{F}}:$$

(Step 4) This structure has 50 electrons from 18 lone pairs and seven bond pairs. We do not need any more valence electrons in this structure.

(Step 5) With the carbon atoms satisfied with their octets, the Lewis structure is complete.

Think about It

In determining the skeletal structure for these molecules, knowing that carbon commonly bonds to four atoms and that the halogens are usually terminal atoms is helpful.

4.73. Collect and Organize

We are to draw correct Lewis structures satisfying the octet rule for all atoms in the oxoanions ClO_2^-, SO_3^{2-}, and HCO_3^-.

Analyze

To draw the Lewis structures, we first must determine the number of valence electrons in each of the structures. Then we arrange the atoms to show the bonding in the molecule by connecting the atoms with single covalent bonds. Finally, we complete the octets of the atoms bonded to the central atoms and then complete the octet of the central atom. All these have negative charges, so we must make sure to add the appropriate number of electrons to the structure.

(a) For ClO_2^-

(Step 1) The number of valence electrons in ClO_2^- is

Element	Cl	2O	
Valence electrons per atom	7 +	(2×6) =	19
Gain of electron due to charge			+1
Total valence electrons			20

(Step 2) Chlorine is the central atom in this molecule because it is less electronegative than oxygen.

$$O\!-\!Cl\!-\!O$$

(Step 3) We add three lone pairs to each oxygen atom to satisfy the octet.

$$:\ddot{\text{O}}—\text{Cl}—\ddot{\text{O}}:$$

(Step 4) This structure has 16 electrons from two bond pairs and six lone pairs. We need two more electrons (one pair) to match the valence electrons determined in step 1. We place these lone pairs on the chlorine atom.

$$:\ddot{\text{O}}—\ddot{\text{Cl}}—\ddot{\text{O}}:$$

(Step 5) The octet on chlorine in this structure is satisfied. We complete the Lewis structure by adding the brackets and charge for the ion.

$$\left[:\ddot{\text{O}}—\ddot{\text{Cl}}—\ddot{\text{O}}:\right]^{-}$$

(b) For SO_3^{2-}

(Step 1) The number of valence electrons in SO_3^{2-} is

Element	S		3O	
Valence electrons per atom	6	+	(3×6)	= 24
Gain of two electrons due to charge				+2
Total valence electrons				26

(Step 2) Sulfur is the central atom in this molecule because it is less electronegative than oxygen.

$$\text{O}—\text{S}—\text{O}$$
$$|$$
$$\text{O}$$

(Step 3) We add three lone pairs to each oxygen atom to satisfy the octet.

$$:\ddot{\text{O}}—\text{S}—\ddot{\text{O}}:$$
$$|$$
$$:\ddot{\text{O}}:$$

(Step 4) This structure has 24 electrons from three bond pairs and nine lone pairs. We need two more electrons (one pair) to match the valence electrons determined in step 1. We place these lone pairs on the sulfur atom.

$$:\ddot{\text{O}}—\text{S}—\ddot{\text{O}}:$$
$$|$$
$$:\ddot{\text{O}}:$$

(Step 5) The octet on sulfur in this structure is satisfied. We complete the Lewis structure by adding the brackets and charge for the ion.

$$\left[:\ddot{\text{O}}—\text{S}—\ddot{\text{O}}: \atop \qquad | \atop \qquad :\ddot{\text{O}}:\right]^{2-}$$

(c) For HCO_3^-

(Step 1) The number of valence electrons in HCO_3^- is

Element	H		C		3O	
Valence electrons per atom	1	+	4	+	(3×6)	= 23
Gain of electron due to charge						+1
Total valence electrons						24

(Step 2) Carbon is the central atom in this molecule because it has the highest bonding capacity. Hydrogen will be a terminal atom on one of the oxygen atoms.

$$\text{O}—\text{C}—\text{O}—\text{H}$$
$$|$$
$$\text{O}$$

(Step 3) We add lone pairs to each oxygen atom to satisfy the octet on each.

$$:\ddot{\text{O}}—\text{C}—\ddot{\text{O}}—\text{H}$$
$$|$$
$$:\ddot{\text{O}}:$$

(Step 4) This structure has 24 electrons from four bond pairs and eight lone pairs. We do not need any more electrons to complete the structure.

(Step 5) We can satisfy the octet on the carbon atom by forming a double bond with one of the oxygen atoms.

$$:\ddot{O} \overset{\frown}{\curvearrowright} C - \ddot{O} - H$$
$$\underset{:\ddot{O}:}{|}$$

$$:O = C - \ddot{O} - H$$
$$\underset{:\ddot{O}:}{|}$$

We complete the Lewis structure by adding the brackets and charge for the ion.

$$\left[:O = C - \ddot{O} - H \atop \underset{:\ddot{O}:}{|} \right]^{-}$$

Think about It
Hydrogen cannot be a central atom because its bonding capacity is only 1.

4.75. **Collect and Organize**
Using the method described in the textbook, we are to draw Lewis structures for $CH_3CH_2CH_2CH_2SH$ and H_2S.

Analyze
To draw the Lewis structures, we first must determine the number of valence electrons in each of the structures, then arrange the atoms to show the bonding in the molecule by connecting the atoms with single covalent bonds. Finally, we complete the octets of the atoms bonded to the central atoms, then complete the octet of the central atom. Considering that hydrogen is always terminal, the carbon atoms must be bonded together in a chain as indicated in the formula given in the problem.

Solve
Butanethiol
(Step 1) The number of valence electrons in $CH_3CH_2CH_2CH_2SH$ is

Element	4C	10H	S
Valence electrons per atom	(4×4) +	(10×1) +	$6 = 32$

(Step 2) Carbon has the most unpaired electrons (four) in its Lewis symbol and therefore has the highest bonding capacity and will be the central atom in the structure. The hydrogen and sulfur atoms will be bonded to the carbon as indicated in the chemical formula. Also, as indicated in the formula, one H atom is bonded to the sulfur atom.

$$\begin{array}{ccccccc} & H & H & H & H & & \\ & | & | & | & | & & \\ H - & C - & C - & C - & C - & S - & H \\ & | & | & | & | & & \\ & H & H & H & H & & \end{array}$$

(Step 3) We complete the octet on the sulfur atom by adding two lone pairs to it.

$$\begin{array}{ccccccc} & H & H & H & H & & \\ & | & | & | & | & & \\ H - & C - & C - & C - & C - & \ddot{S} - & H \\ & | & | & | & | & & \\ & H & H & H & H & & \end{array}$$

(Step 4) This structure has 32 electrons from two lone pairs and 14 bond pairs. We do not need any more valence electrons in this structure.
(Step 5) With carbon satisfied with its octet and hydrogen satisfied with its duet, the Lewis structure is complete.

Hydrogen sulfide
(Step 1) The number of valence electrons in H_2S is

Element	2H	S
Valence electrons per atom	(2×1) +	$6 = 8$

(Step 2) Sulfur has the most unpaired electrons (two) in its Lewis symbol and therefore has the highest bonding capacity and will be the central atom in the structure.

$$H—S—H$$

(Step 3) We complete the octet on the sulfur atom by adding two lone pairs to it.

$$H—\overset{..}{\underset{..}{S}}—H$$

(Step 4) This structure has eight electrons from two lone pairs and two bond pairs. We do not need any more valence electrons in this structure.

(Step 5) With hydrogen satisfied with its duet, the Lewis structure is complete.

Think about It
Carbon atoms are often bonded in chains, as seen in butanethiol. The bonding of an elemental atom to the same elemental atom to form chains is called *catenation*.

4.77. Collect and Organize
Using the method in the textbook, we are to draw Lewis structures for Cl_2O and ClO_3^-.

Analyze
To draw the Lewis structures, we first must determine the number of valence electrons. Then we arrange the atoms to show the bonding in the molecules by connecting the atoms with single covalent bonds. Finally, we complete the octets of the atoms bonded to the central atoms and then complete the octet of the central atom.

Solve
Cl_2O

(Step 1) The number of valence electrons in Cl_2O is

Element	2Cl		O		
Valence electrons per atom	(2×7)	+	6	=	20

(Step 2) We are given that one of the chlorine atoms is the central atom in this structure.

$$Cl—Cl—O$$

(Step 3) We complete the octets on the oxygen and terminal chlorine atoms by adding three lone pairs to each.

$$:\overset{..}{\underset{..}{Cl}}—Cl—\overset{..}{\underset{..}{O}}:$$

(Step 4) This structure has 16 electrons from six lone pairs and two bond pairs. We need four more electrons (two pairs) to match the valence electrons determined in step 1. We add the lone pairs to the central chlorine atom.

$$:\overset{..}{\underset{..}{Cl}}—\overset{..}{\underset{..}{Cl}}—\overset{..}{\underset{..}{O}}:$$

(Step 5) The central chlorine atom is satisfied with its octet, so this Lewis structure is complete.

ClO_3^-

(Step 1) The number of valence electrons in ClO_3^- is

Element	Cl		3O		
Valence electrons per atom	7	+	(3×6)	=	25
Gain of electron due to charge					+1
Total valence electrons					26

(Step 2) We are given that the chlorine atom is the central atom in this structure.

$$\begin{array}{c} O \\ | \\ O—Cl—O \end{array}$$

(Step 3) We complete the octets on the oxygen atoms by adding three lone pairs to each.

$$\begin{array}{c} :\overset{..}{\underset{..}{O}}: \\ | \\ :\overset{..}{\underset{..}{O}}—Cl—\overset{..}{\underset{..}{O}}: \end{array}$$

(Step 4) This structure has 24 electrons from nine lone pairs and three bond pairs. We need two more electrons (one pair) to match the valence electrons determined in step 1. We add the lone pair to the central chlorine atom.

$$\text{:O:} \atop \overset{|}{\text{:O—Cl—O:}}$$

(Step 5) The central chlorine atom is satisfied with its octet, so this Lewis structure is complete. We add brackets and the charge to indicate the ion.

$$\left[{\text{:O:} \atop \overset{|}{\text{:O—Cl—O:}}} \right]^{-}$$

Think about It

In ClO_3^-, Cl is the central atom as we would guess from the formula, but in Cl_2O, oxygen could be the central atom. As shown below, the arrangement of the molecule with Cl as the central atom gives nonzero formal charges for the atoms (see Section 4.7). In Section 4.7, we will also learn that to reduce the formal charge on Cl in ClO_3^-, we can form a double bond between Cl and one of the O atoms.

$$\underset{-1 \quad +1 \quad \ 0}{\text{:O—Cl—Cl:}} \quad \text{versus} \quad \underset{0 \quad \ 0 \quad \ 0}{\text{:Cl—O—Cl:}}$$

4.79. Collect and Organize

We are asked how we can use electronegativity to define whether a bond is ionic or covalent.

Analyze

When a large difference in electronegativity exists, the transfer of an electron from one atom to another is likely and an ionic bond will form. When the electronegativities of two atoms are similar, the electrons will be shared in a covalent bond.

Solve

The general rule is that an electronegativity difference of 2.0 or greater is present, the bond between the atoms is ionic. Below 2.0, the bond is covalent.

Think about It

Large differences in electronegativity, and thus the occurrence of ionic bonding, are likely between a metallic atom (low electronegativity) and a nonmetallic atom (high electronegativity).

4.81. Collect and Organize

We are asked to explain how trends in electronegativity are related to trends in atomic size.

Analyze

Small atoms such as oxygen and fluorine have high electronegativities, whereas large atoms such as cesium have low electronegativities.

Solve

The size of the atom is the result of the nucleus pulling on the electrons. The higher the nuclear charge, the stronger the pull on the electrons within a given valence shell. This is why the size of the atoms generally decreases across a period. A small atom will form a shorter bond with another atom, and the electrons in the bond will feel a strong pull from the nucleus of a smaller atom since the bonding electrons will be "closer" to the nucleus. This stronger pull results in a higher electronegativity for smaller atoms.

Think about It

Both size and electronegativity trends are more fundamentally a reflection of the trends in effective nuclear charge and the n level of the valence electrons of an atom.

4.83. **Collect and Organize**
We are to define *polar covalent bond.*

Analyze
A covalent bond forms between atoms of close electronegativities and involves the sharing, not the transfer, of electrons between the atoms. When a bond is polar, electron density is unevenly distributed.

Solve
A polar covalent bond is one in which the electrons are shared, but not equally, by the atoms.

Think about It
The more electronegative atom in the bond pulls more of the electron density toward itself, making that atom slightly rich in electron density ($\delta-$), leaving the other atom slightly deficient in electron density ($\delta+$).

4.85. **Collect and Organize**
Of the bonds listed between two atoms, we are to determine which are polar and, in those bonds that are polar, which atom has the greater electronegativity.

Analyze
Polar bonds form between any two dissimilar atoms that have different electronegativity values. To determine the more electronegative atom, we can use knowledge of the periodic trends of electronegativity values in Figure 4.8 in the textbook.

Solve
The polar bonds and the atoms with the greater electronegativity (underlined) are <u>C</u>—Se, C—<u>O</u>, <u>N</u>—H, and <u>C</u>—H.

Think about It
The Cl—Cl and O=O bonds are not polar because the bonded atoms are identical.

4.87. **Collect and Organize**
From the list of pairs of atoms, we are to discriminate between binary compounds with polar covalent bonds and ionic bonds.

Analyze
When the difference in electronegativity between the atoms is zero, the bond is nonpolar. If the electronegativity difference is below 2.0, the bond is polar covalent. If the electronegativity difference is 2.0 or greater, the bond is ionic.

Solve

Bond	Electronegativity Difference	Bond Type
(a) C and S	$2.5 - 2.5 = 0$	Nonpolar covalent
(b) C and O	$3.5 - 2.5 = 1.0$	Polar covalent
(c) Al and Cl	$3.0 - 1.5 = 1.5$	Polar covalent
(d) Ca and O	$3.5 - 1.0 = 2.5$	Ionic

Binary compounds of (b) C and O and (c) Al and Cl have polar covalent bonds. The binary compound of (d) Ca and O has ionic bonds.

Think about It
Although both C—O and Al—Cl bonds are polar covalent, the Al—Cl bond has greater ionic character (is more polar) than the C—O bond.

4.89. **Collect and Organize**
We are asked to compare the atmospheric greenhouse gases to the panes of a greenhouse.

Analyze

The atmospheric gases considered greenhouse gases include CO and CH_4. By acting as greenhouse gases they trap radiation, acting as a blanket to warm the earth.

Solve

Like the panes of glass in a greenhouse, the greenhouse gases in the atmosphere are transparent to visible light. Once the visible light warms the surface of the earth and is reemitted as infrared (lower energy) light, the greenhouse gases absorb the infrared light, in the same way that the panes of glass do not allow the heat from inside the greenhouse to escape.

Think about It

For a molecule to absorb infrared radiation and act as a greenhouse gas, it must have a molecular vibration that has a change in dipole moment upon stretching or bending. Nitrogen (N_2) and oxygen (O_2), with no dipole moment change upon stretching, are not greenhouse gases.

4.91. **Collect and Organize**

We are asked to consider which bond stretching in N_2O is responsible for the absorption of infrared radiation.

Analyze

Infrared radiation is absorbed by molecules with polar bonds when the fluctuating electric fields in the molecule do not cancel each other out (asymmetric stretching). The Lewis structure of N_2O shows that this molecule is linear.

$$:N{\equiv}N{-}\ddot{\underset{..}{O}}: \quad \text{or} \quad :\ddot{N}{=}N{=}\ddot{\underset{..}{O}}:$$

Solve

To a first approximation, the N—N bond is not polar, and so the stretching of that bond would not absorb IR radiation. However, the N—O bond is polar and would be expected to absorb IR radiation upon stretching.

Think about It

N_2O is estimated to be about 300 times more potent a greenhouse gas than CO_2. It is, however, present in much lower concentrations (320 ppb versus 385 ppm) than CO_2.

4.93. **Collect and Organize**

We are asked to consider whether carbon monoxide is infrared active (can absorb IR radiation).

Analyze

Infrared radiation is absorbed by a molecular vibration (bond stretch or bend) when the bond is polar and when the fluctuating electric fields do not cancel each other out. The Lewis structure of carbon monoxide is

$$:C{\equiv}O:$$

Solve

The C—O bond is polar because of the difference in electronegativity of carbon and oxygen. Stretching the linear C—O bond in carbon monoxide would give a fluctuating electric field, and therefore CO does absorb IR radiation.

Think about It

Carbon monoxide is a weak greenhouse gas, but it reacts with hydroxyl (OH) radicals, which then cannot react with other greenhouse gases such as methane to "neutralize" them and reduce their effects.

4.95. **Collect and Organize**

For this question we consider why infrared radiation causes vibrations, but not breakage, of chemical bonds.

Analyze

Infrared radiation has wavelengths in the range of 10^{-6} to 10^{-4} m, whereas ultraviolet radiation has wavelengths in the range of 10^{-6} to 10^{-8} m.

Solve

The shorter the wavelength, the higher the energy of the radiation. Thus, infrared radiation, with its longer wavelengths and lower energy, causes chemical bonds only to stretch and bend. Higher energy ultraviolet radiation can cause chemical bonds to break.

Think about It

Ultraviolet radiation, along with X-ray and gamma radiation, can cause bonds to break and are classified as ionizing radiation.

4.97. Collect and Organize

For this question we compare the bonds in CO_2 to CO to determine whether the energy to vibrate the C—O bond in CO is greater or less than the energy to vibrate the C—O bond in CO_2.

Analyze

The Lewis structure of CO shows that the C—O bond is a triple bond, whereas the C—O bond in CO_2 is a double bond.

$$:C\equiv O: \qquad :\ddot{O}=C=\ddot{O}:$$

Solve

Because the triple bond in CO is stronger than the double bond in CO_2, the energy required to vibrate the C—O bond in CO is higher.

Think about It

As we will see in Section 4.9 the bond strength is also related to bond length. The stronger the bond, the shorter the bond distance. The triple bond in CO is 113 pm, whereas the double bond in CO_2 is 123 pm.

4.99. Collect and Organize

We are to explain the concept of resonance.

Analyze

Resonance structures are equivalent Lewis structures that differ only in the placement of electrons.

Solve

Resonance occurs when two or more valid Lewis structures may be drawn for a molecular species. The true structure of the species is a hybrid of the structures drawn.

Think about It

When drawing resonance structures for a molecule, keep two important items in mind: (1) each Lewis structure must be valid (that is, the atoms must have complete octets [or duets, if hydrogen atoms]) and (2) the positions of the atoms must not change—only the distribution of the electrons in bonding pairs and lone pairs will differ between resonance structures.

4.101. Collect and Organize

We are asked to describe what factors determine resonance in molecules or ions.

Analyze

We find out whether a molecule has resonance structures by drawing their Lewis structures.

Solve

A molecule or ion shows resonance when more than one correct Lewis structure exists, that is, when the electrons in the correct Lewis structure may be distributed in more than one way. Often, when the central atom has both a single and a double bond, resonance is possible.

Think about It
Remember that resonance structures differ from each other only in the arrangement of the electrons, not in the atoms of the structure.

4.103. **Collect and Organize**
By drawing the Lewis structures of NO_2 and CO_2, we are to explain why NO_2 is more likely to exhibit resonance.

Analyze
The Lewis structures of NO_2 and CO_2 are as follows:

$$:\ddot{O}-\dot{N}=\ddot{O}: \qquad :\ddot{O}=C=\ddot{O}:$$

Solve
Either N—O bond in the NO_2 structure could be double-bonded, and the formal charges for each structure are identical, so more than one correct Lewis structure exists and NO_2 will exhibit resonance.

$$\overset{-1}{:\ddot{O}}-\overset{+1}{\dot{N}}=\overset{0}{\ddot{O}}: \longleftrightarrow \overset{0}{:\ddot{O}}=\overset{+1}{\dot{N}}-\overset{-1}{\ddot{O}}:$$

The resonance forms of CO_2 show that one is dominant (the one in which all formal charges are zero), and so the other forms contribute little to the true structure of CO_2.

$$\overset{0}{:\ddot{O}}=\overset{0}{C}=\overset{0}{\ddot{O}}: \longleftrightarrow \overset{+1}{:O}\equiv\overset{0}{C}-\overset{-1}{\ddot{O}}: \longleftrightarrow \overset{-1}{:\ddot{O}}-\overset{0}{C}\equiv\overset{+1}{O}:$$

Think about It
The following is *not* a correct Lewis structure for CO_2.

$$:O\equiv C=\ddot{O}:$$

4.105. **Collect and Organize**
For cyclic C_4H_4 we are to draw two Lewis structures showing resonance.

Analyze
To draw the Lewis structures, we first must determine the number of valence electrons in each of the structures. Then we arrange the atoms to show the bonding in the molecule by connecting the atoms with single covalent bonds. Finally, we complete the octets of the atoms bonded to the central atoms and then complete the octet of the central atom. Once one Lewis structure is drawn, we can then consider alternate structures in resonance with the first.

Solve
(Step 1) The number of valence electrons in C_4H_4 is

Element	4C	4H
Valence electrons per atom	(4×4) +	(4×1) = 20

(Step 2) Carbon has the most unpaired electrons (four) in its Lewis symbol and therefore has the highest bonding capacity and will be the central atom in the structure. We are told that the carbon atoms form a ring, and so they are each bonded to two other carbon atoms and one hydrogen atom.

(Step 3) The duets on the terminal H atoms are complete.

(Step 4) This structure has 16 electrons from eight bond pairs. We need four more electrons (two pairs) to match the valence electrons determined in step 1. The carbon atoms do not have octets, so we add the lone pairs to two of the carbon atoms.

(Step 5) The other two carbon atoms do not have an octet. We can complete the octet for each carbon by forming two double bonds between C atoms in the ring.

The two double bonds could have been drawn for the other two carbons as well, so the two resonance forms of C_4H_4 are

Think about It
Cyclic compounds that have alternating single and double bonds often show resonance.

4.107. Collect and Organize
For N_2O_2 and N_2O_3 we are to draw Lewis structures and show all possible resonance forms.

Analyze
To draw the Lewis structures we must first determine the number of covalent bonds in each structure and then complete the octets (duets for hydrogen) as necessary and check the structure with electron bookkeeping. Once one Lewis structure is drawn, we can then consider alternate structures in resonance with the first.

Solve
For N_2O_2
(Step 1) The number of valence electrons is

Element	2N	2O	
Valence electrons per atom	(2×5) +	(2×6) =	22

(Step 2) Nitrogen has more unpaired electrons (three) than oxygen and is less electronegative, so the two nitrogen atoms are the central atoms in the structure.

$$O—N—N—O$$

(Step 3) We complete the octets on the oxygen atoms by adding three lone pairs to each.

$$:\ddot{O}—N—N—\ddot{O}:$$

(Step 4) This structure has 18 electrons from six lone pairs and three bond pairs. We need four more electrons (two pairs) to match the valence electrons determined in step 1. The nitrogen atoms do not have octets yet, so we will add one lone pair to each N atom.

$$:\ddot{O}—\ddot{N}—\ddot{N}—\ddot{O}:$$

(Step 5) We can complete the octet for each nitrogen by forming double bonds between the oxygen and nitrogen atoms.

$$:\ddot{O}{\overset{\curvearrowright}{—}}\ddot{N}—\ddot{N}{—}\ddot{O}: \qquad :\ddot{O}\!=\!\ddot{N}—\ddot{N}\!=\!\ddot{O}:$$

The electrons could also be distributed in five more resonance forms that also complete the octet on all the atoms.

$$\ddot{O}\!=\!N—\ddot{N}\!=\!\ddot{O} \longleftrightarrow :O\!\equiv\!N—\ddot{N}—\ddot{O}: \longleftrightarrow \ddot{O}\!=\!N\!=\!N—\ddot{O}: \longleftrightarrow$$

$$:\ddot{O}—N\!\equiv\!N—\ddot{O}: \longleftrightarrow :\ddot{O}—\ddot{N}—N\!\equiv\!O: \longleftrightarrow :\ddot{O}—N\!=\!N\!=\!\ddot{O}$$

For N_2O_3

(Step 1) The number of valence electrons is

Element	2N	3O
Valence electrons per atom	(2×5) +	(3×6) = 28

(Step 2) Nitrogen has more unpaired electrons (three) than oxygen and is less electronegative, so the two nitrogen atoms are the central atoms in the structure.

$$\begin{array}{c} O \\ | \\ O—N—N—O \end{array}$$

(Step 3) We complete the octets on the oxygen atoms by adding three lone pairs to each.

$$\begin{array}{c} :\ddot{O}: \\ | \\ :\ddot{O}—N—N—\ddot{O}: \end{array}$$

(Step 4) This structure has 26 electrons from nine lone pairs and four bond pairs. We need two more electrons (one pair) to match the valence electrons determined in step 1. The nitrogen atoms do not have octets yet, so we will add one lone pair to a N atom.

$$\begin{array}{c} :\ddot{O}: \\ | \\ :\ddot{O}—\ddot{N}—N—\ddot{O}: \end{array}$$

(Step 5) We can complete the octet for each nitrogen by forming double bonds between the oxygen and nitrogen atoms.

$$\begin{array}{cc} \begin{array}{c} :\ddot{O}: \\ {\overset{\curvearrowleft}{|}} \\ :\ddot{O}{\overset{\curvearrowright}{—}}N—\ddot{N}—\ddot{O}: \end{array} & \begin{array}{c} \ddot{O}: \\ \| \\ :\ddot{O}\!=\!\ddot{N}—N—\ddot{O}: \end{array} \end{array}$$

The electrons could also be distributed in three more resonance forms that also complete the octet on all the atoms.

Think about It

In N_2O_3 a resonance structure that has a triple bond between the N atoms would violate the octet rule for the N bound to two O atoms and for one of the O atoms.

4.109. **Collect and Organize**

Fulminic acid has a linear structure with atom connectivity as described by the molecular formula given. From this framework we are to draw valid resonance structures for HCNO.

Analyze

We first draw one of the valid Lewis structures by the method described in the textbook; then we redistribute the bonding pairs and lone pairs in the structure to draw resonance forms.

Solve

For HCNO, fulminic acid

(Step 1) The number of valence electrons is

Element	H		C		N		O		
Valence electrons per atom	1	+	4	+	5	+	6	=	16

(Step 2) We are given that fulminic acid is a linear molecule with the connectivity of the atoms as

$$H-C-N-O$$

(Step 3) We complete the octets on the oxygen atom by adding three lone pairs. The duet on the terminal H atom is already satisfied.

$$H-C-N-\overset{\cdot\cdot}{\underset{\cdot\cdot}{O}}:$$

(Step 4) This structure has 12 electrons from three lone pairs and three bond pairs. We need four more electrons (two pairs) to match the valence electrons determined in step 1. The nitrogen and carbon atoms do not have octets yet, so we will add lone pairs.

$$H-\underset{\cdot\cdot}{C}-\overset{\cdot\cdot}{N}-\overset{\cdot\cdot}{\underset{\cdot\cdot}{O}}:$$

(Step 5) We can complete the octet for the carbon and nitrogen atoms by forming a triple bond between them.

$$H-C\overset{\cdot\cdot}{\underset{\cdot\cdot}{N}}-\overset{\cdot\cdot}{\underset{\cdot\cdot}{O}}: \qquad H-C\equiv N-\overset{\cdot\cdot}{\underset{\cdot\cdot}{O}}:$$

The electrons could also be distributed in two additional resonance forms that also complete the octet on all the atoms.

$$H-C\equiv N-\overset{\cdot\cdot}{\underset{\cdot\cdot}{O}}: \longleftrightarrow H-\overset{\cdot\cdot}{\underset{\cdot\cdot}{C}}-N\equiv O: \longleftrightarrow H-\overset{\cdot\cdot}{C}=\overset{\cdot\cdot}{N}=O:$$

Think about It

The following resonance form is not valid because it has more than a duet for the H atom and has less than an octet for the C atom.

$$H\!=\!C\!-\!\ddot{N}\!=\!\ddot{O}\!:$$

4.111. **Collect and Organize**

We are asked in this problem to first draw a complete Lewis structure of N_2O_5 and then show all its resonance forms.

Analyze

We first draw one of the valid Lewis structures by the five-step method described in the textbook, and then we redistribute the bonding pairs and lone pairs in the structure to draw resonance forms.

Solve

For N_2O_5

(Step 1) The number of valence electrons is

Element	2N		5O	
Valence electrons per atom	(2×5)	$+$	(5×6)	$= 40$

(Step 2) In this molecule one of the oxygen atoms will be a bridging atom between two "NO_2" units.

(Step 3) We complete the octets on the outside oxygen atoms by adding three lone pairs to each.

(Step 4) This structure has 40 electrons from 14 lone pairs and six bond pairs. No more electrons are needed for this Lewis structure.

(Step 5) We can complete the octet for the nitrogen atoms by forming a double bond between each of them and one of the oxygen atoms bonded to that nitrogen atom.

The electrons could also be distributed in three additional resonance forms that also complete the octet on all the atoms.

Think about It

Because the real structure of dinitrogen pentoxide is a hybrid of these four resonance structures, we would expect each nitrogen–oxygen bond to be the same length and strength, with a bond order of 1.5.

4.113. **Collect and Organize**

We are to explain how we can use formal charges to choose the best molecular structure for a given chemical formula.

Analyze

Formal charge (FC) is not a real charge on the atoms but rather a method to assign the apparent charges on atoms in covalently bonded compounds. FC is determined as follows:

$$FC = \text{(number of valence e}^- \text{ for the atom)}$$
$$- [\text{(number of e}^- \text{ in lone pairs)} + (\tfrac{1}{2} \times \text{number of e}^- \text{ in bonding pairs)}]$$

Solve

The best possible structure for a molecule, judging by formal charges, is the structure in which the formal charges are minimized and the negative formal charges are on the most electronegative atoms in the structure.

Think about It

The sum of the formal charges on the atoms in a structure must equal the charge on the molecule.

4.115. **Collect and Organize**

In a sulfur–oxygen bond, we can use their electronegativity values to predict which atom would carry the negative formal charge for the structure most likely to contribute to the bonding. We are asked whether a structure with a negative formal charge on S rather than O is more likely to contribute to bonding in a molecule containing S and O atoms.

Analyze

The more electronegative atom is more likely to carry the negative formal charge.

Solve

No. The electronegativity of oxygen (3.5) is higher than that of sulfur (2.5), so the negative formal charge must be on the O atom in the structure that contributes most to the bonding.

Think about It

The most electronegative elements are F, O, N, and Cl, and these are the elements most likely to carry negative formal charges, if they must, in Lewis structures that contribute significantly to the bonding.

4.117. **Collect and Organize**

After drawing the Lewis structures for HNC and HCN and assigning formal charges to the atoms, we are asked to analyze the differences in their formal charges (and choose the best, most stable arrangement for the atoms).

Analyze

After drawing the Lewis structures for both HNC and HCN, we assign the formal charge (FC) for each atom from the formula

$$FC = \text{(number of valence e}^- \text{ for the atom)}$$
$$- [\text{(number of e}^- \text{ in lone pairs)} + (\tfrac{1}{2} \times \text{number of e}^- \text{ in bonding pairs)}]$$

Solve

Both HNC and HCN have 10 valence electrons, and the Lewis structures with formal charges are

$$\overset{0}{\text{H}}-\overset{+1}{\text{N}}\equiv\overset{-1}{\text{C}}: \qquad \overset{0}{\text{H}}-\overset{0}{\text{C}}\equiv\overset{0}{\text{N}}:$$

The formal charges are zero for all the atoms in HCN, whereas in HNC the carbon atom, with a lower electronegativity than N, has a –1 formal charge.

Think about It

The HCN arrangement, being more stable, is the preferred structure.

4.119. Collect and Organize

We are to draw Lewis structures for cyanamide, H_2NCN, and assign formal charges to each atom.

Analyze

Because we are asked to draw *structures* for the compound, we suspect that the compound may show resonance. After drawing the possible resonance structures, we assign formal charges to all atoms in each structure by using

$$FC = \text{(number of valence } e^- \text{ for the atom)}$$
$$- [\text{(number of } e^- \text{ in lone pairs)} + (\tfrac{1}{2} \times \text{number of } e^- \text{ in bonding pairs)}]$$

Solve

Cyanamide, H_2NCN, has 16 valence electrons, and the possible structures, with formal charges assigned for the atoms, are

The preferred structure is the one with the C triple bonded to N because all the formal charges on the structure are zero.

Think about It

Be careful in drawing the resonance structures. The structure below is not valid because it violates the octet rule for both nitrogen atoms.

4.121. Collect and Organize

For the arrangement of atoms in nitrous oxide (N_2O), where oxygen is the central atom, we are to assign formal charges and suggest why this structure is not stable.

Analyze

After drawing the possible resonance structures, we assign formal charges to all atoms in each structure by using

$$FC = \text{(number of valence } e^- \text{ for the atom)}$$
$$- [\text{(number of } e^- \text{ in lone pairs)} + (\tfrac{1}{2} \times \text{number of } e^- \text{ in bonding pairs)}]$$

Solve

Nitrous oxide, N_2O, has 16 valence electrons, and the Lewis structures with formal charges assigned to the atoms are

Because oxygen is more electronegative than nitrogen, none of these structures is likely to be stable because the formal charge on O is positive, when it would be predicted from electronegativity to be negative.

Think about It

The Lewis structure for the arrangement N—N—O is far better by formal charge, particularly with the resonance structure that has a N to N triple bond.

4.123. **Collect and Organize**

We are to draw the Lewis structures (with resonance forms) for nitromethane (CH_3NO_2) and $CNNO_2$ (which has two possible skeletal structures), and we are to determine whether the two molecules are resonance structures of each other.

Analyze

For each Lewis structure, we have to be sure that in drawing the resonance structures, we only redistribute electrons and do not move atoms.

Solve

(a) CH_3NO_2 has 24 valence electrons. Completing the octets for all the atoms (duet for hydrogen), drawing an alternate resonance structure, and assigning formal charges to the atoms gives

(b) $CNNO_2$ has 26 valence electrons. Completing the octets for all the atoms, drawing the alternate resonance structures, and assigning formal charges to the atoms gives

Formal charges are minimized in the two bottom structures, with the negative formal charge on the most electronegative atom (oxygen), so these are the preferred structures.

(c) The two structures of $CNNO_2$ given in the text are not resonance structures because their atoms differ in connectivity. When two molecules have the same number of atoms, but in a different arrangement, they are called *isomers*.

Think about It

Be careful to make sure that all atoms in a resonance form have complete octets. The following Lewis structure for $NCNO_2$ is not valid because the terminal nitrogen atom has fewer than 8 e⁻.

4.125. **Collect and Organize**

We are asked to consider whether all odd-electron molecules are inconsistent with the octet rule.

Analyze

When the octet rule is applied to the drawing of any Lewis structure, the number of electrons needed will be a multiple of 8 (ignoring any duets required for H).

Solve

The number of electrons (multiple of 8) needed to follow the octet rule is always even; therefore, yes, odd-electron molecules are always exceptions to the octet rule.

Think about It
When an odd-electron molecule (radical) either gains or loses an electron, it may then satisfy the octet rule for the atoms in the molecule.

4.127. Collect and Organize
We are asked why C, N, O, and F always obey the octet rule in Lewis structures.

Analyze
C, N, O, and F are all second-period elements with electron configurations of $[He]2s^2 2p^x$, where $x = 2, 3, 4, 5$. Once the $2p$ shell is filled with 6 e^-, a closed-shell configuration is formed.

Solve
To accommodate more than 8 e^- in covalently bonded molecules, the atom would have to use orbitals beyond s and p. The d orbitals are not available to the small elements in the second period but do become available for the third-period (and subsequent periods) elements such as P, S, and Cl.

Think about It
The octet rule strictly applies for only second-period elements but remains a starting place for drawing Lewis structures for compounds where larger elements are the central atoms in the structure.

4.129. Collect and Organize
To determine which of the sulfur–fluorine molecules have an expanded octet, we need to consider the number of electrons around the central atom required to form the compound.

Analyze
In each of these compounds sulfur is the central atom, as it is the least electronegative and has the highest bonding capacity. If the number of electrons in bonding pairs and lone pairs on the sulfur atom in the Lewis structure of each compound is greater than 8, then sulfur in that compound has an expanded octet.

Solve

Molecule	Lewis Structure	Number of Electrons around S
(a) SF_6		12
(b) SF_5		11
(c) SF_4		10
(d) SF_2		8

SF_6, SF_5, and SF_4 (a–c) require sulfur to expand its octet.

Think about It
SF_5 is an odd-electron (radical) species.

4.131. Collect and Organize
To determine the number of electrons in the covalent bonds around each sulfur atom in the molecules, we first draw the Lewis structures for each.

Analyze

For these Lewis structures, we might have to expand octets for the sulfur atom (sulfur bonded to >2 atoms has to have more than 8 e⁻ to form the compound). We also have to consider whether the expansion of the octet on sulfur through double bonding, for example, reduces the formal charges on the atoms in the structure.

Solve

(a) SF_4O has 40 valence electrons, and its Lewis structure with formal charges assigned to its atoms is

To reduce the formal charges on S and O, the oxygen may form a double bond with S.

SF_4O has 12 e⁻ in six covalent bonds around sulfur.

(b) SOF_2 has 26 valence electrons, and its Lewis structure with formal charges assigned to its atoms is

To reduce the formal charges on S and O, we could add a double bond between the oxygen and sulfur atoms.

This gives 8 e⁻ in four covalent bonds on sulfur in SOF_2.

(c) SO_3 has 24 valence electrons, and its Lewis structure with formal charges assigned to its atoms is

To reduce the formal charges on S and O, we could add double bonds between the other oxygen atoms and sulfur.

This gives 12 e⁻ in six covalent bonds on sulfur in SO_3.

(d) SF_5^- has 42 valence electrons, and its Lewis structure with formal charges assigned to its atoms is

$$
\begin{bmatrix}
& & \overset{0}{\underset{..}{:F:}} & & \\
\overset{0}{..} & \overset{..}{:F} & | & \overset{..}{F:} & \overset{0}{} \\
& & S & & \\
\overset{0}{..} & \diagup & \underset{-1}{} & \diagdown & \overset{0}{..:O} \\
& :F & & F: &
\end{bmatrix}^-
$$

If we were to add a double bond between a fluorine atom and the sulfur atom, the formal charge buildup would *not* be preferred over the previous structure.

$$
\begin{bmatrix}
& & \overset{+1}{\overset{..}{F}} & & \\
\overset{0}{..} & :F & \| & F: & \overset{0}{} \\
& & S & & \\
\overset{0}{..} & :F & \underset{-2}{} & F: & \overset{0}{}
\end{bmatrix}^-
$$

SF_5^- has 10 e^- in five covalent bonds.

Think about It
Double bonding of an atom to fluorine, as in the second structure in part d, gives a positive formal charge on F. This arrangement is never preferred since fluorine is the most electronegative element.

4.133. Collect and Organize
By drawing the Lewis structures of NOF_3 and POF_3 we are to describe the differences in bonding between these molecules.

Analyze
Nitrogen is a second-period element that cannot expand its octet, but phosphorus, as a third-period element, can expand its octet.

Solve
Both molecules have 32 valence electrons. The Lewis structures with formal charges are as follows:

$$
\begin{array}{cc}
\overset{-1}{:\overset{..}{O}:} & \overset{-1}{:\overset{..}{O}:} \\
\overset{0}{:F} - \overset{+1}{N} - \overset{0}{F:} & \overset{0}{:F} - \overset{+1}{P} - \overset{0}{F:} \\
\underset{0}{:F:} & \underset{0}{:F:}
\end{array}
$$

Because oxygen is more electronegative than N, these structures where the O atom has a –1 formal charge seem reasonable. However, the formal charges on P and O in POF_3 can be reduced to zero because P can expand its octet to form a double bond with O.

$$
\begin{array}{c}
\overset{0}{:\overset{..}{O}:} \\
\overset{0}{:F} - \overset{0}{P} - \overset{0}{F:} \\
\underset{0}{:F:}
\end{array}
$$

POF_3 contains a double bond and no formal charges; NOF_3 has only single bonds, and formal charges are present on the N and O atoms.

Think about It
In Lewis structures, always try to minimize formal charges. For elements in the third or higher period, you can reduce formal charge by expanding the octets to form double bonds.

4.135. **Collect and Organize**

By drawing the Lewis structures of SeF_4 and SeF_5^- we can determine in which structure the Se atom has expanded its octet.

Analyze

Selenium, in the fourth period, expands its octet by making use of its $4d$ orbitals. For each Lewis structure, we use the method in the textbook. If the number of electrons around the central Se atom in the structures is greater than 8, selenium expands its octet to form the compound.

Solve

SeF_4 has 34 valence electrons, and its Lewis structure shows 10 electrons around the central selenium atom.

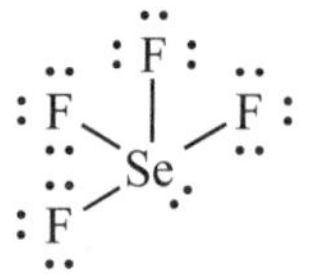

SeF_5^- has 42 valence electrons, and its Lewis structure shows 12 electrons around the central selenium atom.

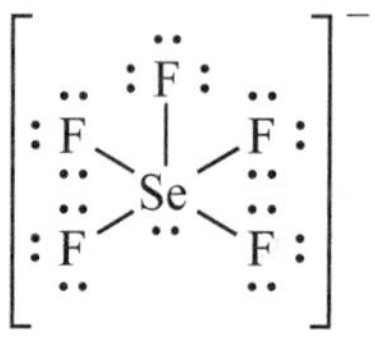

In both SeF_4 and SeF_5^-, Se has more than 8 valence electrons.

Think about It

In both SeF_4 and SeF_5^-, a lone pair of electrons is present on the selenium atom to give 10 and 12 electrons around Se, respectively.

4.137. **Collect and Organize**

From the arrangement of atoms given in Figure P4.137 for Cl_2O_2, we are to draw the Lewis structure and determine whether any of the Cl atoms needs to expand its octet to form the molecule.

Analyze

The arrangement of atoms in Cl_2O_2 requires 26 valence electrons.

Solve

The Lewis structure for Cl_2O_2 is

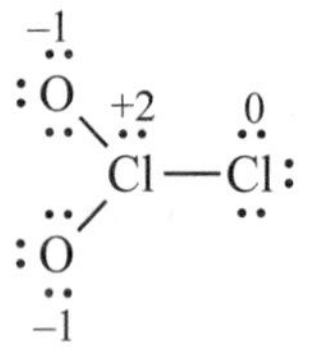

In this structure, neither Cl atom needs to expand its octet. However, the formal charges on the atoms of this structure are fairly high. To reduce formal charges, we could form double bonds between the Cl and O atoms.

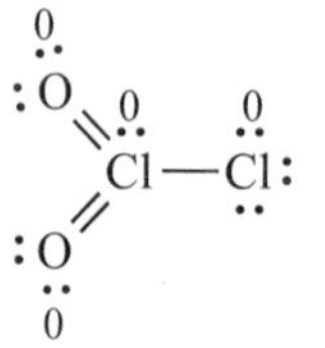

In this structure, all formal charges of all atoms are zero, and the central chlorine atom has an expanded octet.

Think about It

Use formal charges to seek out when an atom will expand its octet. At first glance Cl_2O_2 did not appear to have any more than 8 e⁻ surrounding the central Cl atom.

4.139. Collect and Organize

For each molecule combining Cl with O we are to determine which are odd-electron molecules.

Analyze

To answer this we need only add up the valence electrons for each molecule.

Solve

(a) Cl_2O_7 has $(2\ Cl \times 7\ e^-) + (7\ O \times 6\ e^-) = 56\ e^-$
(b) Cl_2O_6 has $(2\ Cl \times 7\ e^-) + (6\ O \times 6\ e^-) = 50\ e^-$
(c) ClO_4 has $(1\ Cl \times 7\ e^-) + (4\ O \times 6\ e^-) = 31\ e^-$
(d) ClO_3 has $(1\ Cl \times 7\ e^-) + (3\ O \times 6\ e^-) = 25\ e^-$
(e) ClO_2 has $(1\ Cl \times 7\ e^-) + (2\ O \times 6\ e^-) = 19\ e^-$
The odd-electron molecules are (c) ClO_4, (d) ClO_3, and (e) ClO_2.

Think about It

For these chlorine–oxygen molecules, the odd-electron species have an odd number of Cl atoms in their formulas.

4.141. Collect and Organize

For the species named, we are to decide which atom in the molecule most likely has an unpaired electron.

Analyze

An unpaired electron in a molecule is a lone electron. This occurs when a molecule has an odd number of valence electrons. The atom that bears the odd electron is the least electronegative. The electronegativities of the atoms are S = 2.5, O = 3.5, N = 3.0, C = 2.5, H = 2.1.

Solve

(a) For SO^+, since S is less electronegative than O, the unpaired electron is on S.

$$\left[:\!\!\cdot S \equiv O : \right]^+$$

(b) For NO, since N is less electronegative than O, the unpaired electron is on N.

$$\cdot \ddot{N} \equiv O :$$

(c) For CN, since C is less electronegative than N, the unpaired electron is on C.

$$\cdot C \equiv N :$$

(d) For OH, since H is less electronegative than O, we expect the unpaired electron to be on H. Hydrogen, however, must be bonded to O and obey the duet rule, so the unpaired electron must be on O.

$$\cdot \ddot{O} - H$$

Think about It

The unpaired electron is where a lone pair normally is shown in a Lewis structure, not where a bonding pair is drawn. This could not be done for the H in OH because the H atom would not have a lone pair on it; H cannot have more than its duet surrounding it.

4.143. Collect and Organize

From the Lewis structures given we can use formal charge arguments to determine which structure contributes most to the bonding in CNO.

Analyze

The resonance structure that contributes the most to the bonding has the lowest possible formal charges on the atoms and, if formal charges are present, then the negative formal charges should be on the most electronegative atoms in the structure.

Solve

The formal charge assignments on each of the structures are as follows:

(a) $\overset{-2}{\cdot\ddot{C}}-\overset{+1}{N}\equiv\overset{+1}{O}:$

(b) $\overset{-1}{\cdot C}=\overset{+1}{N}=\overset{0}{\ddot{O}}\cdot$

(c) $:\overset{-1}{C}\equiv\overset{+1}{N}-\overset{0}{\ddot{O}}\cdot$

(d) $\cdot\overset{0}{C}\equiv\overset{+1}{N}-\overset{-1}{\ddot{O}}:$

The structure that contributes the most to the bonding in CNO is (d).

Think about It

Because all these structures are in resonance, each resonance form contributes to the bonding. However, because structure (d) is favored with the −1 formal charge placed on the oxygen atom, the form with a $C\equiv N$ bond and with the unpaired electron on C contributes the most to the bonding.

4.145. **Collect and Organize**

Using the Lewis structures for the nitrate ion (NO_3^-) and the nitrite ion (NO_2^-), we can determine whether we expect their nitrogen–oxygen bond lengths to be the same.

Analyze

In Lewis structures, single bonds are longer than double bonds, which are longer than triple bonds. We must also consider any resonance forms that these molecules might have.

Solve

Each bond in the nitrate ion is 1.33 bonds because of resonance.

Each bond in the nitrite ion is 1.5 bonds because of resonance.

No, the nitrogen–oxygen bond lengths in NO_3^- and NO_2^- are not the same; they are different.

Think about It

We would expect that the nitrogen–oxygen bond length in NO_2^- is shorter than the bond length in NO_3^-.

4.147. **Collect and Organize**

Using the Lewis structures (with resonance forms, if necessary), we can explain why the nitrogen–oxygen bonds in N_2O_4 and N_2O are nearly identical in length.

Analyze

In Lewis structures, single bonds are longer than double bonds, which are longer than triple bonds. We must also consider any resonance forms that these molecules might have.

Solve

The nitrogen–oxygen bond in N_2O_4 has a bond order of 1.5 because of four equivalent resonance forms.

The nitrogen–oxygen bond in N_2O has a bond order of 1.5 because of resonance among three resonance forms (where the last resonance structure shown does not significantly contribute to the structure of the molecule because of the buildup of too much formal charge).

$$\overset{-1}{\underset{\cdot\cdot}{:}}\overset{+1}{N}=\overset{0}{N}=\overset{\cdot\cdot}{O}\overset{\cdot}{:} \longleftrightarrow :\overset{0}{N}\equiv\overset{+1}{N}-\overset{-1}{\underset{\cdot\cdot}{O}}: \longleftrightarrow :\overset{-2}{\underset{\cdot\cdot}{N}}-\overset{+1}{N}\equiv\overset{+1}{O}:$$

Therefore, owing to resonance, N_2O_4 and N_2O are expected to have nearly equal bond lengths.

Think about It
Remember that all resonance forms, even though they may not contribute equally, do contribute some to the structure.

4.149. **Collect and Organize**
To rank the bond lengths in NO_2^-, NO^+, and NO_3^- we need to draw the Lewis structures, with resonance forms if necessary.

Analyze
In Lewis structures, single bonds are longer than double bonds, which are longer than triple bonds. We must also consider any resonance forms that these molecules might have.

Solve
For NO_2^-, the bond order for the N—O bond is 1.5 because of resonance.

$$\left[:\!O\!=\!N\!-\!\ddot{O}\!:\right]^- \longleftrightarrow \left[:\!\ddot{O}\!-\!N\!=\!O\!:\right]^-$$

For NO^+, the bond order for the N—O bond is 3.0.

$$\left[:N\equiv O:\right]^+$$

For NO_3^-, the bond order for the N—O bond is 1.33 because of resonance.

In order of increasing bond length: $NO^+ < NO_2^- < NO_3^-$.

Think about It
Resonance has quite an effect on bond order and length.

4.151. **Collect and Organize**
To rank the bond energies for NO_2^-, NO^+, and NO_3^-, we need to draw the Lewis structures, with resonance structures if necessary.

Analyze
In Lewis structures, single bonds have the lowest bond energy. Double bonds are stronger (have higher bond energies) than single bonds, and triple bonds are stronger than double bonds. The higher the bond order, the higher the bond energy.

Solve
For NO_2^-, the bond order for the N—O bond is 1.5 because of resonance.

$$\left[:\!\ddot{O}\!=\!N\!-\!\ddot{O}\!:\right]^- \longleftrightarrow \left[:\!\ddot{O}\!-\!N\!=\!\ddot{O}\!:\right]^-$$

For NO^+, the bond order for the N—O bond is 3.0.

$$\left[:N\equiv O:\right]^+$$

For NO_3^-, the bond order for the N—O bond is 1.33 because of resonance.

In order of increasing bond energy: $NO_3^- < NO_2^- < NO^+$.

Think about It
This ranking is the reverse of the ranking for increasing bond length in Problem 4.149.

4.153. Collect and Organize
To reflect the valence electrons available for bonding, the electron dot placement around the element symbol in a Lewis symbol should show the lone electrons that may form covalent bonds with other atoms. We are to select the preferred symbol in each pair listed.

Analyze
The valence electrons available for bonding in the atom are Be = 2, Al = 3, C = 4, He = 0.

Solve
(a)   ·Be·   (b)   ·Al·   (c)   ·C·   (d)   :He

Think about It
This placement method can be extended to other atoms. For example, oxygen, which tends to form two bonds to other atoms, has the Lewis dot symbol

·Ö·

4.155. Collect and Organize
Carbon disulfide could have either carbon or sulfur as the central atom in its structure. Using the formal charge assignments in the two possible Lewis structures, we are to determine which is the preferred structure.

Analyze
A structure is preferred when the formal charges on the atoms are minimized and when any negative formal charges are located on the most electronegative elements. The electronegativities of carbon and sulfur are the same, namely, 2.5.

Solve
Carbon disulfide has 16 valence electrons.

$$\overset{0}{\text{:S}}=\overset{0}{\text{C}}=\overset{0}{\text{S:}} \qquad \overset{0}{\text{:S}}=\overset{+2}{\text{S}}=\overset{-2}{\text{C:}}$$

When C is the central atom, the atoms all carry zero formal charge; this structure is preferred for carbon disulfide.

Think about It
Because sulfur can expand its octet, the formal charges on CSS may be reduced:

$$\overset{0}{\text{:S}}=\overset{+1}{\text{S}}\equiv\overset{-1}{\text{C:}}$$

This still leaves formal charges on the atoms. For reasons you will see when you study valence bond theory, carbon cannot quadruple bond to reduce the formal charges on the atoms in this structure down to zero.

4.157. Collect and Organize
For the poisonous substance phosgene, $COCl_2$, we are to draw the Lewis structure.

Analyze

$COCl_2$ has 24 valence electrons. Carbon has the largest bonding capacity and is the least electronegative of the atoms, so it is the central atom in the structure.

Solve

$$:\overset{\overset{\displaystyle ::}{O}}{\underset{\underset{\displaystyle }{C}}{\|}}$$

$$:\ddot{\underset{..}{Cl}}\diagup \quad \diagdown \ddot{\underset{..}{Cl}}:$$

Think about It

Symptoms of human phosgene inhalation include choking, painful breathing, severe eye irritation, and skin burns. Death may result from lack of oxygen.

4.159. **Collect and Organize**

Neutral OCN reacts with itself to form OCNNCO, and OCN⁻ reacts with BrNO to give OCNNO, and with Br_2 and NO_2 to give OCN(CO)NCO. For these three products we are to draw Lewis structures with any appropriate resonance forms.

Analyze

(a) OCNNCO has 30 valence electrons.
(b) BrNO has 18 valence electrons.
(c) OCN(CO)NCO has 40 valence electrons.

Solve

(a)

$$\overset{+1}{:O}\overset{0}{\equiv}\overset{-1}{C}-\overset{-1}{N}-\overset{0}{N}-\overset{+1}{C}\equiv\overset{}{O:} \longleftrightarrow \overset{0}{:O}=\overset{0}{C}=\overset{0}{N}-\overset{0}{N}=\overset{0}{C}=\overset{0}{O}. \longleftrightarrow \overset{0}{:O}=\overset{-1}{C}-\overset{+1}{N}\equiv\overset{+1}{N}-\overset{-1}{C}=\overset{0}{O}. \longleftrightarrow$$

$$\overset{-1}{:O}-\overset{0}{C}\equiv\overset{+1}{N}-\overset{+1}{N}\equiv\overset{0}{C}-\overset{-1}{O:} \longleftrightarrow \overset{0}{:O}=\overset{0}{C}=\overset{0}{N}-\overset{+1}{N}\equiv\overset{0}{C}-\overset{-1}{O:} \longleftrightarrow \overset{-1}{:O}-\overset{0}{C}\equiv\overset{+1}{N}-\overset{0}{N}=\overset{0}{C}=\overset{0}{O:}$$

(b)

$$:\ddot{Br}-\overset{..}{N}=\overset{..}{O}:$$

$$\overset{+1}{:O}\equiv\overset{0}{C}-\overset{0}{N}=\overset{0}{N}-\overset{-1}{O:} \longleftrightarrow \overset{0}{:O}=\overset{-1}{C}-\overset{0}{N}=\overset{+1}{N}=\overset{0}{O}. \longleftrightarrow \overset{-1}{:O}-\overset{-1}{C}=\overset{0}{N}-\overset{+1}{N}\equiv\overset{+1}{O}:$$

(c)

$$\overset{\overset{\displaystyle ..O..}{}}{}$$
$$\overset{+1}{:O}\equiv\overset{0}{C}-\overset{-1}{N}-\overset{\overset{\displaystyle \|}{C}}{}-\overset{-1}{N}-\overset{0}{C}\equiv\overset{+1}{O:} \longleftrightarrow \overset{0}{:O}=\overset{0}{C}=\overset{0}{N}-\overset{\overset{\displaystyle \|}{C}}{}-\overset{0}{N}=\overset{0}{C}=\overset{0}{O:} \longleftrightarrow$$

$$\overset{\overset{\displaystyle :O:^{-1}}{}}{}$$
$$\overset{0}{:O}=\overset{0}{C}=\overset{0}{N}-\overset{\overset{\displaystyle |}{C}}{}=\overset{+1}{N}=\overset{0}{C}=\overset{0}{O:} \longleftrightarrow \overset{-1}{:O}-\overset{0}{C}\equiv\overset{+1}{N}-\overset{\overset{\displaystyle \|}{C}}{}-\overset{+1}{N}\equiv\overset{0}{C}-\overset{-1}{O:} \longleftrightarrow$$

$$\overset{\overset{\displaystyle ..O..}{}}{}$$
$$\overset{-1}{:O}-\overset{0}{C}\equiv\overset{+1}{N}-\overset{\overset{\displaystyle \|}{C}}{}-\overset{0}{N}=\overset{0}{C}=\overset{0}{O:} \longleftrightarrow \overset{0}{:O}=\overset{0}{C}=\overset{0}{N}-\overset{\overset{\displaystyle \|}{C}}{}-\overset{+1}{N}\equiv\overset{0}{C}-\overset{-1}{O:} \longleftrightarrow$$

$$\overset{\overset{\displaystyle :\!\overset{\cdot\cdot}{O}\!:}{\big|}^{-1}}{\underset{\cdot\cdot}{:}\overset{0}{\underset{\cdot\cdot}{O}}\!\!=\!\!\overset{0}{C}\!\!=\!\!\overset{+1}{N}\!\!=\!\!\overset{\underset{0}{C}}{}\!\!-\!\!\overset{0}{\underset{\cdot\cdot}{N}}\!\!=\!\!\overset{0}{C}\!\!=\!\!\overset{0}{\underset{\cdot\cdot}{\overset{\cdot\cdot}{O}}\!\!:}}$$

Think about It

The resonance structure that contributes the most to the bonding in each of these compounds is the one that minimizes formal charges on the atoms.

$$:\overset{0}{\underset{\cdot\cdot}{O}}\!\!=\!\!\overset{0}{C}\!\!=\!\!\overset{0}{\underset{\cdot\cdot}{N}}\!\!-\!\!\overset{0}{\underset{\cdot\cdot}{N}}\!\!=\!\!\overset{0}{C}\!\!=\!\!\overset{0}{\underset{\cdot\cdot}{O}}\!\!: \qquad :\overset{+1}{O}\!\!\equiv\!\!\overset{0}{C}\!\!-\!\!\overset{0}{\underset{\cdot\cdot}{N}}\!\!=\!\!\overset{0}{\underset{\cdot\cdot}{N}}\!\!-\!\!\overset{-1}{\underset{\cdot\cdot}{O}}\!: \qquad :\overset{0}{\underset{\cdot\cdot}{O}}\!\!=\!\!\overset{0}{C}\!\!=\!\!\overset{0}{\underset{\cdot\cdot}{N}}\!\!-\!\!\overset{\overset{\displaystyle \overset{0}{\underset{\cdot\cdot}{O}}}{\|}}{\underset{0}{C}}\!\!-\!\!\overset{0}{\underset{\cdot\cdot}{N}}\!\!=\!\!\overset{0}{C}\!\!=\!\!\overset{0}{\underset{\cdot\cdot}{O}}\!\!:$$

4.161. Collect and Organize

We are to draw two Lewis structures of Cl_2O_6; one structure with a chlorine–chlorine bond and the other with a Cl—O—Cl arrangement of atoms.

Analyze

Cl_2O_6 has 50 valence electrons. We will draw the Lewis structures with the minimum formal charge on all atoms.

Solve

Think about It

The formal charges on all the atoms for both arrangements of atoms in Cl_2O_6 are zero. From formal charges alone, therefore, we would not be able to predict the actual atom arrangement in Cl_2O_6 because we were able to draw structures for both arrangements in which all atoms have zero formal charge. The actual structure is thought to be as a perchlorate salt, $ClO_2^+ClO_4^-$.

4.163. Collect and Organize

Cyanogen (C_2N_2) is formed from CN, a radical species, and reacts with water to give oxalic acid. We are to draw the Lewis structures for the two possible arrangements of cyanogen and then, through comparing the structures with oxalic acid, rationalize a choice for the actual structure of cyanogen.

Analyze

(a) CN has 9 valence electrons, and as an odd-electron species we expect the structure to have 1 unpaired electron. C_2N_2 has 18 valence electrons.
(b) Oxalic acid's structure contains a C—C bond, which would derive from the carbon–carbon bond in cyanogen.

Solve

(a) CN has the Lewis structure

$$\cdot C\!\!\equiv\!\!N:$$

The more likely structure for cyanogen is the one with no formal charges on the atoms. This is the one that contains the C—C bond:

$$:\overset{0}{N}\!\!\equiv\!\!\overset{0}{C}\!\!-\!\!\overset{0}{C}\!\!\equiv\!\!\overset{0}{N}: \qquad :\overset{-1}{C}\!\!\equiv\!\!\overset{+1}{N}\!\!-\!\!\overset{+1}{N}\!\!\equiv\!\!\overset{-1}{C}:$$

(b) It would be expected that oxalic acid would retain the C—C bond from the cyanogen from which it is formed in the reaction of cyanogen with water. This is consistent with the structure for cyanogen predicted from formal charge analysis.

Think about It
Formal charge analysis is a method that works often, but not always, in predicting atom connectivity in a molecule or the major contributing resonance form in bonding. The prediction, however, must stand up to experimental scrutiny.

4.165. **Collect and Organize**
The structure of SF_3CN shows bond lengths of 116 pm (C—N), 174 pm (S—C), and 160 pm (F—S). We can compare these bond lengths to those in Table 4.7 to determine the type of bond each might be (single, double, or triple). This information can help us draw the Lewis structure for the molecule and assign formal charges.

Analyze
From Table 4.7, the only bond length listed that corresponds to any of the bond lengths in SF_3CN is $C \equiv N$ (116 pm). To draw the Lewis structure, we need 36 valence electrons.

Solve

Formal charges are nonzero and the carbon–nitrogen bond is not triple.

All formal charges are zero and the carbon–nitrogen bond is triple.

Think about It
In the preferred structure, sulfur has expanded its octet.

4.167. **Collect and Organize**
Tellurium will expand its octet to form $TeOF_6^{2-}$. Using this information and formal charges, we can draw the best Lewis structure for this ion.

Analyze
$TeOF_6^{2-}$ has 56 valence electrons, and tellurium is the central atom, as it is the least electronegative atom in the structure.

Solve

This structure has the lowest formal charges. Oxygen is highly electronegative, so it will carry a negative formal charge.

Think about It
Another resonance structure of $TeOF_6^{2-}$ would be

$$\left[\begin{array}{c} \ddot{O} \\ F \quad \parallel_2 \quad F \\ F - Te \\ F \quad \quad F \\ F \quad F \end{array}\right]^{2-}$$

but this places all the negative formal charge on the least electronegative atom in the structure, so it is not preferred to the structure shown above.

4.169. **Collect and Organize**
Both calcium carbonate and magnesium hydroxide are ionic compounds. To draw their Lewis structures, we have to draw the Lewis diagrams separately for the cation and anion.

Analyze
Calcium carbonate is $CaCO_3$, where the cation is Ca^{2+} and the anion is CO_3^{2-}. Magnesium hydroxide is $Mg(OH)_2$, where the cation is Mg^{2+} and the anion is OH^-.

Solve

$$[Ca]^{2+} \left[\begin{array}{c} \ddot{O} \\ \parallel \\ C \\ :\ddot{O} \quad \ddot{O}: \end{array}\right]^{2-} \quad 2[Mg]^{2+}[:\ddot{O} - H]^-$$

Think about It
The carbonate anion in calcium carbonate has two additional resonance structures that we could draw (see Problem 4.152).

4.171. **Collect and Organize**
In considering the Lewis structures of linear N_4 and cyclic N_4, by assigning formal charges we may be able to choose which form might be preferred by this short-lived allotrope of nitrogen.

Analyze
N_4 has 20 valence electrons.

Solve
(a, b)

$$\overset{0}{:}N\equiv\overset{+1}{N}-\overset{0}{N}=\overset{-1}{\ddot{N}} \longleftrightarrow \overset{-1}{:\ddot{N}}=\overset{+1}{N}=\overset{+1}{N}=\overset{-1}{\ddot{N}} \longleftrightarrow \overset{-1}{:\ddot{N}}=\overset{0}{N}-\overset{+1}{N}\equiv\overset{0}{N}:$$

All these resonance forms have atoms with nonzero formal charges. The middle structure has the most nonzero formal charges separated over three bond lengths, so this one is least preferred. The first and last resonance structures are preferred and are indistinguishable from each other.

(c) The resonance structures for cyclic N_4 have no formal charges on any of the nitrogen atoms.

$$\begin{array}{cc} \ddot{N} - \ddot{N} \\ \parallel \quad \parallel \\ \ddot{N} - \ddot{N} \end{array} \longleftrightarrow \begin{array}{cc} \ddot{N} = \ddot{N} \\ \mid \quad \mid \\ \ddot{N} = \ddot{N} \end{array}$$

Think about It
We would predict the structure of N_4 to be cyclic on the basis of formal charge considerations.

4.173. **Collect and Organize**

By drawing the Lewis structures for each of the molecules to minimize formal charges on the atoms, we can determine which molecules contain an atom with an expanded octet.

Analyze

All these molecules contain Cl, which may expand its octet because it is a third-period element.

Solve

(a) $:Cl{-}Cl:$ All formal charges are 0; no expanded octet

(b)   F—Cl—F structure   All formal charges are 0; expanded octet on Cl

(c)   I—Cl—I structure   All formal charges are 0; expanded octet on Cl

(d) $\left[:Cl{-}\overset{-1}{O}:\right]^{-}$ Formal charges are minimized and negative formal charge is on the more electronegative element; no expanded octet

ClF_3 (b) and ClI_3 (c) have an atom with an expanded octet.

Think about It

Remember to not expand octets on atoms so that you obtain less-preferred formal charges on the atoms. For example,

$$\left[:\overset{-1}{Cl}{=}O:\right]^{-}$$

is not preferred over the structure in part d above.

4.175. **Collect and Organize**

After drawing the Lewis structure (with resonance forms) for N_5^-, we can determine, using formal charges, which resonance forms contribute the most to the bonding in the molecule and compare the bonding of N_5^- to that of N_3^- in terms of average bond order.

Analyze

N_5^- has 26 valence electrons.

Solve

(a, b) All possible resonance structures for N_5^- with formal charge assignment are as follows:

$$\left[:\overset{-2}{N}{-}\overset{0}{N}{=}\overset{0}{N}{-}\overset{+1}{N}{\equiv}\overset{0}{N}:\right]^{-} \longleftrightarrow \left[:\overset{-2}{N}{-}\overset{0}{N}{=}\overset{+1}{N}{=}\overset{+1}{N}{=}\overset{-1}{N}:\right]^{-} \longleftrightarrow \left[:\overset{-2}{N}{-}\overset{+1}{N}{\equiv}\overset{+1}{N}{-}\overset{0}{N}{=}\overset{-1}{N}:\right]^{-} \longleftrightarrow$$

$$\left[:\overset{-1}{N}{=}\overset{0}{N}{-}\overset{+1}{N}{\equiv}\overset{+1}{N}{-}\overset{-2}{N}:\right]^{-} \longleftrightarrow \left[:\overset{0}{N}{\equiv}\overset{+1}{N}{-}\overset{0}{N}{=}\overset{0}{N}{-}\overset{-2}{N}:\right]^{-} \longleftrightarrow \left[:\overset{-1}{N}{=}\overset{0}{N}{-}\overset{0}{N}{=}\overset{+1}{N}{=}\overset{-1}{N}:\right]^{-} \longleftrightarrow$$

$$\left[:\overset{-1}{N}{=}\overset{+1}{N}{=}\overset{0}{N}{-}\overset{0}{N}{=}\overset{-1}{N}:\right]^{-} \longleftrightarrow \left[:\overset{0}{N}{\equiv}\overset{+1}{N}{-}\overset{-1}{N}{-}\overset{0}{N}{=}\overset{-1}{N}:\right]^{-} \longleftrightarrow \left[:\overset{-1}{N}{=}\overset{0}{N}{-}\overset{-1}{N}{-}\overset{+1}{N}{\equiv}\overset{0}{N}:\right]^{-}$$

The structures that contribute most have the lowest formal charges (last four structures shown). This means that the terminal nitrogen–nitrogen bonds will be close to the length of a double bond, and the middle nitrogen–nitrogen bonds in the structure will be close to a bond order of 1.5 (between a single and double bond).

(c) N_3^- has the Lewis structures

$$\left[:\overset{-2}{\overset{\cdot\cdot}{N}}-\overset{+1}{N}\equiv\overset{0}{N}:\right]^- \longleftrightarrow \left[:\overset{-1}{\overset{\cdot\cdot}{N}}=\overset{+1}{N}=\overset{-1}{\overset{\cdot\cdot}{N}}:\right]^- \longleftrightarrow \left[:\overset{0}{N}\equiv\overset{+1}{N}-\overset{-2}{\overset{\cdot\cdot}{N}}:\right]^-$$

From these resonance structures we see that each bond is predicted to be of double-bond character in N_3^-. Therefore, in N_5^- there are two longer N—N bonds than in N_3^-. N_3^- has the higher average bond order.

Think about It
The longer (and weaker) N—N bonds in N_5^- might be the ones broken in a chemical reaction.

4.177. **Collect and Organize**
By plotting the electronegativity (y-axis) versus the ionization energy (x-axis) for the elements in the second period ($Z = 3$ to 9), we can determine whether the trend is linear and then estimate the electronegativity for neon, knowing that its first ionization energy is 2081 kJ/mol.

Analyze
Figure 4.8 shows the electronegativities of the second-period main group elements, and Appendix 3 lists the ionization energies. Using Excel, we can plot the values for Li, Be, B, C, N, O, and F. We can estimate the electronegativity of Ne with the equation for the line for the trend seen for the other second-period elements.

Solve

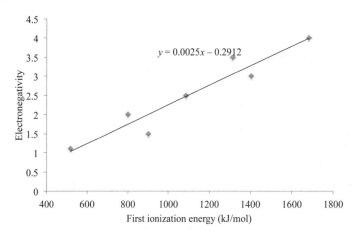

Using the equation for the best-fit line where x = the ionization energy of neon (2081 kJ/mol) gives a value of y (electronegativity) of neon:

$$y = 0.002(2081) - 0.2912 = 4.9$$

Think about It
The calculated electronegativity for neon is higher than that of fluorine, as we would expect from periodic trends. Electronegativity values, however, for the noble gases (especially the lighter ones such as He and Ne) are not that meaningful. Remember that electronegativity is the power of an atom *in a bond* to attract electrons to itself. Because He and Ne form no known compounds, the electronegativity value is not useful in the way that electronegativity values are used to determine bond polarity, for example.

4.179. **Collect and Organize**
We consider the structure of N_2F^+, including its possible resonance structures, the formal charges on its atoms in each resonance structure, and whether fluorine could be the central atom in the molecule.

Analyze
N_2F^+ has 16 valence electrons.

Solve

(a) Isoelectronic means that the two species have the same number of electrons. N_2O also has 16 valence electrons ($2\,N \times 5\,e^- + 1\,O \times 6\,e^-$).

(b–d)

$$\left[\overset{-2}{\underset{\cdot\cdot}{:}}\overset{}{\underset{\cdot\cdot}{N}}\!\!-\!\!\overset{+1}{N}\!\!\equiv\!\!\overset{+2}{F}:\right]^+ \longleftrightarrow \left[\overset{-1}{\underset{\cdot\cdot}{:}}\overset{}{N}\!\!=\!\!\overset{+1}{N}\!\!=\!\!\overset{+1}{\underset{\cdot\cdot}{F}}\right]^+ \longleftrightarrow \left[:\overset{0}{N}\!\!\equiv\!\!\overset{+1}{N}\!\!-\!\!\overset{0}{\underset{\cdot\cdot}{F}}:\right]^+$$

The central nitrogen atom in all the resonance structures always carries a +1 formal charge. The first and second resonance forms shown are unacceptable because they have greater than the minimal formal charges on the atoms.

(e) Yes, the fluorine could be the central atom in the molecule, but this would place significant positive formal charge on the fluorine atom (the most electronegative element). These structures are unlikely:

$$\left[\overset{-2}{\underset{\cdot\cdot}{:}}\overset{}{\underset{\cdot\cdot}{N}}\!\!-\!\!\overset{+3}{F}\!\!\equiv\!\!\overset{0}{N}:\right]^+ \longleftrightarrow \left[\overset{-1}{\underset{\cdot\cdot}{:}}\overset{}{N}\!\!=\!\!\overset{+3}{F}\!\!=\!\!\overset{-1}{\underset{\cdot\cdot}{N}}\right]^+ \longleftrightarrow \left[:\overset{0}{N}\!\!\equiv\!\!\overset{+3}{F}\!\!-\!\!\overset{-2}{\underset{\cdot\cdot}{N}}:\right]^+$$

Think about It

We could try to reduce the formal charge on fluorine in part e by drawing

$$\left[:\overset{0}{N}\!\!\equiv\!\!\overset{+1}{F}\!\!\equiv\!\!\overset{0}{N}:\right]^+$$

As a second-period element, however, fluorine cannot expand its octet.

CHAPTER 5 | Bonding Theories: Explaining Molecular Geometry

5.1. Collect and Organize

Dipole moments are a result of permanent partial charge separation in a molecule due to differences in atom electronegativities and molecular geometry. We can use the given structures for $C_2H_3F_3$ to determine whether we can distinguish them by their dipole moments.

Analyze

The electronegativity of H is 2.1, of C is 2.5, and of F is 4.0. The polarities of the C—F and C—H bonds, therefore, are

$$\overset{+\longrightarrow}{C \underline{\qquad} F} \qquad \overset{\longleftarrow +}{C \underline{\qquad} H}$$

In the C—F bond, the C atom carries a partial positive charge ($\delta+$) and the F atom carries a partial negative charge ($\delta-$). In the C—H bond, the C atom carries a partial negative charge ($\delta-$) and the H atom carries a partial positive charge ($\delta+$).

Solve

The geometry of structure (a) is such that all the fluorine atoms are bonded to the same carbon. When adding up the bond dipole vectors for this compound, we can see that this placement of the fluorine atoms in (a) gives the more polar molecule and, therefore, the molecule with the greater dipole moment.

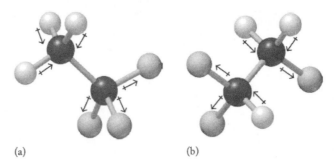

(a)   (b)

Yes, we can differentiate between these structures. The arrangement of atoms on the left has a dipole moment, whereas the one on the right does not.

Think about It

Both the difference in electronegativities of bonded elements and the molecular geometry are important in establishing molecular polarity.

5.3. Collect and Organize

For the molecules shown, N_2F_2, H_2NNH_2, and NCCN, we are to determine whether the molecules are planar and whether any of the molecules have delocalized π electrons through resonance structures.

Analyze

To determine the planarity of the molecules, we need to draw the Lewis structures for each and determine the molecular geometry.

Solve

Electron pair geometry on
N = trigonal planar
Molecular geometry =
bent

Electron pair geometry on
N = tetrahedral
Molecular geometry =
trigonal pyramidal

Electron pair geometry on
N = linear
Molecular geometry =
linear

$: N \equiv C - C \equiv N :$

Planar
No delocalized π electrons

Not planar
No delocalized π electrons

Planar
No delocalized π electrons
No resonance forms

N_2F_2 and NCCN are planar molecules. No delocalized π electrons are present in any of these molecules.

Think about It
For a molecule with two central atoms to be planar, its molecular geometry must be linear, trigonal planar, or square planar.

5.5. **Collect and Organize**
For each species, O_2^+ and O_2^{2+}, we are to fill the molecular orbital (MO) diagram for homonuclear diatomic oxygen. From the filled diagram, we can determine whether O_2^+ has more or fewer electrons in antibonding molecular orbitals than O_2^{2+}.

Analyze
The number of valence electrons in O_2^+ is $(2\ O \times 6\ e^-) - 1\ e^- = 11\ e^-$, and in O_2^{2+} the number of electrons is $(2\ O \times 6\ e^-) - 2\ e^- = 10\ e^-$. Antibonding orbitals in the MO diagram are designated with an asterisk (*).

Solve
For O_2^+, filling of the MO diagram gives

$$(\sigma_{2s})^2 (\sigma_{2s}^*)^2 (\sigma_{2p})^2 (\pi_{2p})^4 (\pi_{2p}^*)^1$$

3 electrons in antibonding orbitals
For O_2^{2+}, filling of the MO diagram gives

$$(\sigma_{2s})^2 (\sigma_{2s}^*)^2 (\sigma_{2p})^2 (\pi_{2p})^4$$

2 electrons in antibonding orbitals

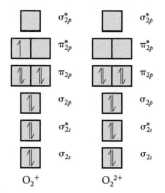

Therefore, O_2^+ has more electrons populating antibonding orbitals than O_2^{2+}.

Think about It
For these species, the bond orders are as follows:

$$O_2^+ \text{ bond order} = \tfrac{1}{2}(8-3) = 2.5$$
$$O_2^{2+} \text{ bond order} = \tfrac{1}{2}(8-2) = 3$$

5.7. **Collect and Organize**
Given the structure of a constituent of pine oil, we are to determine whether the compound is chiral.

Analyze
A compound is chiral if any of its sp^3 carbon atoms is bonded to four different atoms or groups of atoms.

Solve
Of the eight sp^3 carbon atoms in this structure, one is indeed bonded to four different groups, so this molecule is chiral.

Think about It
The way to tell experimentally whether a molecule is chiral is to determine whether it rotates plane-polarized light when pure.

5.9. **Collect and Organize**
ReF$_7$ has a geometry in which a pentagon is "capped" on the top and bottom by atoms.

We are asked to calculate the F—Re—F bond angles in this molecule.

Analyze
Three F—Re—F angles are present in the molecule: axial F—Re—axial F, axial F—Re—equatorial F, and equatorial F—Re—equatorial F.

Solve
Looking at the diagram, we see that the axial F—Re—axial F bond is linear, so the angle is 180°. The axial F—Re—equatorial F angle is 90°. Finally, because the sum of the internal angles of the regular pentagon must add up to 360°, the equatorial F—Re—equatorial F bonds are all equal: 360°/5 = 72°.

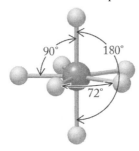

Think about It
The equatorial fluorine atoms are quite crowded together around the Re metal center with small bond angles.

5.11. **Collect and Organize**
The shape of a molecule depends on the repulsions around the central atom(s) between electrons in lone pairs and bonding pairs. We are asked why repulsions between electron pairs, not between nuclei, determine molecular geometry.

Analyze
Atoms contain very small, positively charged nuclei surrounded by relatively large electron clouds.

Solve
Because the electrons take up most of the space in the atom and because the nucleus is located in the center of the electron cloud, the electron clouds repel each other before the nuclei get close enough to each other.

Think about It
All of chemistry, in essence, is due to the behavior of electrons (are they lost, gained, or shared?); that behavior, of course, is influenced by the attraction of electrons to the nucleus.

5.13. **Collect and Organize**
Considering that they differ by one oxygen atom, we are to explain why NO_3^- and NO_2^- have similar O–N–O bond angles.

Analyze
Bond angles are determined by molecular geometry, which is influenced by the steric number (number of lone pairs and bond pairs) around the central atom. To determine steric number, we will need to look at the Lewis structures for NO_3^- and NO_2^-.

$$\left[:\overset{..}{\underset{..}{O}}: \\ :\overset{..}{\underset{..}{O}}=N-\overset{..}{\underset{..}{O}}: \right]^- \qquad \left[:\overset{..}{\underset{..}{O}}=N-\overset{..}{\underset{..}{O}}: \right]^-$$

Solve
Since the Lewis structures of both NO_3^- and NO_2^- show a steric number of 3 for the central N atoms, both ions have a trigonal planar electron-group geometry with bond angles of 120°.

Think about It
Both NO_3^- and NO_2^- have resonance structures, but resonance will not change the steric number for these molecules, so the molecular structures and bond angles will not change between resonance forms.

5.15. Collect and Organize

Using ammonia as an example, we consider why lone pair–bonding pair interactions are more repulsive than bonding pair–bonding pair interactions.

Analyze

The electrons in a bonding pair are located between two nuclei and therefore "feel" the attractive force from both nuclei. Lone pairs of electrons are attracted by only one nucleus.

Solve

Because the lone pair feels attraction from only one nucleus, it is less confined than bonding pairs and therefore occupies more space around the central N atom in ammonia. It will therefore "bump into" and repel a neighboring bonding pair that takes up less space.

Think about It

The presence of the lone pair in ammonia means that the H—N—H bond angles are less than the ideal 109.5° for a steric number of 4.

5.17. Collect and Organize

In considering the two structures for AB_4, seesaw and trigonal pyramidal, we are to explain why the seesaw geometry has the lower energy.

Analyze

In VSEPR theory, the repulsive interactions between bonding pairs (bp) and lone pairs (lp) at 90° decrease in order as follows:

$$lp–lp \gg lp–bp \gg bp–bp$$

The lowest energy geometry has the lowest number of lp–lp interactions. If no lp–lp interactions are present or if they are equal for two geometries, then the geometry with the lowest number of lp–bp interactions has the lowest energy.

Solve

Seesaw geometry
0 lp–lp, 2 lp–bp, 4 bp–bp

Trigonal pyramidal geometry
0 lp–lp, 3 lp–bp, 3 bp–bp

The seesaw geometry has only two lp–bp interactions at 90° (compared with three for trigonal pyramidal), so it has the lower energy.

Think about It

Remember that in comparing possible geometries by VSEPR theory, we need only look at interactions at 90° or less.

5.19. Collect and Organize

We are to rank the trigonal planar, linear, and tetrahedral molecular geometries in order of increasing bond angle.

Analyze

In trigonal planar molecules, all bond angles are 120°. In tetrahedral molecules, all bond angles are 109.5°. In linear molecules, the bond angles are 180°.

Solve

In order of increasing bond angle, (c) tetrahedral < (a) trigonal planar < (b) linear.

Think about It

In general, as steric number increases, the smallest bond angle for the geometry decreases.

5.21. **Collect and Organize**

We are to determine for which electron-group geometries a linear molecular geometry is inconsistent.

Analyze

For each geometry, we will take atoms away to obtain the VSEPR geometry until we obtain a triatomic molecule and then see whether that molecular geometry is linear.

Solve

(a)

Tetrahedral   Bent

(b)

Octahedral   Linear

(c)

Trigonal planar   Bent

Neither tetrahedral (a) nor trigonal planar (c) triatomic molecules will be linear.

Think about It

A linear triatomic molecule would also be possible for the trigonal bipyramidal electron-group geometry.

5.23. **Collect and Organize**

Using Lewis structures and VSEPR theory, we can determine the molecular geometries of GeH_4, PH_3, H_2S, and $CHCl_3$.

Analyze

After drawing the Lewis structure for each molecule, we can determine the steric number for the central atom, then locate the atoms about the central atom to see the bond angles, and finally determine the molecular shape from the location of the atoms.

Solve

(a)

SN = 4
Electron-group geometry = tetrahedral
No lone pairs
Molecular geometry = tetrahedral

(b)

$$H—\overset{..}{P}—H$$
$$\underset{H}{|}$$

SN = 4
Electron-group geometry = tetrahedral
One lone pair
Molecular geometry = trigonal pyramidal

(c)

$$H—\overset{..}{\underset{..}{S}}—H$$

SN = 4
Electron-group geometry = tetrahedral
Two lone pairs
Molecular geometry = bent

(d)

$$\overset{:\overset{..}{C}l:}{\underset{:\overset{..}{C}l:}{H—\overset{|}{C}—\overset{..}{C}l:}}$$

SN = 4
Electron-group geometry = tetrahedral
No lone pairs
Molecular geometry = tetrahedral

Think about It

Molecules with SN = 4 may have molecular geometries of tetrahedral, trigonal pyramidal, bent, or linear—for example,

$$H—\overset{..}{\underset{..}{F}}:$$

depending on the number of lone pairs on the central atom.

5.25. Collect and Organize

Using Lewis structures and VSEPR theory, we can determine the molecular geometries of NH_4^+, CO_3^{2-}, NO_2^-, and XeF_5^+.

Analyze

After drawing the Lewis structure for each molecule, we can determine the steric number for the central atom, then locate the atoms about the central atom to see the bond angles, and finally determine the molecular shape from the location of the atoms.

Solve

(a)

$$\left[\overset{H}{\underset{H}{H—\overset{|}{N}—H}} \right]^+$$

SN = 4
Electron-group geometry = tetrahedral
No lone pairs
Molecular geometry = tetrahedral

(b)

$$\left[\overset{\cdot\overset{..}{O}\cdot}{\underset{:\overset{..}{O}:\quad\overset{..}{O}:}{\|\atop C}} \right]^{2-}$$

SN = 3
Electron-group geometry = trigonal planar
No lone pairs
Molecular geometry = trigonal planar

(c)

$$\left[:\overset{..}{O}=N—\overset{..}{\underset{..}{O}}: \right]^-$$

SN = 3
Electron-group geometry = trigonal planar
One lone pair
Molecular geometry = bent

(d)

$$\left[\begin{array}{c} :\!F\!: \\ :\!F\!\cdots\!\overset{|}{\underset{|}{Xe}}\!\cdots\!F\!: \\ :\!F\!\blacktriangle\!\ \ \blacktriangledown\!: \\ :\!F\!: \end{array} \right]^{+}$$

SN = 6
Electron-group geometry = octahedral
One lone pair
Molecular geometry = square pyramidal

$$\overset{F}{\underset{F}{\underset{\cdots}{F_{\cdots}\!\overset{|}{\underset{|}{Xe}}\!\cdots\!F}}}$$

Think about It

Notice how the other resonance structure of NO_2^- also has a bent geometry because the steric number remains 3 at the central N atom.

$$\left[:\!\overset{..}{\underset{..}{O}}\!-\!N\!=\!\overset{..}{\underset{..}{O}}\!: \right]^{-} \qquad \overset{..}{\underset{O}{\overset{|}{\underset{}{N}}}}\!\underset{O}{\diagdown}$$

5.27. Collect and Organize

Using Lewis structures and VSEPR theory, we can determine the molecular geometries of $S_2O_3^{2-}$, PO_4^{3-}, NO_3, and NCO.

Analyze

After drawing the Lewis structure for each molecule, we can determine the steric number for the central atom, then locate the atoms about the central atom to see the bond angles, and finally determine the molecular shape from the location of the atoms.

Solve

(a)

$$\left[\begin{array}{c} \overset{..}{\underset{}{O}} \\ \| \\ :\!S\!=\!\overset{..}{\underset{..}{S}}\!-\!\overset{..}{\underset{..}{O}}\!: \\ | \\ :\!\overset{..}{\underset{..}{O}}\!: \end{array} \right]^{2-}$$

SN = 4
Electron-group geometry = tetrahedral
No lone pairs
Molecular geometry = tetrahedral

$$\overset{O}{\underset{S}{\overset{\|}{\underset{}{S}}}}\!\overset{\cdots\!O}{\underset{O}{}}$$

(b)

$$\left[\begin{array}{c} :\!\overset{..}{\underset{}{O}}\!: \\ | \\ :\!\overset{..}{\underset{}{O}}\!=\!P\!-\!\overset{..}{\underset{..}{O}}\!: \\ | \\ :\!\overset{..}{\underset{..}{O}}\!: \end{array} \right]^{3-}$$

SN = 4
Electron-group geometry = tetrahedral
No lone pairs
Molecular geometry = tetrahedral

$$\overset{O}{\underset{O}{\overset{\|}{\underset{}{P}}}}\!\overset{\cdots\!O}{\underset{O}{}}$$

(c)

$$\overset{:\!\overset{..}{\underset{}{O}}\!:}{\underset{:\!O\!=\!\overset{|}{\underset{}{N}}\!\cdots\!\overset{..}{\underset{..}{O}}\!:}{}}$$

SN = 3
Electron-group geometry = trigonal planar
No lone pairs
Molecular geometry = trigonal planar

$$\overset{O}{\underset{O\!=\!\overset{|}{\underset{}{N}}\!\diagdown_O}{}}$$

(d)

$$\cdot\!\overset{..}{\underset{..}{N}}\!-\!C\!\equiv\!O\!:$$

SN = 2
Electron-group geometry = linear
No lone pairs
Molecular geometry = linear

$$N\!-\!C\!\equiv\!O$$

Think about It

Remember that the presence of resonance structures for a molecule does not change its geometry.

5.29. Collect and Organize

By drawing the Lewis structures and determining the molecular geometry of O_3, SO_2, and CO_2 we can determine which two of these molecules have the same molecular geometry.

Analyze

After drawing the Lewis structure for each molecule, we can determine the steric number for the central atom, then locate the atoms about the central atom to see the bond angles, and finally determine the molecular shape from the location of the atoms.

Solve

Lewis structure	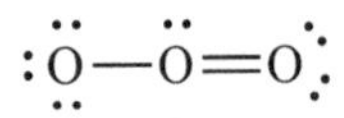 :Ö—Ö=O:	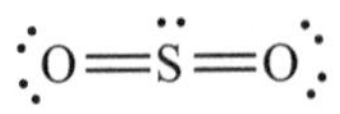 :O=S=O:	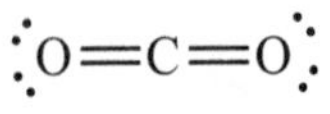 :O=C=O:
SN	3	3	2
Electron-group geometry	Trigonal planar	Trigonal planar	Linear
Number of lone pairs	1	1	0
Molecular geometry	Bent	Bent	Linear
Bond angle	<120°	<120°	180°

Both O_3 and SO_2 are bent with ~120° angles and have the same molecular geometry.

Think about It

At first these triatomic molecules may all appear to have the same geometry from their formulas. Be careful to draw correct Lewis structures because the presence of lone pairs on the central atom is important in determining overall geometry.

5.31. **Collect and Organize**

By drawing the Lewis structures and determining the molecular geometry of SCN^-, CNO^-, and NO_2^- we can determine which two of these ions have the same molecular geometry.

Analyze

After drawing the Lewis structure for each molecule, we can determine the steric number for the central atom, then locate the atoms about the central atom to see the bond angles, and finally determine the molecular shape from the location of the atoms.

Solve

Lewis structure	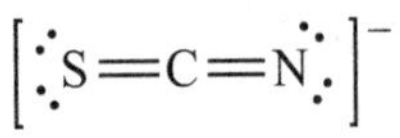 [:S=C=N:]⁻	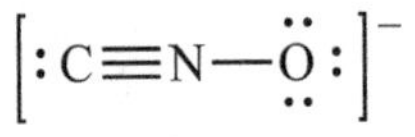 [:C≡N—Ö:]⁻	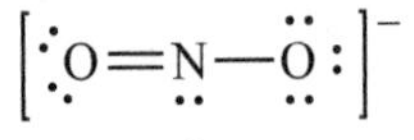 [:O=N—Ö:]⁻
SN	2	2	3
Electron-group geometry	Linear	Linear	Trigonal planar
Number of lone pairs	0	0	1
Molecular geometry	Linear	Linear	Bent
Bond angle	180°	180°	<120°

Both SCN^- and CNO^- are linear and therefore have the same molecular geometry.

Think about It

The Lewis structures shown are the resonance structures that, by formal charge arguments, contribute most to the bonding. The other resonance structures for each molecule have the same molecular structure as for the resonance structure shown.

5.33. **Collect and Organize**

From the Lewis structures of S_2O and S_2O_2 we can use VSEPR theory to determine the molecular geometry of these two compounds detected in the atmosphere of Venus.

Analyze

After drawing the Lewis structure for each molecule, we can determine the steric number for the central atom, then locate the atoms about the central atom to see the bond angles, and finally determine the molecular shape from the location of the atoms. S_2O_2 has two possible geometries: one with two central S atoms and one with one central S atom.

Solve

:S=S=O: SN = 3
Electron-group geometry = trigonal planar
One lone pair
Molecular geometry = bent

:O=S=S=O: On each S, SN = 3
Electron-group geometry = trigonal planar
One lone pair
Molecular geometry = bent at each S atom

or S_2O_2 may have only one central S atom
SN = 3
Electron-group geometry = trigonal planar
No lone pairs
Molecular geometry = trigonal planar

Think about It

S_2O_2 could also have the geometry

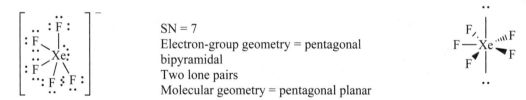

We could differentiate these isomers by measuring their dipole moments.

5.35. **Collect and Organize**

After drawing the Lewis structure for XeF_5^- we can use VSEPR theory to predict its molecular structure.

Analyze

Xenon brings eight electrons, a closed-shell configuration, so it must expand its octet (as we saw in Chapter 4) to bond with F atoms in XeF_5^-.

Solve

SN = 7
Electron-group geometry = pentagonal bipyramidal
Two lone pairs
Molecular geometry = pentagonal planar

Think about It

Placing the lone pairs in the axial positions of the pentagonal bipyramid gives the lowest energy geometry because no lp–lp interactions occur for this structure.

5.37. **Collect and Organize**

Using the given skeletal structure of Sarin (Figure P5.37), we can complete the Lewis structure, assign formal charges to the P and O atoms, and then predict the geometry around P by using VSEPR theory.

Analyze

The molecular formula of Sarin is $C_4H_{10}FOP$, which has 44 e$^-$ and needs 76 e$^-$ to complete the octets (and duets) on all the atoms. This gives a difference of 32 e$^-$ for 16 covalent bonds and leaves 12 e$^-$ in six lone pairs to complete the Lewis structure.

Solve

SN = 4 for the P atom in this molecule, and no lone pairs are present, so the geometry around the P atom in Sarin is tetrahedral.

Think about It
The Lewis structure drawn is for all atoms with the lowest formal charge. This was accomplished by double bonding the terminal oxygen to phosphorus to reduce the +1 formal charge on phosphorus and the –1 formal charge on oxygen to zero. Remember from Chapter 4 that phosphorus may expand its octet to reduce formal charge.

5.39. **Collect and Organize**
Both molecules and bonds may be polar. For this review question, the definitions of the two terms allow us to differentiate between a polar bond and a polar molecule.

Analyze
A bond is polar when two bonded atoms have different electronegativities. Molecular polarity is the result of bond polarity and molecular geometry.

Solve
A polar bond occurs only between two atoms in a molecule. The more electronegative atom in the bond carries a partial negative charge and the least electronegative atom in the bond carries a partial positive charge. Molecular polarity takes into account all the individual bond polarities and the geometry of the molecule. A polar molecule has a permanent, measurable dipole moment.

Think about It
To determine molecular polarity we have to first determine the individual bond polarities.

5.41. **Collect and Organize**
We are asked whether a nonpolar molecule may contain polar covalent bonds.

Analyze
Molecular polarity is determined by adding the vectors of the individual bond polarities.

Solve
Yes. As long as the individual bond polarities are equal in magnitude and opposite in direction (as vectors), a molecule may be nonpolar overall even if the bonds themselves are polar.

Think about It
If the bond polarities (as vectors) do not cancel, then the molecule will be polar.

5.43. **Collect and Organize**
We can look at the bond polarities and the molecular structure by VSEPR theory to determine which molecules (CCl_4, $CHCl_3$, CO_2, H_2S, and SO_2) are polar and which are nonpolar.

Analyze

All the individual bonds in these molecules are polar, so the molecular geometry of each compound will determine the overall molecular polarity. We can represent each bond polarity with a vector, with the head of the arrow pointed toward the more electronegative atom, which carries a partial negative charge. We then visually inspect the molecule to see whether the individual bond dipoles add up or cancel out.

Solve

(a)

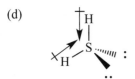

All bond polarities are equal in magnitude and cancel each other, so CCl_4 is nonpolar.

(b)

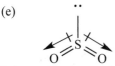

The electronegativity of the atoms in $CHCl_3$ are in order $Cl > C > H$. Because the bond polarities do not cancel, $CHCl_3$ is polar.

(c)

O$=$C$=$O

The bond polarities in CO_2 cancel, so it is nonpolar.

(d)

The molecular geometry of H_2S is bent, so it is polar.

(e)

The molecular geometry of SO_2 is bent, so it is polar.

Polar molecules are (b) $CHCl_3$, (d) H_2S, and (e) SO_2. Nonpolar molecules are (a) CCl_4 and (c) CO_2.

Think about It

Molecules with polar bonds are nonpolar only for highly symmetrical geometries (linear, trigonal planar, tetrahedral, trigonal bipyramidal, and octahedral).

5.45. **Collect and Organize**

By looking at the molecular structures and individual bond polarities present in $CFCl_3$, CF_2Cl_2, and Cl_2FCCF_2Cl we can determine which of these CFCs are polar and which are nonpolar.

Analyze

To determine bond polarities, we need the electronegativity values for C (2.5), F (4.0), and Cl (3.0). In each of these molecules the halogens are bonded to the carbon atoms. Because the electronegativities of the halogens are higher than that of carbon, the bonds are polarized so that the halogen carries a partial negative charge.

Solve

(a)

(b)

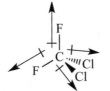

(c)

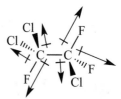

All these molecules have a tetrahedral geometry around the carbon atoms. Because of the different bond polarities of C—F and C— Cl, however, none of the molecules have bond dipoles that cancel. All these molecules (a–c) are polar.

Think about It
Only molecules with completely symmetric geometries with all the same atoms attached to the central atoms are nonpolar.

5.47. Collect and Organize
To determine which molecule is more polar in each pair given, we need to compare not only the molecules' geometries but also the magnitude of the individual bond dipoles.

Analyze
We predict the bond polarity by the difference in electronegativity of the bonded atoms (EN values are C = 2.5, Cl = 3.0, F = 4.0, H = 2.1, Br = 2.8). All the molecules have halogens bonded to the carbon with a tetrahedral geometry. The more electronegative the atom on carbon, the more polar is that bond. Each C—X bond is polarized so that the halogen carries a partial negative charge.

Solve
(a) Because the Br in $CBrF_3$ has a lower electronegativity than the Cl in $CClF_3$, it does not counteract the electron pull from the three F atoms on the C as well as a Cl atom, so $CBrF_3$ (Freon 13B1) is more polar than $CClF_3$.
(b) Because the H in CHF_2Cl has a lower electronegativity than the Cl in CF_2Cl_2, it does not counteract the electron pull from the two F atoms on the C as well as a Cl atom, so CHF_2Cl (Freon 22) is more polar than CF_2Cl_2.

Think about It
In these molecules where all the bonds are polarized in the same direction (X is partially negative), the replacement of one atom by a less electronegative atom results in a more polar molecule.

5.49. Collect and Organize
For each of the COX_2 molecules (X = I, Br, Cl), we can use the different electronegativities of the atoms in the molecule along with the molecular geometry to place the molecules in order of increasing molecular polarity.

Analyze
The carbonyl dihalides have a trigonal planar geometry. The electronegativities of the elements in these compounds are C = 2.5, O = 3.5, Cl = 3.0, Br = 2.8, I = 2.5.

Solve
The greatest electronegativity difference in the C—X bond is between C and Cl. The least electronegativity difference in the C—X bond is between C and I. Therefore these compounds in order of increasing polarity of the C—X bond are: COI_2 (ΔEN C—I = 0) < $COBr_2$ (ΔEN C—Br = 0.3) < $COCl_2$ (ΔEN C—Cl = 0.5).

Think about It
To compare the overall molecular polarity for these compounds we would have to examine how the C—X bond polarity pulls opposite the polarity of C=O bond (ΔEN = 1.0). As the electronegativity of the halogen atom decreases (Cl > Br > I), the overall molecular polarity of the COX_2 molecule increases because the C—X bonds pull less to balance the C=O bond dipole. In order of increasing molecular polarity, $COCl_2$ < $COBr_2$ < COI_2.

5.51. **Collect and Organize**

In this question we consider how atomic orbitals mix to form hybrid orbitals. Specifically, we consider what atomic orbitals need to have in common in order to mix.

Analyze

The types of hybrid orbitals we have seen in the textbook include mixing of the *s* and *p* orbitals to form sp, sp^2, and sp^3 orbitals. In making hybrid orbitals we can consider requirements of size (energy) and orientation.

Solve

Atomic orbitals will hybridize if they are of similar size (energy), which means that they should be of the same principal quantum number. Also they must be oriented to overlap and hybridize; if the two atomic orbitals are pointed away from each other in space, they could not hybridize.

For hybridization, atomic orbitals should be of similar size:

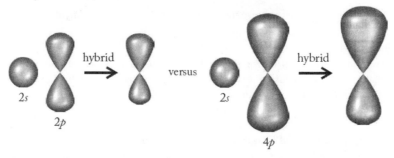

For hybridization, atomic orbitals should have the correct orientation for overlap:

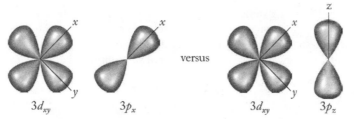

Think about It

Hybridization of orbitals can also be thought of as adding or overlapping the wave functions of two atomic orbitals, and hybridization often results in a new shape for the orbital to use in bonding.

5.53. **Collect and Organize**

From the steric number obtained from the Lewis structures of SO, SO_2, S_2O, and SO_3 we can determine the hybridization of each of the sulfur atoms.

Analyze

Hybridization is directly obtained from the steric number (SN). When SN = 2, the hybridization is sp; when SN = 3, the hybridization is sp^2; when SN = 4, the hybridization is sp^3; when SN = 5, the hybridization is sp^3d; when SN = 6, the hybridization is sp^3d^2.

Solve

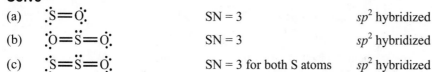

(a)	$\ddot{S}=\ddot{O}$	SN = 3	sp^2 hybridized
(b)	$\ddot{O}=\ddot{S}=\ddot{O}$	SN = 3	sp^2 hybridized
(c)	$\ddot{S}=\ddot{S}=\ddot{O}$	SN = 3 for both S atoms	sp^2 hybridized

(d)

:O:
‖
S
:O⸗ ⸗O:

SN = 3 sp^2 hybridized

The steric numbers for S in SO_2, S_2O, and SO_3 are all 3, which gives a trigonal planar molecular geometry. From our study of chemistry so far this would also mean that the hybridization would be assigned as sp^2. However, the central S forms at least two π bonds to the other atoms, which requires that some of the p orbitals on S not be involved in the hybridization so that they can form parallel π bonds. Therefore, S must use a low-lying d orbital in place of one of the p orbitals for spd hybridization in SO_2 and S_2O and sd^2 hybridization in SO_3 to form the two σ bonds to terminal atoms and to "hold" the lone pairs, leaving enough p orbitals unhybridized to form the π bonds.

Think about It
Any resonance forms we can draw for these molecules give the same hybridization for the central S atom.

5.55. **Collect and Organize**
From the two Lewis structures of N_2F_2 we are shown in Figure P5.55, we can determine whether differences in structure are due to the hybridization on the N atoms in each structure. Second, we will compare the hybridization of the N in this molecule with the hybridization of carbon in C_2H_2.

Analyze
The steric number around the N and C atoms in the Lewis structures indicates the hybridization. When SN = 2, the hybridization is sp; when SN = 3, the hybridization is sp^2; when SN = 4, the hybridization is sp^3.

Solve
Both Lewis structures of N_2F_2 show a steric number of 3 for the N atoms, so both structures have sp^2 hybridized orbitals on N. The difference in the structures lies in the relative placement of the F atoms in space. The steric number on each F atom is 4, so each F atom is sp^3 hybridized. Acetylene, C_2H_2, shows SN = 2 for the carbon atoms in its Lewis structure, so they are sp hybridized and not sp^2 hybridized as for N in N_2F_2.

$$H-C\equiv C-H$$

Think about It
The structures shown for N_2F_2 are not resonance forms, but they are isomers. They differ in the arrangement of the atoms in space, and the two isomers can be separated on the basis of their difference in polarity.

5.57. **Collect and Organize**
Using Lewis structures and the steric number around the central atom, we can determine how orbital hybridization changes in CO_2, NO_2, O_3, and ClO_2.

Analyze
We draw the Lewis structures in the usual way. Hybridization is directly obtained from the steric number (SN). When SN = 2, the hybridization is sp; when SN = 3, the hybridization is sp^2; when SN = 4, the hybridization is sp^3; when SN = 5, the hybridization is sp^3d; when SN = 6, the hybridization is sp^3d^2.

Solve

:O=C=O: :Ö—N̈=Ö: :Ö—Ö=Ö: :O=C̈l=O:

                                                                         SN = 4
SN = 2   SN = 3   SN = 3   "sp^3" according to
sp sp^2 sp^2 steric number
                                                                         alone

From our study of chemistry so far, the hybridization of Cl in ClO_2 is assigned as sp^3. We have to think here, though. We need to form a π bond from the Cl to both oxygen atoms, which requires that two of the p orbitals on Cl not be involved in the hybridization so that they can form parallel π bonds with the oxygens. What this means is that Cl must use low-lying d orbitals in place of the p orbitals for spd^2 hybridization to form the two σ bonds to the oxygens and to "hold" the lone pair and the electron.

Think about It

An unpaired electron in NO_2 and ClO_2 "counts" as one for the steric number. It will occupy one of the hybridized orbitals.

5.59. Collect and Organize

After drawing the Lewis structures for ClO_4^- for which formal charges are minimized, we can determine the molecular shape and the hybridization on the central Cl atom.

Analyze

We draw the Lewis structures in the usual way. The structure contributing the most to the actual geometry of the molecule is that with the lowest formal charges and with the most electronegative atom (here, oxygen) carrying a negative formal charge if necessary.

Solve

The first resonance structure has the best formal charge arrangement. The steric number for Cl in this structure is 4, which gives a tetrahedral molecular geometry. At first glance this would also mean that the hybridization would be assigned as sp^3. However, the Cl forms three π bonds to three of the oxygen atoms, which requires that three of the p orbitals on Cl not be involved in the hybridization so that it can form parallel π bonds. Therefore, Cl must use low-lying d orbitals in place of the p orbitals for sd^3 hybridization to form the four σ bonds to oxygen.

Think about It

On central atoms with expanded octets, we need to use d orbitals in place of p orbitals for the σ-bonded hybrid orbitals so as to leave the unhybridized p orbitals available for π bonding.

5.61. Collect and Organize

From the Lewis structure of HArF we can use the steric number to determine the molecular geometry and the hybridization of the central Ar atom.

Analyze

We draw the Lewis structure in the usual way. HArF has 16 e⁻ and needs 4 e⁻ to form the two covalent bonds from Ar to F and H. This leaves 12 e⁻ in six lone pairs on Ar and F to complete the structure. Since this is a compound of a noble gas, we expect Ar to have to an expanded octet. Hybridization is directly obtained from the steric number (SN). When SN = 2, the hybridization is sp; when SN = 3, the hybridization is sp^2; when SN = 4, the hybridization is sp^3; when SN = 5, the hybridization is sp^3d; when SN = 6, the hybridization is sp^3d^2.

Solve

H—Ar—F:

SN = 5
sp^3d hybridized
Electron-pair geometry = trigonal bipyramidal
Molecular geometry = linear
H—Ar—F bond angle = 180°

Think about It
This question has placed many of the components of structure and bonding theories together—Lewis structure, VSEPR theory, and valence bond theory—to fully describe the molecular structure of HArF.

5.63. **Collect and Organize**
After drawing resonance structures for N_2O we can compare the hybridization of the central N atom among the structures.

Analyze
N_2O has 16 e^- and needs 24 e^- to complete the octets on all the atoms. The difference of 8 e^- corresponds to four covalent bonds. This leaves 8 e^- in four lone pairs to complete the structure.

Solve

$$\overset{..}{:}\overset{-1}{N}=\overset{+1}{N}=\overset{0}{O}\overset{..}{:} \longleftrightarrow :\overset{-2}{\overset{..}{N}}-\overset{+1}{N}\equiv\overset{+1}{O}: \longleftrightarrow :N\equiv\overset{0}{N}-\overset{-1}{\overset{..}{O}}:$$

For each resonance structure the central N atom has a steric number of 2, so yes, all these resonance structures have the central N atom as *sp* hybridized.

Think about It
If we had a change in hybridization, we would also have a change in structure (how the atoms are arranged in space).

5.65. **Collect and Organize**
Using the Lewis structure of $SO_2F_3^-$ we can determine the geometry of the anion and describe the bonding by valence bond theory.

Analyze
The tetramethylammonium cation has 32 e^- and needs 32 to complete octets or duets on all its atoms. To connect the atoms we need four bonds from carbon to the central nitrogen atom and one bond from each hydrogen atom to carbon atoms. $SO_2F_3^-$ has 40 e^- and needs 40 e^- to complete the octets on all the atoms. To connect the atoms we need five bonds that use 10 e^-, leaving 30 e^- in 15 lone pairs.

Solve
(a) The Lewis structure of the tetramethylammonium cation below shows that the central nitrogen atom has a steric number of 4. Therefore, the geometry around this nitrogen atom is tetrahedral and the C—N—C bond angles are 109.5°.

$$\left[\begin{array}{c} CH_3 \\ | \\ H_3C-N-CH_3 \\ | \\ CH_3 \end{array} \right]^+$$

(b) Because the steric number of the central N atom in the tetramethylammonium cation is 4, the hybridization of the N atom is sp^3.
(c) Table A4.1 in the textbook appendix lists bond distance of the sulfur–oxygen double bond as 143 pm. The Lewis structure of the $SO_2F_3^-$ anion below, where the sulfur atom has expanded its octet to hold 14 electrons, is consistent with the sulfur–oxygen bonds lengths in this compound.

$$\left[\begin{array}{c} :\overset{..}{F}: \\ | \\ :\overset{..}{F}-\overset{|}{S}=\overset{..}{O}. \\ :\overset{..}{F} \diagdown O: \end{array} \right]^-$$

(d) Because the sulfur atom has expanded its octet to 14 electrons, the hybridization of the S atom in this anion is sp^3d^3.

Think about It

The geometry of the $SO_2F_3^-$ anion is trigonal bipyramidal.

5.67. Collect and Organize

We consider in this question whether a molecule with more than one central atom can have resonance forms.

Analyze

Resonance forms are Lewis structures that show alternative (yet still valid) electron distributions in a molecule.

Solve

We have already seen several examples of molecules that have several central atoms and that have multiple resonance forms in Chapter 4. In that chapter, a good example of resonance in a molecule with more than one central atom is benzene. So, yes, molecules with more than one central atom can indeed have resonance forms.

Think about It

As long as another way exists to distribute the electrons in a molecule, we have resonance.

5.69. Collect and Organize

We are asked to explain whether resonance structures are examples of the delocalization of electrons in a molecule.

Analyze

Resonance structures show different possible electron distributions over the atoms in the molecule. Each one contributes to the actual structure of the molecule.

Solve

To obtain the actual molecular structure, we mix the resonance forms together. The molecule does not exist in one form at one instant and another form the next. The electron distribution is blurred across all the resonance forms, which in essence defines the delocalization of electrons.

Think about It

Resonance forms help us see which atoms and bonds are involved in sharing the delocalized electrons.

5.71. Collect and Organize

We are given the skeletal arrangement for the nitramide molecule. We first need to complete the Lewis structure for the molecule to describe the geometry and hybridization around each N atom to see whether they are the same.

Analyze

H_2NNO_2 has 24 e$^-$ and needs 36 e$^-$, giving a difference of 12 e$^-$ in six covalent bonds and leaving 12 e$^-$ in six lone pairs to complete the structure.

Solve

One N atom has SN = 4 with one lone pair, so it has trigonal pyramidal geometry and is sp^3 hybridized. The other N atom has SN = 3 with no lone pairs, so it has trigonal planar geometry and is sp^2 hybridized. No, the hybridization of both N atoms is not the same.

Think about It
Only the resonance structure with the lowest formal charges on the atoms is shown above.

5.73. **Collect and Organize**
We are given the skeletal arrangement for the sulfamate ion. We first need to complete the Lewis structure for the molecule to describe the geometry and hybridization around the S and N atoms. We are asked which atomic or hybrid orbitals overlap to form the S—O and S—N bonds.

Analyze
$SO_3NH_2^-$ has 32 e^- and needs 44 e^-, giving a difference of 12 e^- in six covalent bonds and leaving 20 e^- in 10 lone pairs to complete the structure. To reduce formal charges on the atoms, sulfur may expand its octet.

Solve

Both the S and N atoms have SN = 4 for an electron-pair geometry of tetrahedral. The presence of a lone pair on N gives this atom trigonal pyramidal geometry and the nitrogen atom is sp^3 hybridized. The steric number for S is also 4, which at first glance would also mean that the hybridization would be assigned as sp^3. However, the S forms two π bonds to two of the oxygen atoms, which requires that two p orbitals on S not be involved in the hybridization so that it can form parallel π bonds. Therefore, S must use two low-lying d orbitals in place of two of the p orbitals for spd^2 hybridization to form the four σ bonds to oxygen and nitrogen.

Think about It
On central atoms with expanded octets we need to use d orbitals in place of p orbitals for the σ-bonded hybrid orbitals so as to leave the unhybridized p orbitals available for π bonding.

5.75. **Collect and Organize**
Given some ordinary objects, we are to determine which are chiral.

Analyze
A chiral object is not superimposable on its mirror image.

Solve
A spoon (b) (if we ignore the any design on the handle) is superimposable on its mirror image, but (a) a golf club, (c) a glove, and (d) a shoe are not, and so they are chiral objects.

Think about It
You might also learn later that an object is not chiral if it contains a plane of symmetry or has an inversion center.

5.77. Collect and Organize

In this question we consider whether an *sp*-hybridized carbon center would be chiral.

Analyze

A chiral object is not superimposable on its mirror image.

Solve

When a carbon atom is *sp* hybridized, the SN = 2 and therefore the geometry around this carbon is linear. A carbon center is chiral when it has four different groups bonded to it. An *sp*-hybridized carbon, however, has only two atoms or groups bonded to it, so it cannot be a chiral center.

Think about It

You might also learn later that an object is not chiral if it contains a plane of symmetry or has an inversion center, but the general rule of chirality for carbon atoms as having four different groups bonded to it is a reliable way to determine whether a particular carbon atom in a molecule is a chiral center.

5.79. Collect and Organize

We are to determine whether a racemic mixture is a homogeneous or heterogeneous mixture.

Analyze

For a mixture to be heterogeneous, we must be able to discern by eye (or with a microscope) the different components of the mixture. A racemic mixture is a mixture of two enantiomers.

Solve

A racemic mixture is mixed at the molecular level, so it is a homogeneous mixture.

Think about It

When successfully separated, the components of a racemic mixture rotate plane-polarized light in opposite directions.

5.81. Collect and Organize

Given four molecular structures, we are to determine whether each is chiral.

Analyze

For any of these molecules to be chiral, it would have to contain an sp^3-hybridized carbon atom bonded to four different groups.

Solve

(a) Chiral

(b) Not chiral   The carbon atoms either are not sp^3 hybridized (the doubly bonded C atoms) or do not have four different substituents (the –CH_3 groups).

(c) Chiral

(d) Not chiral   One carbon atom is not sp^3 hybridized (the doubly bonded C $=$ O), and the other carbon atom does not have four different substituents (the –CH_3 group).

Think about It
Remember to look carefully for four different substituents on the sp^3-hybridized carbons in the structures.

5.83. **Collect and Organize**
From the line drawings of three carboxylic acids (Figure P5.83), we are to determine which are chiral.

Analyze
A molecule is chiral if it has at least one carbon atom bonded to four different groups.

Solve
Only molecule (a) has a chiral carbon center and so is the only molecule shown that is chiral:

5.85. **Collect and Organize**
In each structure in Figure P5.85, we are to circle the chiral centers.

Analyze
Wherever in the molecule a carbon is bonded to four different groups, a chiral center exists.

Solve

Saccharin   Sodium cyclamate   Aspartame

Think about It
Because the ring of carbon atoms in sodium cyclamate is symmetrical, the carbon to which the $-NHSO_3^-$ group is bound is not chiral.

5.87. **Collect and Organize**
Optical isomers are nonsuperimposable mirror images that contain a chiral carbon center with four different groups bonded to the carbon. We are asked to identify the chiral center in the compound in Figure P5.87.

Analyze
Wherever in the molecule a carbon is bonded to four different groups, a chiral center exists.

Solve

Think about It
Having even one chiral center in a molecule makes the molecule chiral, and each enantiomer will rotate plane-polarized light in opposite but equal directions.

5.89. **Collect and Organize**
Between valence bond theory and molecular orbital theory, we are asked which better explains emission in the visible range.

Analyze
Emission involves the relaxation of an electron from a higher energy orbital (atomic or molecular) to a lower energy orbital.

Solve
Molecular orbital theory better explains the emission of light from a molecule because it has descriptions of electronic energy levels in its theory.

Think about It
Valence bond theory is better than molecular orbital theory in describing bond angles and molecular geometry.

5.91. **Collect and Organize**
We are asked whether all σ molecular orbitals are from the overlap of one *s* orbital with another *s* orbital.

Analyze
Sigma (σ) bonds are defined as those bonds where the highest electron density is along the internuclear axis between the bonded atoms.

Solve
No. Although *s–s* overlap always gives σ molecular orbitals, other orbitals may overlap to also give σ bonds such as the following:

s + *p* orbital   *p* + *p* orbital d_{z^2} + *p* orbital

Think about It
When these atomic orbitals mix to form molecular orbitals, remember that two molecular orbitals form: the sigma bonding (σ) and the sigma antibonding (σ*) orbitals.

5.93. **Collect and Organize**
When an *s* orbital overlaps with another *s* orbital, a sigma (σ) bond forms. We are to consider the effectiveness of the *s–s* orbital overlap between orbitals of different *n* values.

Analyze

A difference between a $1s$ orbital and a $2s$ orbital, for example, is the volume that the electrons occupy. A $2s$ orbital is larger than a $1s$ orbital.

Solve

No. The overlap of $1s$ and $2s$ orbitals is not as efficient as $1s–1s$ or $2s–2s$ overlaps. The mismatch in size and energy is poor.

Think about It

One guideline for molecular orbital diagrams for homonuclear diatomic molecules states that the better mixing of orbitals from the same n level leads to greater bond stabilization.

5.95. Collect and Organize

We are to make a sketch to show the overlap of two $1s$ orbitals to form σ_{1s} and σ_{1s}^* molecular orbitals.

Analyze

When mixing atomic orbitals (AOs) to give molecular orbitals (MOs), the number of MOs equals the number of AOs. Here we obtain two MOs because we are mixing two $1s$ orbitals. One MO is bonding (lower in energy) and the other is antibonding (higher in energy).

Solve

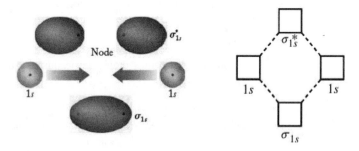

Think about It

This molecular orbital diagram is appropriate for neutral and ionic species of H_2 and He_2.

5.97. Collect and Organize

For the species N_2^+, O_2^+, C_2^+, and Br_2^{2-} we are to place electrons into the appropriate molecular orbital energy levels to predict the bond order for each diatomic molecule.

Analyze

Due to $s–p$ orbital mixing, the order of MOs for $Li_2–N_2$ is

$$\sigma_{2s}\sigma_{2s}^*\pi_{2p}\sigma_{2p}\pi_{2p}^*\sigma_{2p}^*$$

For $O_2–Ne_2$, which have less $s–p$ orbital mixing, the order of the MOs is

$$\sigma_{2s}\sigma_{2s}^*\sigma_{2p}\pi_{2p}\pi_{2p}^*\sigma_{2p}^*$$

For each species we fill the MO energy levels from lowest to highest energy with the total number of electrons. The bond order (BO) is calculated from

$$BO = \tfrac{1}{2}\,(\text{number of } e^- \text{ in bonding MOs} - \text{number of } e^- \text{ in antibonding MOs})$$

For Br_2^{2-} we assume the same MO energies as for F_2, but the MOs involve the $4s$ and $4p$ atomic orbitals.

Solve

N_2^+ Total number of electrons = 9 e^-

$$(\sigma_{2s})^2(\sigma_{2s}^*)^2(\pi_{2p})^4(\sigma_{2p})^1$$
$$BO = \tfrac{1}{2}\,(7-2) = 2.5$$

O_2^+ Total number of electrons = 11 e⁻

$(\sigma_{2s})^2(\sigma_{2s}^*)^2(\sigma_{2p})^2(\pi_{2p})^4(\pi_{2p}^*)^1$

BO = $\frac{1}{2}$ (8 – 3) = 2.5

C_2^+ Total number of electrons = 7 e⁻

$(\sigma_{2s})^2(\sigma_{2s}^*)^2(\pi_{2p})^3$

BO = $\frac{1}{2}$(5 – 2) = 1.5

Br_2^{2-} Total number of electrons = 16 e⁻

$(\sigma_{4s})^2(\sigma_{4s}^*)^2(\sigma_{4p})^2(\pi_{4p})^4(\pi_{4p}^*)^4(\sigma_{4p}^*)^2$

BO = $\frac{1}{2}$(8 – 8) = 0

All species with nonzero bond order (N_2^+, O_2^+, and C_2^+) are expected to exist.

Think about It
N_2^+ and O_2^+ have the same bond order but very different MO filling. N_2^+ has two fewer electrons than O_2^+.

5.99. Collect and Organize
For the species N_2^+, O_2^+, C_2^{2+}, and Br_2^{2-} we can place electrons into the appropriate molecular orbital energy levels to predict which species have one or more unpaired electrons.

Analyze
Due to *s–p* orbital mixing, the order of MOs for Li_2–N_2 is

$$\sigma_{2s}\sigma_{2s}^*\pi_{2p}\sigma_{2p}\pi_{2p}^*\sigma_{2p}^*$$

For O_2–Ne_2, which have less *s–p* orbital mixing, the order of the MOs is

$$\sigma_{2s}\sigma_{2s}^*\sigma_{2p}\pi_{2p}\pi_{2p}^*\sigma_{2p}^*$$

For Br_2^{2-} we assume the same MO energies as for F_2, but the MOs involve the 4*s* and 4*p* atomic orbitals. The species will have unpaired electrons and be paramagnetic when, after filling, a σ or σ* orbital has one electron in it or when a π or π* orbital has one, two, or three electrons in them.

Solve
(a) N_2^+ Total number of electrons = 9 e⁻

$(\sigma_{2s})^2(\sigma_{2s}^*)^2(\pi_{2p})^4(\sigma_{2p})^1$

One unpaired electron

(b) O_2^+ Total number of electrons = 11 e⁻

$(\sigma_{2s})^2(\sigma_{2s}^*)^2(\sigma_{2p})^2(\pi_{2p})^4(\pi_{2p}^*)^1$

One unpaired electron

(c) C_2^{2+} Total number of electrons = 6 e⁻

$(\sigma_{2s})^2(\sigma_{2s}^*)^2(\pi_{2p})^2$

Two unpaired electrons

(d) Br_2^{2-} Total number of electrons = 16 e⁻

$(\sigma_{4s})^2(\sigma_{4s}^*)^2(\sigma_{4p})^2(\pi_{4p})^4(\pi_{4p}^*)^4(\sigma_{4p}^*)^2$

No unpaired electrons

The paramagnetic species are (a) N_2^+, (b) O_2^+, and (c) C_2^{2+}.

Think about It
The π orbital filling according to Hund's rule shows how the π orbitals have unpaired electrons when one, two, or three electrons occupy them, but not with four electrons.

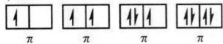

5.101. **Collect and Organize**
For the species C_2^{2-}, N_2^{2-}, O_2^{2-}, and Br_2^{2-} we can place electrons into the appropriate molecular orbital energy levels to predict which species have electrons in π^* orbitals.

Analyze
Due to s–p orbital mixing, the order of MOs for Li_2–N_2 is

$$\sigma_{2s}\sigma_{2s}^*\pi_{2p}\sigma_{2p}\pi_{2p}^*\sigma_{2p}^*$$

For O_2–Ne_2, which have less s–p orbital mixing, the order of the MOs is

$$\sigma_{2s}\sigma_{2s}^*\sigma_{2p}\pi_{2p}\pi_{2p}^*\sigma_{2p}^*$$

For each dianionic species, we fill the MO energy levels from lowest to highest energy with the total number of electrons. For Br_2^{2-} we assume the same MO energies as for F_2, but the MOs involve the $4s$ and $4p$ atomic orbitals.

Solve
(a) C_2^{2-} Total number of electrons = 10 e^-
$$(\sigma_{2s})^2(\sigma_{2s}^*)^2(\pi_{2p})^4(\sigma_{2p})^2$$
No electrons in π^* molecular orbitals

(b) N_2^{2-} Total number of electrons = 12 e^-
$$(\sigma_{2s})^2(\sigma_{2s}^*)^2(\pi_{2p})^4(\sigma_{2p})^2(\pi_{2p}^*)^2$$
Two electrons in π^* molecular orbitals

(c) O_2^{2-} Total number of electrons = 14 e^-
$$(\sigma_{2s})^2(\sigma_{2s}^*)^2(\sigma_{2p})^2(\pi_{2p})^4(\pi_{2p}^*)^4$$
Four electrons in π^* molecular orbitals

(d) Br_2^{2-} Total number of electrons = 16 e^-
$$(\sigma_{4s})^2(\sigma_{4s}^*)^2(\sigma_{4p})^2(\pi_{4p})^4(\pi_{4p}^*)^4(\sigma_{4p}^*)^2$$
Four electrons in π^* molecular orbitals

The species with electrons in π^* orbitals are (b) N_2^{2-}, (c) O_2^{2-}, and (d) Br_2^{2-}.

Think about It
The bond orders for each species are 3 for C_2^{2-}, 2 for N_2^{2-}, 1 for O_2^{2-}, and 0 for Br_2^{2-}.

5.103. **Collect and Organize**
For B_2, C_2, N_2, and O_2 we are to determine which increases its bond order on acquiring two electrons to become a dianion.

Analyze
Bond order increases when the two extra electrons are placed into bonding MOs. If the two extra electrons are placed into antibonding MOs, the bond order decreases.

Solve
(a) B_2 has the MO configuration of

$$(\sigma_{2s})^2(\sigma_{2s}^*)^2(\pi_{2p})^2$$

The two electrons added to form the dianion are placed into the π_{2p} orbital, so the bond order increases.

(b) C_2 has the MO configuration of

$$(\sigma_{2s})^2(\sigma_{2s}^*)^2(\pi_{2p})^4$$

The two electrons added to form the dianion are placed into the σ_{2p} orbital, so the bond order increases.

(c) N_2 has the MO configuration of

$$(\sigma_{2s})^2(\sigma_{2s}^*)^2(\pi_{2p})^4(\sigma_{2p})^2$$

The two electrons added to form the dianion are placed into the π_{2p}^* orbital, so the bond order decreases.

(d) O_2 has the MO configuration of

$$(\sigma_{2s})^2(\sigma_{2s}^*)^2(\sigma_{2p})^2(\pi_{2p})^4(\pi_{2p}^*)^2$$

The two electrons added to form the dianion are placed into the π_{2p}^* orbital, so the bond order decreases.

Bond order increases with a gain of two electrons for (a) B_2 and (b) C_2.

Think about It
The species above that have unpaired electrons (and thus are paramagnetic) are B_2, N_2^{2-}, and O_2.

5.105. **Collect and Organize**
For the diatomic 1+ cations of Li_2, Be_2, B_2, C_2, N_2, O_2, F_2, and Ne_2 we are to consider whether the cations always have shorter bonds than the neutral molecules.

Analyze
Shorter bonds have higher bond orders. Longer bonds have lower bond orders. Bond order decreases when the electron is removed from a bonding MO. If the electron is removed from an antibonding MO, the bond order increases.

Solve
Li_2 has the MO configuration of

$$(\sigma_{2s})^2$$

Removing one electron decreases the bond order, and the bond is lengthened.
Be_2 has the MO configuration of

$$(\sigma_{2s})^2(\sigma_{2s}^*)^2$$

Removing one electron increases the bond order, and the bond is shortened.

B_2 has the MO configuration of

$$(\sigma_{2s})^2(\sigma_{2s}^*)^2(\pi_{2p})^2$$

Removing one electron decreases the bond order, and the bond is lengthened.
C_2 has the MO configuration of

$$(\sigma_{2s})^2(\sigma_{2s}^*)^2(\pi_{2p})^4$$

Removing one electron decreases the bond order, and the bond is lengthened.
N_2 has the MO configuration of

$$(\sigma_{2s})^2(\sigma_{2s}^*)^2(\pi_{2p})^4(\sigma_{2p})^2$$

Removing one electron decreases the bond order, and the bond is lengthened.
O_2 has the MO configuration of

$$(\sigma_{2s})^2(\sigma_{2s}^*)^2(\sigma_{2p})^2(\pi_{2p})^4(\pi_{2p}^*)^2$$

Removing one electron increases the bond order, and the bond is shortened.
F_2 has the MO configuration of

$$(\sigma_{2s})^2(\sigma_{2s}^*)^2(\sigma_{2p})^2(\pi_{2p})^4(\pi_{2p}^*)^4$$

Removing one electron increases the bond order, and the bond is shortened.
Ne_2 has the MO configuration of

$$(\sigma_{2s})^2(\sigma_{2s}^*)^2(\sigma_{2p})^2(\pi_{2p})^4(\pi_{2p}^*)^4(\sigma_{2p}^*)^2$$

Removing one electron increases the bond order, and the bond is shortened.

No. The cations N_2^+, C_2^+, B_2^+, and Li_2^+, which lose an electron from bonding orbitals in the corresponding neutral molecules, decrease their bond order and have longer bond lengths.

Think about It

All the 1+ cations will be paramagnetic.

5.107. **Collect and Organize**

For NH_4^+ and ClO_4^- we are asked to determine the molecular geometries of the two ions.

Analyze

First, we must draw the Lewis structures of each ion. Then, through the steric number (SN), we can determine the electron-pair geometry. If lone electron pairs are on the central atom, we have to take that into account to translate the electron-pair geometry into the molecular geometry.

Solve

SN = 4
Electron-pair geometry = tetrahedral
Molecular geometry = tetrahedral

SN = 4
Electron-pair geometry = tetrahedral
Molecular geometry = tetrahedral

Think about It

The structure drawn for ClO_4^- has the lowest formal charges on the atoms. The expanded octet on Cl is possible because it is a third-period element.

5.109. **Collect and Organize**

We are given a skeletal structure in Figure 5.109. By completing the Lewis structure and applying VSEPR theory, we can determine the N—C—C, O=C—O, and C—O—H bond angles.

Analyze

From the Lewis structure and steric number (SN) we can determine the electron-pair geometry around the carbon and oxygen atoms. If the electron-pair geometry is linear, the bond angles are 180°; if it is trigonal planar, the bond angles are 120°; if it is tetrahedral, the bond angles are 109.5°.

Solve

SN = 3
Electron-pair geometry = trigonal planar
O–C–O bond angle = 120°

SN = 4
Electron-pair geometry = tetrahedral
C–O–H bond angle = 109.5°

SN = 4
Electron-pair geometry = tetrahedral
N–C–C bond angle = 109.5°

Think about It
Remember, these are idealized bond angles. Because lone pairs take up more space than bonding pairs, the C—O—H bond angle is probably <109.5°.

5.111. **Collect and Organize**
We are given two alternate skeletal structures for Cl_2O_2. We are to complete the Lewis structures, and from those we can find the molecular geometry to determine whether either isomer is linear and whether either or both have a permanent dipole.

Analyze
Cl_2O_2 has 26 e⁻ and needs 32 e⁻, giving a difference of 6 e⁻ in three covalent bonds. This leaves 20 e⁻ in 10 lone pairs to complete the octets on the atoms. Chlorine may expand its octet to minimize formal charges on the atoms in the Lewis structure.

Solve
The Lewis structures for the two different skeletal arrangements of Cl_2O_2 are

$$:\ddot{\text{C}}\text{l}—\ddot{\text{O}}—\ddot{\text{O}}—\ddot{\text{C}}\text{l}: \qquad :\ddot{\text{C}}\text{l}—\ddot{\text{O}}—\ddot{\text{C}}\text{l}=\ddot{\text{O}}:$$

Structure 1   Structure 2

(a) All the central atoms in both structures (O—O and O—Cl) have SN = 4, so their electron-group geometries are tetrahedral. Each central atom also has two lone pairs and two bonding pairs, which gives them a bent molecular geometry. Therefore, neither molecule is linear.
(b) Free rotation about the O—O bond in Structure 1 and its symmetry means that this molecule would not have a permanent dipole. Structure 2, however, because of its asymmetry, will have a permanent dipole.

Think about It
These compounds may be drawn three-dimensionally as

5.113. **Collect and Organize**
For the diatomic ion ClO^+ we are to draw the Lewis structure and complete the molecular orbital (MO) diagram (see Figure P5.113) to determine the Cl—O bond order.

Analyze
ClO^+ has 12 e⁻. To complete the octets on the atoms for the Lewis structure, ClO^+ would need 16 e⁻, giving a difference of 4 e⁻ in two covalent bonds. This leaves 8 e⁻ in four lone pairs to complete the structure. Chlorine may expand its octet to reduce the formal charges on the atom in the Lewis structure.

Solve
(a) $$\left[:\ddot{\text{C}}\text{l}=\ddot{\text{O}}:\right]^+$$

(b) The MO diagram would fill as
$$(\sigma_{3s})^2(\sigma_{3s}^*)^2(\sigma_{3p})^2(\pi_{3p})^4(\pi_{3p}^*)^2$$
$$\text{BO} = \tfrac{1}{2}(8-4) = 2$$

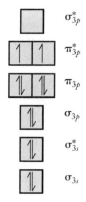

Think about It
For ClO⁺ the bond order drawn in the Lewis structure matches the bond order calculated with MO theory.

5.115. Collect and Organize
Given the skeletal structure of phosphoric acid, we are to complete its Lewis structure and use VSEPR theory to determine the molecular geometry around the phosphorus atom.

Analyze
H_3PO_4 has 32 e⁻ and needs 46 e⁻, giving a difference of 14 e⁻ in seven covalent bonds. This leaves 18 e⁻ in nine lone pairs to complete the octets on the atoms in the structure. Phosphorus may expand its octet to reduce the formal charges on the atoms.

Solve

All formal charges = 0
SN at phosphorus = 4
Electron-pair and molecular geometry around P = tetrahedral

Think about It
In this structure phosphorus forms three σ bonds to OH, and a σ plus a π bond to oxygen.

5.117. Collect and Organize
For BBCO and OCBBCO we are to draw the Lewis structures that minimize the formal charges on the atoms. Using these structures, we can predict the B–B–C bond angle in each.

Analyze
BBCO has 16 e⁻ and needs 32 e⁻, giving a difference of 16 e⁻ in eight covalent bonds. This leaves no lone pairs of electrons. OCBBCO has 26 e⁻ and needs 48 e⁻, giving a difference of 22 e⁻ in 11 covalent bonds. This leaves 4 e⁻ in two lone pairs to complete the octets on the atoms.

Solve
(a) and (b)

:B—B=C=O:

All formal charges = 0
On both central B and C atoms SN = 2
Molecular geometry = linear
B—B═C = 180°

:O=C=B—B=C=O:

All formal charges = 0
On all central B and C atoms SN = 2
Molecular geometry = linear
B—B═C = 180°

Think about It

In both compounds when formal charge is minimized, the boron atoms do not have complete octets in the Lewis structure and are thus electron deficient. These compounds might be predicted to gain some stability through the other (less favorable) resonance forms where the formal charges do not equal zero.

5.119. **Collect and Organize**

We are to draw the resonance structures of methyl isothiocyanate (CH_3NCS) and use formal charges to identify the resonance form that contributes most to the bonding. From the Lewis structure, we can determine the steric number (SN) at the carbon atoms in the molecule and predict the molecular geometry at each carbon atom.

Analyze

CH_3NCS has 22 e^- and needs 38 e^-, giving a difference of 16 e^- in eight covalent bonds. This leaves 6 e^- in three lone pairs on the molecule.

Solve

(a) and (b)

The resonance structure in which all the formal charges equal zero contributes the most to the bonding.
(c) At the methyl (CH_3) carbon, SN = 4, so this carbon is tetrahedral. At the isothiocyanate (NCS) carbon, SN = 2, so the molecular geometry at this carbon is linear.

Think about It

The molecular geometries at the carbon atoms stay the same in all the resonance structures.

5.121. **Collect and Organize**

If borazine is isoelectronic with benzene, it has the same number of electrons. To determine whether delocalized π electrons also exist in borazine, we must draw the Lewis structure of $B_3N_3H_6$ with resonance forms.

Analyze

$B_3N_3H_6$ has 30 e^- and needs 60 e^-, giving a difference of 30 e^- in 15 covalent bonds. This leaves no lone pairs in the molecule.

Solve

In these resonance structures the π electrons are delocalized just as in benzene. In the resonance forms, the formal charge on B is –1 and that on N is +1.

Think about It

The resonance structure that minimizes the formal charges on all the atoms gives a structure in which the B atoms are electron deficient.

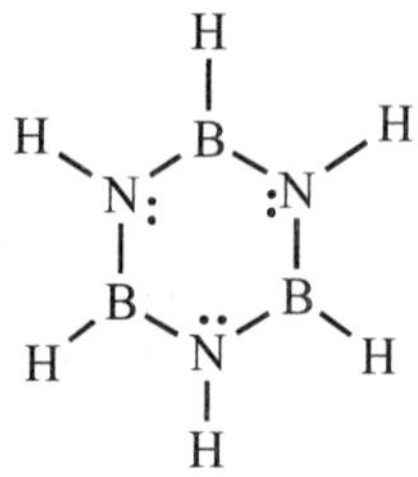

5.123. **Collect and Organize**

If the molecule HArF contains ArF^-, we can use molecular orbital theory to determine the bond order in ArF^-.

Analyze

ArF^- would have 16 valence electrons and bonding would involve overlap of the $3s$ and $3p$ orbitals on Ar with the $2s$ and $2p$ orbitals on F. Although the overlap would not be as effective as the overlap of orbitals of the same n level, we can assume that the overlap gives similar molecular orbitals. The MO diagram, then, would look similar to that for F_2.

Solve

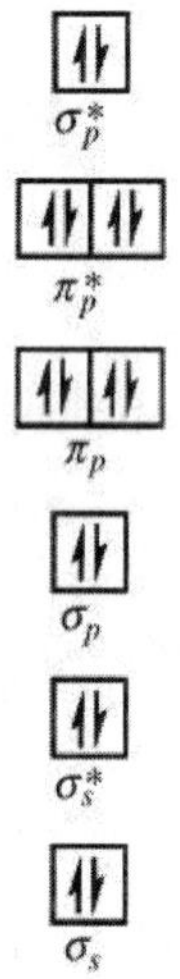

$BO = \frac{1}{2}(8 - 8) = 0$

ArF^- is not expected to be stable because its bond order is zero.

Think about It

The argon–fluorine bond would be stable, however, as a neutral species (ArF) or as a cation (ArF^+).

5.125. **Collect and Organize**

To determine the polarity of N_2O_2, N_2O_5, and N_2O_3 we must draw Lewis structures and then consider the direction and magnitude of the individual bond dipoles.

Analyze

We draw the Lewis structures in the usual way and then use VSEPR theory to draw the structures' geometries on the basis of the steric number of the central N and O atoms. The electronegativity for O is greater than that for N, so each N—O bond is polarized so that partial negative charge is on the oxygen atom. Once we have assigned the individual bond dipoles, we can then see whether the vectors representing those bond dipoles cancel to give a nonpolar molecule or add to give a polar molecule.

Solve

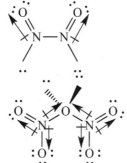

The N_2O_2 molecule is nonpolar as drawn, but we can imagine the N—N bond rotating to give a polar molecule.

Because of free rotation around the N—N bond, N_2O_2 is nonpolar.

The N_2O_5 molecule is polar.

The N_2O_3 molecule is polar.

Think about It

Be careful to consider geometry in assigning polarity to a molecule. The bent geometry around the central oxygen atom in N_2O_5 makes that molecule polar.

5.127. Collect and Organize

We can use the molecular orbital diagram for O_2 to determine the bond order in O_2^{2-} and O_2^{-} and compare these bond orders with those predicted from the Lewis structures.

Analyze

O_2^{2-} has 14 e^{-} to fill up the MO diagram. Its Lewis structure needs 16 e^{-}, giving a difference of 2 e^{-} in one covalent bond and leaving 12 e^{-} in six lone pairs to complete the octets on the oxygen atoms. O_2^{-} has 13 e^{-} to fill up the MO diagram. For its Lewis structure, it needs 16 e^{-}, giving a difference of 3 e^{-} in one covalent bond and one unpaired electron and leaving 10 e^{-} in five lone pairs to complete the octets on the oxygen atoms.

Solve

For O_2^{2-} the bond order is
BO $= \frac{1}{2}(8-6) = 1$.

The Lewis structure is consistent with this bond order:

$$\left[:\ddot{O}-\ddot{O}:\right]^{2-}$$

MO diagram for O_2^{2-}

For O_2^- the bond order is
BO $= \frac{1}{2}(8-5) = 1.5$.

The Lewis structure is not consistent with this bond order:

$$\left[\cdot\ddot{O}-\ddot{O}:\right]^-$$

MO diagram for O_2^-

Think about It
Lewis structures cannot show fractional bond orders and so cannot show the lengthening of the bond in going from O_2^- to O_2^{2-}.

5.129. Collect and Organize
To determine the hybridization and bond angles in cyclic S_8 we can use the steric number (SN) of the S atoms obtained from the Lewis structure.

Analyze
S_8 has 48 e^- and needs 64 e^-, for a difference of 16 e^- in eight covalent bonds. This leaves 32 e^- in 16 lone pairs to complete the octets on the S atoms.

Solve

Each S atom has SN = 4, so the electron-pair geometry is tetrahedral.
Orbital hybridization on S = sp^3.

Think about It
With two lone pairs on each S atom, the molecular geometry at each S atom is predicted to be bent with an angle of approximately 109.5°. The actual bond angles (108°) are less than the ideal because the two lone pairs occupy more space and therefore the bond pair–bond pair angle is reduced.

5.131. Collect and Organize
We are given that ozone has only one kind of atom but has a permanent dipole moment. We have to look closely at the molecular geometry of O_3 to explain this molecule's polarity.

Analyze
For the Lewis structure, O_3 has 18 e^- and needs 24 e^-, giving a difference of 6 e^- in three covalent bonds and leaving 12 e^- in six lone pairs to complete the octets on the oxygen atoms. The molecular geometry is obtained from the steric number (SN) around the central O atom in the structure.

Solve

$$:\overset{\displaystyle ..}{\underset{}{O}}=\overset{\displaystyle .. }{\underset{..}{O}}\overset{..}{\underset{..}{O}}:$$

SN = 3 for an electron-pair geometry of trigonal planar.
The presence of one lone pair on the central O atom makes the molecular geometry at the central O atom bent.

This molecule is polar because, although the oxygen–oxygen bonds themselves are nonpolar, the lone pair has its own "pull" on the electrons in the molecule. Also, the π bonds between the oxygen atoms place slightly more electron density on the terminal O atoms and make the "nonpolar O—O bond" actually polar.

Think about It

Geometry around an atom, not just difference in electronegativity, is important to the overall polarity of a molecule.

CHAPTER 6 | Intermolecular Forces: Attractions between Particles

6.1. **Collect and Organize**
Of the hydrocarbons shown in Figure P6.1, we are to choose the one with the highest boiling point.

Analyze
As constitutional isomers, all these hydrocarbons have the same molecular formula, C_7H_{16}, with the same molar masses, so their boiling points cannot be distinguished by their relative masses. However, they do have structures that are different from each other in terms of branching, with (d) more branched than (c), which in turn is more branched than (b), with (a) being an unbranched, linear hydrocarbon.

Solve
The more branching, the lower the dispersion forces between the molecules and the lower the boiling point. Therefore, the linear *n*-heptane (a), with no branching of the hydrocarbon chain, is the isomer with the highest boiling point.

Think about It
In the series *n*-pentane, *n*-hexane, *n*-heptane, and *n*-octane, the molar mass difference leads us to predict that *n*-octane will have the highest boiling point.

6.3. **Collect and Organize**
From the phase diagram for compound X shown in Figure P6.3, we are to determine whether on a hot summer day the substance will be in the solid, liquid, or gas form.

Analyze
The conditions of a hot summer day are pressure at 1 atm and temperature at about 30°C. We find this point on the phase diagram. The green-shaded area on the phase diagram in Figure P6.3 is for the solid phase, the blue-shaded area is for the liquid phase, and the pink-shaded area is for the gas phase.

Solve
The point for 1 atm and 30°C is in the green-shaded, or solid, phase.

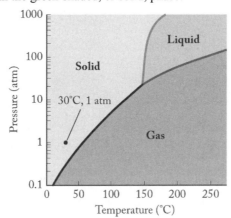

Think about It
Heating compound X further in the closed container to above 55°C would sublime the solid into the gas phase.

6.5. **Collect and Organize**
For compound X in Problems 6.3 and 6.4, we are to predict the phase change, if any, that will occur when we take the compound at 50 atm from 0°C to 250°C at the same pressure.

Analyze

We can plot both points on the phase diagram. If the change from one condition to the other crosses any phase equilibrium line, a phase change will occur. The green-shaded area on the phase diagram in Figure P6.3 is for the solid phase, the blue-shaded area is for the liquid phase, and the pink-shaded area is for the gas phase.

Solve

The point for 50 atm and 0°C is in the green-shaded, or solid, phase. The point for 50 atm and 250°C is in the gas phase. When we connect these two states, we see that the compound undergoes both melting (crossing the solid–liquid equilibrium line) and boiling (crossing the liquid–gas equilibrium line). This compound, therefore, undergoes the solid-to-liquid and the liquid-to-gas phase changes.

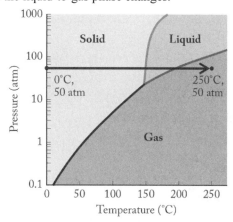

Think about It

Below the triple point, an increase in temperature at the same pressure results only in sublimation, not melting.

6.7. **Collect and Organize**

Using the phase diagram shown in Figure P6.3 for compound X, we are to predict whether the solid form will float on the liquid form as the liquid freezes at 300 atm.

Analyze

In the phase diagram we see that as pressure is applied at a particular temperature, say 160°C, compound X will form a solid from the liquid form. This change indicates that the solid is the denser form, as it is favored at higher pressures.

Solve

Because the solid is the denser form, it will not float on the liquid form.

Think about It

The right-sloping solid-to-liquid equilibrium line shows that the solid is the denser phase. This is unlike water, which has a left-sloping solid-to-liquid line, which means that ice does float on water.

6.9. **Collect and Organize**

Using Figure P6.8 we are to determine what, if any, phase change occurs when the water at −25°C and 2500 atm undergoes heating and a pressure reduction to −15°C and 1000 atm.

Analyze

We can plot both points on the phase diagram. If the change from one condition to the other crosses the phase equilibrium line, a phase change will occur. The pink-shaded area on the phase diagram in Figure P6.8 is for the solid phase, and the blue-shaded area is for the liquid phase.

Solve

In decreasing the pressure and increasing the temperature, we see on the phase diagram that the liquid will freeze to become a solid.

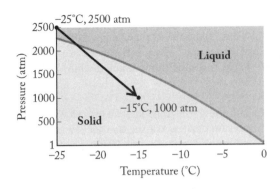

Think about It
This result for lowering pressure and increasing temperature is counterintuitive because water is quite different from most other liquids.

6.11. **Collect and Organize**
We are to explain why a branched alkane (hydrocarbon) has a lower boiling point than a normal (linear) alkane if they have the same molar mass.

Analyze
A higher boiling point means that the intermolecular forces between the molecules in the liquid phase are greater.

Solve
The intermolecular forces between molecules of a branched alkane are less than those of a linear, unbranched alkane because a branched molecule has less available surface area for the intermolecular forces than the linear form. Therefore, with lower intermolecular forces between the molecules, the branched alkane has a lower boiling point than its linear analogue.

Think about It
Compare the boiling points of the constitutional isomers of pentane:

$$\underset{36°C}{\text{structure}} \qquad \underset{27.7°C}{\text{structure}} \qquad \underset{9.5°C}{\text{structure}}$$

6.13. **Collect and Organize**
For each pair of substances we are to determine which one has the stronger London dispersion forces.

Analyze
The more atoms and electrons in a compound, the greater the dispersion forces between the molecules.

Solve
(a) CCl_4 has stronger dispersion forces than CF_4 because Cl is a larger atom with more electrons than F.
(b) C_3H_8 has stronger dispersion forces than CH_4 because C_3H_8 has more atoms in its molecular structure.
(c) CS_2 has stronger dispersion forces than CO_2 because S has more electrons than O.

Think about It
The greater number of electrons and atoms in a compound gives rise to stronger dispersion forces because more polarizable electrons are present on the atoms that make up the compound.

6.15. Collect and Organize

From the order of the boiling points of gasoline, jet fuel, kerosene, fuel oil, and diesel oil, we are to predict which fuel has hydrocarbons of the greatest average molar mass.

Analyze

Molecules with higher molar masses generally have greater intermolecular forces.

Solve

Diesel oil has hydrocarbons of the greatest molar mass among these fuels because it has the highest boiling point.

Think about It

We might also expect diesel fuel to be more viscous than gasoline owing to greater dispersion forces present because of the increased molar mass of diesel fuel.

6.17. Collect and Organize

We are to describe how individual water molecules are oriented around dissolved anions.

Analyze

The water molecule is polar because of its bent geometry, with a partial negative charge on the oxygen atom and a partial positive charge on the hydrogen ends.

Solve

The water molecule is oriented around an anion so as to point the partially positive hydrogen atoms toward the anion. This arrangement results in attractive forces between the water molecules and the anion.

Think about It

This interaction between the anion and water molecules is an ion–dipole interaction.

6.19. Collect and Organize

We are to explain the differences in strength between dipole–dipole interactions (weaker) and ion–dipole interactions (stronger).

Analyze

The dipole–dipole interaction involves attractions between two polar molecules with slight charge separation (partial positive and negative charges) on the molecule. An ion–dipole interaction involves attractions between an ion with a full positive or negative charge and a polar molecule.

Solve

Coulomb's law states that as charge increases, the attraction of two oppositely charged species for each other increases. Because of the full positive or negative charge on the ion, the ion–dipole interaction is stronger than the dipole–dipole interaction.

Think about It

Ion–ion is the strongest of all interactions between molecules.

6.21. **Collect and Organize**
We are to explain why hydrogen bonds are considered a special class of dipole–dipole interactions.

Analyze
Hydrogen bonds can form when hydrogen is bonded to a very electronegative element (F, O, N). The hydrogen bond is very polar.

Solve
The charge buildup on H (partially positive) and the electronegative element (partially negative) means that the X—H bond is polar but not ionic. It is still a dipole–dipole interaction, except that its strength is noticeably higher than that of other dipole–dipole interactions.

Think about It
Hydrogen bonds are also important in explaining why ice floats and how proteins fold.

6.23. **Collect and Organize**
We are to explain why CH_3F (melting point, $-142°C$) has a higher melting point than CH_4 (mp, $-182°C$).

Analyze
The higher melting point of CH_3F indicates stronger intermolecular forces between CH_3F molecules than between CH_4 molecules.

Solve
CH_3F is a polar molecule and therefore has stronger intermolecular forces than those of the nonpolar molecules of CH_4, which have only the weak dispersion forces. Because overcoming strong intermolecular forces takes more energy, CH_3F has a higher melting point than CH_4. Second, the dispersion forces between CH_3F molecules will be greater than those between CH_4 molecules because F has more electrons than H. This then is added to the dipole–dipole forces between CH_3F molecules.

Think about It
Molecular polarity and the degree of charge separation are important considerations for comparing some physical properties of compounds (such as boiling point or vapor pressure).

6.25. **Collect and Organize**
We are asked to explain why CH_4 does not form hydrogen bonds but CH_3OH does.

Analyze
Hydrogen bonds can form only when hydrogen is bonded to a very electronegative element (F, O, N).

Solve
The H in methane has just a single bond to the relatively low-electronegativity C atom, and therefore the carbon–hydrogen bond is not polar enough to exhibit hydrogen bonding. In methanol, however, one of the H atoms is bonded to oxygen, which is second to fluorine in electronegativity. This H shows hydrogen bonding in methanol.

Think about It
The other H bonds to C in methanol, CH_3OH, are not capable of hydrogen bonding. They are like the carbon–hydrogen bonds in methane, CH_4.

6.27. **Collect and Organize**
For the covalent molecules CF_4, CF_2Cl_2, CCl_4, and $CFCl_3$ we are to determine which we would expect to have dipole–dipole interactions.

Analyze
We need to first determine whether the molecules are polar or nonpolar. Polar molecules have permanent dipoles that attract each other (δ^- to δ^+); nonpolar molecules have only weak dispersion forces between them. If

all the molecules are polar, then the one with the smallest dipole moment (as determined from differences in electronegativities between the atoms) would be the molecule with the weakest intermolecular forces.

Solve

From the Lewis structures of these molecules, we know that both CF_4 and CCl_4 are nonpolar tetrahedral molecules. These have only dispersion forces as the intermolecular force between the molecules. CF_2Cl_2 (b) and $CFCl_3$ (d) are both polar tetrahedral molecules and therefore have dipole–dipole interactions between their molecules.

Think about It

Between CF_4 and CCl_4 we would expect CCl_4 to have the stronger dispersion forces.

6.29. **Collect and Organize**

We are to explain which ion, Cl^-, Br^-, or I^-, has the strongest ion–dipole interactions with water.

Analyze

Ions with smaller size or higher charge will attract the dipoles of the water molecules more strongly than those of larger size or smaller charge. All the charges on these halide ions are the same, so we need consider only the size of the halide ions.

Solve

Because Cl^- is smaller than either Br^- or I^-, Cl^- will exhibit the strongest ion–dipole interaction with water.

Think about It

The F^- ion would be predicted to have an even stronger ion–dipole interaction with water than the Cl^- anion.

6.31. **Collect and Organize**

We can define *miscible* and *soluble* to delineate the difference between these terms.

Analyze

Two liquids are miscible when they dissolve completely in all proportions into each other. A substance (liquid, solid, or gas) is soluble when it dissolves in a solvent.

Solve

Miscible and soluble are nearly the same in that both describe one substance dissolving into another. Miscibility, however, refers to two liquids mixing, whereas two solids, for example, may be soluble in each other. In addition, the solubility of a substance in a solvent may be limited and so may form a saturated solution or precipitate from the solution if the concentration is too high, but two liquids that are miscible are soluble in each other in all proportions.

Think about It

The classification between soluble and insoluble is also indistinct. Generally speaking, a solute that dissolves at less than 0.1 g in 1.00 L of a solvent is considered insoluble.

6.33. **Collect and Organize**

We are to relate the solubility of substances in water with the terms *hydrophilic* and *hydrophobic*.

Analyze

Hydrophilic means "water-loving" and *hydrophobic* means "water-fearing."

Solve

Hydrophilic substances dissolve in water. Hydrophobic substances do not dissolve, or are immiscible, in water.

Think about It

Ethanol is hydrophilic because it is miscible with water to give a homogeneous solution, but olive oil is hydrophobic because it forms a heterogeneous mixture with water that separates into oil and water layers.

6.35. Collect and Organize

For each pair of compounds, we are to determine which is more soluble in H_2O.

Analyze

Water is a polar solvent capable of forming hydrogen bonds to dissolved substances with X—H bonds (X = F, O, N). In each pair of compounds, the more soluble is the more polar molecule or the one that forms hydrogen bonds. In considering whether a salt is soluble in water, we have to consider the relative strengths of the ionic bonds as well as the relative strengths of the ion–dipole interactions formed on dissolution.

Solve

(a) $CHCl_3$ is polar, whereas CCl_4 is not. $CHCl_3$ is more soluble in water.
(b) CH_3OH is more polar because it has a smaller hydrocarbon chain than $C_6H_{11}OH$. CH_3OH is more soluble in water.
(c) NaF has a weaker ionic bond than MgO because its ions have lower charges. NaF is more soluble in water.
(d) BaF_2 has a weaker ionic bond than CaF_2 because Ba^{2+} is larger than Ca^{2+}. BaF_2 is more soluble in water.

Think about It

Solubility is determined by many factors: polarity, ability to hydrogen bond, and strength of the intermolecular forces between molecules of the solute.

6.37. Collect and Organize

Of the ionic compounds listed, NaCl, KI, $Ca(OH)_2$, and CaO, we are to determine which would be most soluble in water.

Analyze

The weaker the ionic bond, the easier the bond breaks for the cation and anion to dissolve in water. Ionic bonds are weakest for large ions of low charge.

Solve

KI (b) has the largest ions of lowest (1+ and 1–) charge, so it is the most soluble in water because it has the weakest ion–ion bond.

Think about It

CaO, with a 2+ cation and 2– anion, would be expected to be the least soluble in water.

6.39. Collect and Organize

From among the four compounds listed we are to choose the one most soluble in water.

Analyze

Water is a polar solvent capable of forming hydrogen bonds and dipole–dipole interactions with other polar dissolved substances. All the compounds listed have some degree of polarity due to the bent geometry around the oxygen in the middle of the compounds' structure. The compounds, though, have different hydrocarbon ($-CH_2-$) chain lengths.

Solve

The longer the $-CH_2-$ chain, the more hydrophobic (nonpolar) the molecule; therefore, (c) CH_3OCH_3, with the shortest hydrocarbon chain length, will be the most soluble in water.

Think about It

These compounds, however, are all less soluble than their alcohol counterparts ($CH_3(CH_2)_nOH$) because the alcohol –OH can hydrogen bond to water.

6.41. Collect and Organize

We are asked to differentiate between *sublimation* and *evaporation*.

Analyze

Sublimation describes the process in which a substance goes from the solid to the gas phase. Evaporation describes the process in which a substance goes from the liquid to the gas phase.

Solve

Although both processes end with the substance in the gas phase, sublimation "skips" a step in that the solid does not first liquefy before evaporating.

Think about It

A familiar substance that sublimes at room temperature and pressure is dry ice (solid CO_2).

6.43. Collect and Organize

We are asked to define *equilibrium line*.

Analyze

This term applies to the lines in a phase diagram.

Solve

If you are along the equilibrium line in a phase diagram, the two phases that border that line are stable and coexist at that pressure–temperature combination.

Think about It

Where the equilibrium lines meet is called the *triple point*. This is the temperature–pressure combination where all three phases (gas, liquid, and solid) are present and stable.

6.45. Collect and Organize

We are to predict the phase most likely to be present at two different temperature–pressure combinations.

Analyze

At high temperatures, the atoms or molecules of a substance have high kinetic energies and can partially or fully break the intermolecular forces between them. At high pressures the atoms or molecules are close to each other and therefore are attracted to each other through intermolecular forces.

Solve

(a) For low temperatures and high pressures we would expect a solid phase to be present.
(b) For high temperatures and low pressures we would expect a gas phase to be present.

Think about It

As we decrease the pressure at low temperatures, we could melt the solid and even perhaps vaporize it, or sublime the solid.

6.47. Collect and Organize

When freeze-drying food, we sublime the ice in frozen food into the gas phase. We are asked whether the pressure for this process must be below the pressure at the triple point of water.

Analyze

The triple point is where the gas–solid, solid–liquid, and liquid–gas phase boundaries meet in a phase diagram.

Solve

From the phase diagram for water we see that above the triple point, the solid phase must change to the liquid phase to enter the gaseous phase. Below the triple point, changing the temperature at a given pressure will sublime solid water into the gas phase. Yes, the pressure used for the sublimation process for freeze-drying must be below the pressure at the triple point.

Think about It
The triple point is characteristic of a particular substance. The triple point for ethanol is different from that for water.

6.49. Collect and Organize
We are to list the steps to convert water at room temperature and pressure (25°C, 1 atm) to its triple point.

Analyze
The triple point of water is 0.01°C and 0.006 atm.

Solve
To reach the triple point we would (1) reduce the temperature from 25°C to 0.01°C and then (2) reduce the pressure from 1 atm to 0.006 atm.

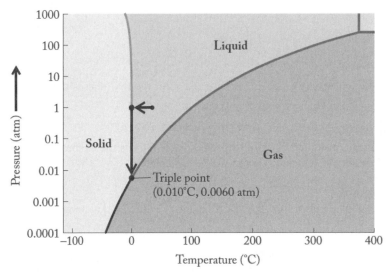

Think about It
At the triple point, all three phases (gas, liquid, and solid) coexist in equilibrium.

6.51. Collect and Organize
We consider the phase changes that water, initially at 5.0 atm and 100°C, undergoes when the pressure is reduced to 0.5 atm while maintaining temperature at 100°C.

Analyze
In the phase diagram for water, the phase of the water at 5.0 atm and 100°C is liquid. The phase of water at 0.5 atm and 100°C is gas.

Solve
Water at 100°C vaporizes from liquid to gas when the pressure is reduced from 5.0 atm to 0.5 atm.

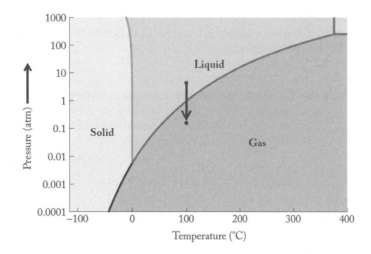

Think about It

At 100°C, water boils at 1.0 atm. At pressures lower than 1.0 atm, water at 100°C is entirely in the gaseous state.

6.53. ### Collect and Organize

From the phase diagram for CO_2 (Figure 6.25) we can determine the temperature below which $CO_2(s)$ sublimes to $CO_2(g)$ simply by lowering the pressure.

Analyze

The direct solid-to-gas conversion occurs below the triple point (–57°C, 5.1 atm).

Solve

The triple point of CO_2 is at –57°C. At any temperature below the triple point, $CO_2(s)$ sublimes directly to $CO_2(g)$ through lowering the pressure.

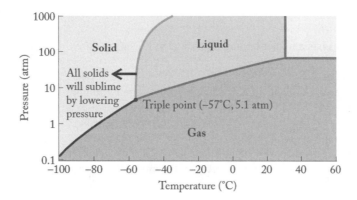

Think about It

Because the triple point of CO_2 is at a low temperature, we do not observe dry ice melting under ambient conditions (25°C, 1 atm).

6.55. Collect and Organize

We can use the phase diagram for water shown in Figure 6.23 to determine which phases of water are present at different temperature and pressure combinations.

Analyze

We use the phase diagram just like a map, locating each pressure and temperature combination and "reading" the phase at that location on the diagram. We are shown locations on the map to orient us: the normal pressure (1 atm), melting point (0°C), and boiling point (100°C) lines are indicated as well as the conditions for the triple point (0.01°C, 0.006 atm).

Solve

(a) 2 atm and 110°C: liquid
(b) 0.5 atm and 80°C: liquid
(c) 7×10^{-3} atm and 3°C: gas

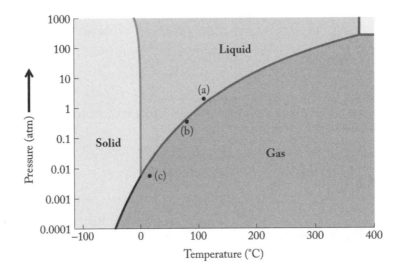

Think about It

Water at high pressures has a higher boiling point than at lower pressures, as seen in (a).

6.57. Collect and Organize

Water and methanol are both polar liquids capable of hydrogen bonding. We are asked why a needle floats on water but not on methanol.

Analyze

Surface tension is the resistance of a liquid to increase its surface area by moving the molecules of the liquid apart. The greater the intermolecular forces between the molecules in the liquid, the greater the surface tension.

Solve

A needle floats on water but not on methanol because of the high surface tension of water. This is because water can hydrogen bond through two O—H bonds with other water molecules, whereas methanol has only one O—H bond through which to form strong hydrogen bonds. The intermolecular forces between the C—H groups on the CH_3OH molecules are only weak dispersion forces.

Think about It

The high surface tension of water also allows some insects to walk on water.

6.59. Collect and Organize

We are to explain why water pipes are in danger of bursting when the temperature is below the freezing point of water.

Analyze

At temperatures below freezing, the water in the pipes freezes. Because the density of ice is less than that of liquid water, the water expands as it freezes.

Solve

The expansion of water in the pipes upon freezing may create sufficient pressure on the wall of the pipes to cause them to burst.

Think about It

To prevent pipes from freezing during the winter months, we must drain the water from the portion of the pipe exposed to freezing temperatures.

6.61. Collect and Organize

We are to explain why the meniscus of liquid Hg is convex, rather than concave as it is for most liquids.

Analyze

The shape of the meniscus is due to the competing adhesive forces (liquid to glass surface that has Si—O—H bonds) and cohesive forces (liquid to liquid).

Solve

The cohesive forces in mercury are stronger than the adhesive forces of the mercury to the glass. This effect yields a convex meniscus.

Think about It

The strong metallic bonding between mercury atoms is not balanced by the adhesive Hg to Si—O—H bonds.

6.63. Collect and Organize

We are to describe the origin of surface tension in terms of intermolecular forces.

Analyze

Surface tension is the resistance of a liquid to increase its surface area by moving the molecules of the liquid apart. The greater the intermolecular forces between the molecules in the liquid, the greater the surface tension.

Solve

Molecules in the bulk liquid are "pulled" by all the other liquid molecules surrounding them, and they are therefore "suspended" in the bulk liquid; their intermolecular forces suspend them by pulling on all sides and directions. Molecules on the surface of a liquid, however, are pulled only by molecules under and beside them by the intermolecular forces between them, creating a tight film of molecules on the surface that we call surface tension.

Think about It

When the surface tension is greater than the force of gravity on a small object placed on top of water, the object floats.

6.65. Collect and Organize

We are to explain why methanol boils at a lower temperature than water (64.7°C versus 100°C) even though methanol has a larger molar mass than water (32.04 g/mol versus 18.02 g/mol).

Analyze

Both the methanol and water are held together in the condensed phases (liquid and solid) by weak van der Waals forces and hydrogen bonds.

Solve

Although the dispersion forces between methanol molecules are greater than those between water molecules because methanol has more electrons and greater molar mass, water can form two hydrogen bonds compared with methanol's one hydrogen bond. This greater number of stronger interactions between water molecules raises the boiling point of water above that of methanol.

Think about It
As we add carbons to the alcohol chain for the series R—OH, the boiling point increases because of increases in the van der Waals forces between the molecules.

$$CH_3OH \ < \ CH_3CH_2OH < CH_3CH_2CH_2OH < CH_3CH_2CH_2CH_2OH$$
bp 64.7°C   bp 78.4°C   bp 97.2°C   bp 117.7°C

6.67. **Collect and Organize**
To explain why the boiling point of CH_2F_2 is lower than that of CH_2Cl_2 despite the greater dipole moment of CH_2F_2, we need to consider all the intermolecular forces that act between the molecules in each substance.

Analyze
Both molecules are polar, so dipole–dipole interactions are present in each substance. Weak dispersion forces are also present between the molecules. These dispersion forces are greater for CH_2Cl_2 because chlorine has more electrons and is more polarizable than fluorine.

Solve
The substance with the higher boiling point is that with the larger sum of intermolecular forces. Here, the greater dispersion forces of CH_2Cl_2 add to the dipole–dipole interactions to give stronger intermolecular forces between the CH_2Cl_2 molecules than those of CH_2F_2 molecules. Also, the molar mass of CH_2Cl_2 is higher than that of CH_2F_2, so it takes more energy to vaporize.

Think about It
Usually dispersion forces are so much weaker that they do not significantly add to the strength of the dominant intermolecular force between molecules. In this problem, we see a clear example where considering dispersion forces is necessary.

6.69. **Collect and Organize**
Using a phase diagram for water, we can determine whether the sublimation point of ice increases or decreases as the pressure is increased.

Analyze
In the phase diagram, the solid–vapor phase boundary slopes up to the right.

Solve
From the slope of the solid–vapor phase boundary, we see that as pressure increases, the temperature at which ice sublimes increases.

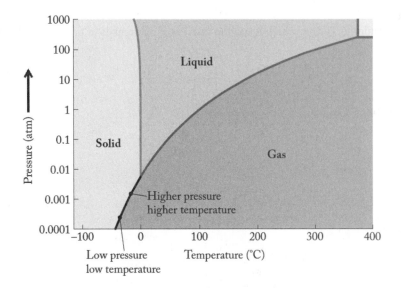

Think about It

With increased pressure, fewer water molecules enter the gas phase from the solid phase. This is also true for the liquid–vapor transition: as pressure increases, the boiling point increases.

6.71. Collect and Organize

Given that the melting point of hydrogen is at a higher temperature than its triple point, we are to determine whether H_2 expands or contracts upon freezing.

Analyze

If the triple point is at a lower temperature than the melting point, then the solid–liquid phase boundary must slope up and to the right in the phase diagram. This positive slope means that the solid phase has a higher density than the liquid phase.

Solve

Hydrogen contracts as it freezes because the phase diagram tells us that the solid phase is denser than the liquid phase.

Think about It

At very high pressures, solid hydrogen forms, in which the H—H bond of the diatomic molecule no longer exists and the solid hydrogen behaves like a metal.

6.73. Collect and Organize

From among the four molecules shown we are to choose the one that would be soluble in both water and octanol.

Analyze

For a substance to dissolve well in both water and octanol, it should have both hydrophilic and hydrophobic groups. Hydrophilic groups are groups that might form hydrogen bonds with water or have strong bond dipoles. Hydrophobic groups are groups that are nonpolar.

Solve

(a) This molecule has few polar groups and mostly is dominated by its nonpolar carbon–hydrogen regions.
(b) This molecule has a balance of polar (–COOH and –NH₂) groups with nonpolar carbon–hydrogen bonds.
(c) This molecule is overall nonpolar; it is very symmetrical despite its polar C—F bonds.
(d) This molecule is dominated by polar OH groups with fewer nonpolar regions.
Because (b) has a balance of hydrophilic and hydrophobic groups, we expect this molecule to have similar solubility in water and in octanol.

Think about It

Molecule (c) is similar to Teflon, which is used to coat cooking utensils to prevent foods from sticking.

$$\left(\begin{array}{cc} F & F \\ | & | \\ -C-C- \\ | & | \\ F & F \end{array}\right)_n$$

CHAPTER 7 | Stoichiometry: Mass Relationships and Chemical Reactions

7.1. Collect and Organize

For each molecule shown in Figure P7.1, we are to write empirical and molecular formulas to determine for which molecule(s) the empirical formula differs from the molecular formula.

Analyze

A molecular formula provides the number of each kind of atom in a molecule of the substance. An empirical formula is the lowest whole-number ratio of the atoms present in the substance.

Solve

(a) Molecular formula: N_2O_5; empirical formula: N_2O_5
(b) Molecular formula: N_2O_4; empirical formula: NO_2
(c) Molecular formula: NO; empirical formula: NO
(d) Molecular formula: N_2O_3; empirical formula: N_2O_3
(e) Molecular formula: NO_2; empirical formula: NO_2
Therefore, the formula for which the molecular formula differs from the empirical formula is (b) N_2O_4.

Think about It

For NO_2 and N_2O_4, the empirical formula is the same.

7.3. Collect and Organize

This exercise has us interpret diagrams (Figure P7.3) drawn from a molecular perspective in order to write a chemical reaction that includes an indication of the state of the substances (solid, liquid, or gas).

Analyze

When the atoms are isolated, they are written as atomic species. If the atoms are bound to each other, they are in the form of molecular species. Any representation of the substances that has a high degree of order (all molecules lined up) and a shape independent of the container represents the solid phase. Representations with less order that conform to the shape of the container show the liquid phase (molecules lined up with some order). Representations with a random distribution of the substances that fill the container indicate the gas phase.

Solve

(a) Four atoms of X (red spheres) and four atoms of Y (blue spheres), both in the gas phase, are on the reactant side of the equation (left of the arrow). On the product side (right of the arrow), four gaseous molecules of XY (red–blue) are present. Therefore, the chemical equation reads

$$4\ X(g) + 4\ Y(g) \rightarrow 4\ XY(g)$$

(b) Four atoms of X (red spheres) and four atoms of Y (blue spheres), both in the gas phase, are on the reactant side of the equation. On the product side, four solid molecules of XY (red–blue) are present. Therefore, the chemical equation reads

$$4\ X(g) + 4\ Y(g) \rightarrow 4\ XY(s)$$

(c) Four atoms of X (red spheres) and four atoms of Y (blue spheres), both in the gas phase, are on the reactant side of the equation. On the product side, four gaseous substances are present: two molecules of XY_2 and two atoms of X. Therefore, the chemical equation reads

$$4\ X(g) + 4\ Y(g) \rightarrow 2\ XY_2(g) + 2\ X(g)$$

(d) Four molecules of X_2 (red spheres bonded together) and four molecules of Y_2 (blue spheres bonded together), both in the gas phase, are on the reactant side of the equation. On the product side, eight gaseous molecules of XY (red–blue) are present. Therefore, the chemical equation reads

$$4\ X_2(g) + 4\ Y_2(g) \rightarrow 8\ XY(g)$$

Think about It

In parts a, b, and d when the reactants react, no leftover atoms of the reactants are present; however, in part c two atoms of X are left over in the reaction on the product side to make XY_2. Here, Y is the limiting reactant, and the number of Y atoms ultimately determines how many molecules of XY_2 will form from the reactant mixture.

7.5. Collect and Organize

Of the four hydrocarbons shown we are to identify those that have the same percent composition.

Analyze

Molecules that have the same empirical formula will have the same percent composition.

Solve

(a) Empirical formula of C_6H_6 is CH.
(b) Empirical formula of C_2H_4 is CH_2.
(c) Empirical formula of C_3H_8 is C_3H_8.
(d) Empirical formula of C_6H_{12} is CH_2.
Therefore, (b) and (d) have the same percent composition of C and H.

Think about It

Another molecule that would have the same percent composition as C_2H_4 and C_6H_{12} would be C_4H_8.

7.7. Collect and Organize

Considering a reaction with the balanced equation

$$A + 2B \rightarrow C$$

in which 1.00 g of A is reacted with 4.00 g of B, we are to determine how many grams of C is formed.

Analyze

For this reaction we can assume that all the reactants form the product C.

Solve

By the law of conservation of mass, we can neither gain nor lose mass in a chemical reaction; therefore, when all of A reacts with all of B, we will have 1.00 + 4.00 = 5.00 g of product C.

Think about It

If we did not have complete reaction between A and B to form C, we would still have a total mass of A, B, and C of 5.00 g.

7.9. Collect and Organize

Considering a reaction with the balanced equation from question 7.8,

$$A + B \rightarrow C + D$$

we are to identify the reactant or product that would have the largest molar mass.

Analyze

The molar mass is the mass of the substance divided by the number of moles of that substance. Although we do not know the mole amount of each substance present in their masses used in the equation, we can use the fact that each one reacts in the equation in equimolar quantities.

Solve

If all are used or produced in the equation in equimolar amounts, then the reactant or product with the highest mass is the one with the highest molar mass. This is reactant B, for which the reaction uses 4.00 g.

Think about It

From the balanced chemical equation we get the information of how many moles of reactant reacts to form how many moles of product, not the number of grams.

7.11. Collect and Organize

If we alter the reaction conditions we can obtain either NO or NO_2 from the reaction of N_2 with O_2. In this problem we are asked to determine how many grams of O_2 would be produced from y grams of N_2 to form NO_2 if we know that x grams of O_2 reacts with y grams of N_2 to form the other product, NO.

Analyze

The ratios of the mass of reactants for the formation of these two products are
$$y \text{ grams } N_2 + x \text{ grams } O_2 \rightarrow NO$$
$$y \text{ grams } N_2 + ? \text{ grams } O_2 \rightarrow NO_2$$

Solve

Because twice as many oxygen atoms are present in NO_2 than in NO, we would need $2x$ grams of O_2 to react with y grams of N_2 to give NO_2.

Think about It

This is an application of the law of multiple proportions.

7.13. Collect and Organize

Given two formulas for oxides of iron, FeO and Fe_2O_3, we are to determine how much more oxygen would be required to combine with the same mass of iron used to form FeO.

Analyze

We have to be careful here: the ratio of iron to oxygen in FeO is 1:1, whereas the same ratio is 2:3 in Fe_2O_3.

Solve

We would need 3/2, or 1.5 times, as much oxygen for the reaction to form Fe_2O_3.

Think about It

You could also say that we need 50% more oxygen for the reaction.

7.15. Collect and Organize

We are asked whether the number of atoms in the reactants in a balanced chemical equation must equal the number of atoms in the products.

Analyze

A balanced chemical reaction follows the law of conservation of mass. This means that for each and every atom present in a reaction, we balance the number of a particular kind of atom (element) in reactants and products.

Solve

The number of atoms of reactants in a balanced chemical equation *must always* equal the number of atoms of the products.

Think about It

Elements in compounds are rearranged in chemical equations, and we may have fewer or more moles present after a reaction. For example, in the balanced equation for the production of ammonia,
$$N_2(g) + 3 H_2(g) \rightarrow 2 NH_3(g)$$
four moles of reactants produces 2 mol of products. Therefore, the number of moles of reactants many not equal the number of moles of products.

7.17. Collect and Organize

For the combustion reaction of methane
$$CH_4(g) + 2 O_2(g) \rightarrow CO_2(g) + 2 H_2O(g)$$
we are to determine the number of moles of water vapor produced when 1 mol of methane is used in the reaction.

Analyze

From the balanced equation we see that the ratio of methane consumed to water produced is 1:2.

Solve

For every mole of methane combusted, 2 mol of water vapor will be produced.

Think about It

Likewise from the balanced equation, for every mole of methane burned, 1 mol of carbon dioxide is produced.

7.19. Collect and Organize

To balance these chemical reactions we use the three steps described in the textbook.

Analyze

To balance each equation we first write the unbalanced equation by using the chemical formulas of the reactants and products and take inventory of the atoms in the reactants and products. Next, we balance an element that is present in only one reactant and product, again taking the inventory of atoms. Finally, we balance the other elements present by placing coefficients in front of the species in the reaction so that the number of the atoms for each element is equal on both sides of the equation. If any fractional coefficients are present, we multiply the entire equation through to eliminate all fractions.

Solve

(a) The unbalanced reaction is
$$N_2(g) + O_2(g) \rightarrow NO(g)$$
Atoms: $\quad 2\,N + 2\,O \rightarrow 1\,N + 1\,O$

We can best start by balancing the N atoms by placing a 2 in front of NO on the right-hand side.
$$N_2(g) + O_2(g) \rightarrow 2\,NO(g)$$
Atoms: $\quad 2\,N + 2\,O \rightarrow 2\,N + 2\,O$

The equation is now balanced.

(b) The unbalanced reaction is
$$N_2(g) + O_2(g) \rightarrow N_2O(g)$$
Atoms: $\quad 2\,N + 2\,O \rightarrow 2\,N + 1\,O$

We start by balancing the O atoms by placing a 2 in front of N_2O on the right-hand side.
$$N_2(g) + O_2(g) \rightarrow 2\,N_2O(g)$$
Atoms: $\quad 2\,N + 2\,O \rightarrow 4\,N + 2\,O$

We next can balance the N atoms by placing a 2 in front of N_2 on the left-hand side.
$$2\,N_2(g) + O_2(g) \rightarrow 2\,N_2O(g)$$
Atoms: $\quad 4\,N + 2\,O \rightarrow 4\,N + 2\,O$

The equation is now balanced.

(c) The unbalanced reaction is
$$NO(g) + NO_3(g) \rightarrow NO_2(g)$$
Atoms: $\quad 2\,N + 4\,O \rightarrow 1\,N + 2\,O$

We can start by balancing the N atoms by placing a 2 in front of NO_2 on the right-hand side.
$$NO(g) + NO_3(g) \rightarrow 2\,NO_2(g)$$
Atoms: $\quad 2\,N + 4\,O \rightarrow 2\,N + 4\,O$

The equation is now balanced.

(d) The unbalanced reaction is
$$NO(g) + O_2(g) + H_2O(\ell) \rightarrow HNO_2(g)$$

Atoms: $1\,N + 4\,O + 2\,H \rightarrow 1\,N + 2\,O + 1\,H$

We can start by balancing the H atoms by placing a coefficient of 2 in front of HNO_2 on the right-hand side.

$$NO(g) + O_2(g) + H_2O(\ell) \rightarrow 2\,HNO_2(g)$$

Atoms: $1\,N + 4\,O + 2\,H \rightarrow 2\,N + 4\,O + 2\,H$

We can then balance the N atoms by placing a coefficient of 2 in front of NO on the left-hand side.

$$2\,NO(g) + O_2(g) + H_2O(\ell) \rightarrow 2\,HNO_2(g)$$

Atoms: $2\,N + 5\,O + 2\,H \rightarrow 2\,N + 4\,O + 2\,H$

We can then balance the O atoms by placing a coefficient of $\frac{1}{2}$ in front of O_2 on the left-hand side.

$$2\,NO(g) + 1/2\,O_2(g) + H_2O(\ell) \rightarrow 2\,HNO_2(g)$$

Atoms: $2\,N + 4\,O + 2\,H \rightarrow 2\,N + 4\,O + 2\,H$

To eliminate the fractional coefficients we multiply all the coefficients by 2.

$$4\,NO(g) + O_2(g) + 2\,H_2O(\ell) \rightarrow 4\,HNO_2(g)$$

Atoms: $4\,N + 8\,O + 4\,H \rightarrow 4\,N + 8\,O + 4\,H$

The equation is now balanced.

Think about It

Many gaseous oxides of nitrogen exist because nitrogen can occur in compounds with several different charges. In these reactions we see nitrogen's charges as 0 (N_2), 1+ (N_2O), 2+ (NO), 4+ (NO_2), and 6+ (NO_3).

7.21. Collect and Organize

We are asked to write balanced chemical equations for the reactions described. Because we are given only the names, not the chemical formulas for the reactants and products, we have to be sure to correctly write the formulas to balance the equations. To balance these chemical reactions we use the three steps described in the textbook.

Analyze

To balance each equation we first write the unbalanced equation by using the chemical formulas of the reactants and products and take inventory of the atoms in the reactants and products. Next, we balance an element that is present in only one reactant and product, again taking the inventory of atoms. Finally, we balance the other elements present by placing coefficients in front of the species in the reaction so that the number of the atoms for each element is equal on both sides of the equation. If any fractional coefficients are present, we multiply the entire equation through to eliminate all fractions.

Solve

(a) The unbalanced reaction is

$$N_2O_5(g) + Na(s) \rightarrow NaNO_3(s) + NO_2(g)$$

Atoms: $2\,N + 5\,O + 1\,Na \rightarrow 2\,N + 5\,O + 1\,Na$

The numbers of Na, N, and O atoms on the reactants and products side are all equal. This reaction is already balanced.

(b) The unbalanced reaction is

$$N_2O_4(g) + H_2O\,(\ell) \rightarrow HNO_3(aq) + HNO_2(aq)$$

Atoms: $2\,N + 5\,O + 2\,H \rightarrow 2\,N + 5\,O + 2\,H$

The numbers of N, O, and H atoms on the reactants and products side are all equal. This reaction is already balanced.

(c) The unbalanced reaction is

$$NO(g) \rightarrow N_2O(g) + NO_2(g)$$

Atoms: $1\,N + 1\,O \rightarrow 3\,N + 3\,O$

We can start by balancing the N atoms. We can do this by placing a 3 in front of NO on the left-hand side.

$$3\,NO(g) \rightarrow N_2O(g) + NO_2(g)$$

Atoms: $\quad 3\,N + 3\,O \rightarrow 3\,N + 3\,O$

This also resulted in the O atoms being balanced. The equation is now balanced.

Think about It

The first two chemical reactions were balanced as written, and we did not need to change the coefficients. When writing chemical equations, however, making sure that the equation is balanced is always best.

7.23. **Collect and Organize**

For the combustion of several hydrocarbons we are to complete the equations and balance the equations.

Analyze

In the combustion of hydrocarbons, the only products are carbon dioxide and water. To balance the reactions we will use the three steps described in the textbook.

Solve

(a) The unbalanced reaction is

$$C_3H_8(g) + O_2(g) \rightarrow CO_2(g) + H_2O(g)$$

Atoms: $\quad 3\,C + 8\,H + 2\,O \rightarrow 1\,C + 2\,H + 3\,O$

We can start by balancing the C atoms, as they appear in only one reactant and product, by placing a 3 in front of CO_2 on the right-hand side.

$$C_3H_8(g) + O_2(g) \rightarrow 3\,CO_2(g) + H_2O(g)$$

Atoms: $\quad 3\,C + 8\,H + 2\,O \rightarrow 3\,C + 2\,H + 7\,O$

Next we can balance the H atoms by placing a 4 in front of H_2O on the right-hand side.

$$C_3H_8(g) + O_2(g) \rightarrow 3\,CO_2(g) + 4\,H_2O(g)$$

Atoms: $\quad 3\,C + 8\,H + 2\,O \rightarrow 3\,C + 8\,H + 10\,O$

Finally we can balance the O atoms by placing a 5 in front of O_2 on the left-hand side.

$$C_3H_8(g) + 5\,O_2(g) \rightarrow 3\,CO_2(g) + 4\,H_2O(g)$$

Atoms: $\quad 3\,C + 8\,H + 10\,O \rightarrow 3\,C + 8\,H + 10\,O$

The equation is now balanced.

(b) The unbalanced reaction is

$$C_4H_{10}(g) + O_2(g) \rightarrow CO_2(g) + H_2O(g)$$

Atoms: $\quad 4\,C + 10\,H + 2\,O \rightarrow 1\,C + 2\,H + 3\,O$

We can start by balancing the C atoms, as they appear in only one reactant and product, by placing a 4 in front of CO_2 on the right-hand side.

$$C_4H_{10}(g) + O_2(g) \rightarrow 4\,CO_2(g) + H_2O(g)$$

Atoms: $\quad 4\,C + 10\,H + 2\,O \rightarrow 4\,C + 2\,H + 9\,O$

Next we can balance the H atoms by placing a 5 in front of H_2O on the right-hand side.

$$C_4H_{10}(g) + O_2(g) \rightarrow 4\,CO_2(g) + 5\,H_2O(g)$$

Atoms: $\quad 4\,C + 10\,H + 2\,O \rightarrow 4\,C + 10\,H + 13\,O$

Finally we can balance the O atoms by placing 13/2 in front of O_2 on the left-hand side.

$$C_4H_{10}(g) + 13/2\,O_2(g) \rightarrow 4\,CO_2(g) + 5\,H_2O(g)$$

Atoms: $\quad 4\,C + 10\,H + 13\,O \rightarrow 4\,C + 10\,H + 13\,O$

To eliminate the fractional coefficients we multiply all the coefficients by 2.

$$2\,C_4H_{10}(g) + 13\,O_2(g) \rightarrow 8\,CO_2(g) + 10\,H_2O(g)$$

Atoms: $\quad 8\,C + 20\,H + 26\,O \rightarrow 8\,C + 20\,H + 26\,O$

The equation is now balanced.

(c) The unbalanced reaction is
$$C_6H_6(\ell) + O_2(g) \rightarrow CO_2(g) + H_2O(g)$$
Atoms: $6\,C + 6\,H + 2\,O \rightarrow 1\,C + 2\,H + 3\,O$

We can start by balancing the C atoms, as they appear in only one reactant and product, by placing a 6 in front of CO_2 on the right-hand side.
$$C_6H_6(\ell) + O_2(g) \rightarrow 6\,CO_2(g) + H_2O(g)$$
Atoms: $6\,C + 6\,H + 2\,O \rightarrow 6\,C + 2\,H + 13\,O$

Next we can balance the H atoms by placing a 3 in front of H_2O on the right-hand side.
$$C_6H_6(\ell) + O_2(g) \rightarrow 6\,CO_2(g) + 3\,H_2O(g)$$
Atoms: $6\,C + 6\,H + 2\,O \rightarrow 6\,C + 6\,H + 15\,O$

Finally we can balance the O atoms by placing 15/2 in front of O_2 on the left-hand side.
$$C_6H_6(\ell) + 15/2\,O_2(g) \rightarrow 6\,CO_2(g) + 3\,H_2O(g)$$
Atoms: $6\,C + 6\,H + 15\,O \rightarrow 6\,C + 6\,H + 15\,O$

To eliminate the fractional coefficients we multiply all the coefficients by 2.
$$2\,C_6H_6(\ell) + 15\,O_2(g) \rightarrow 12\,CO_2(g) + 6\,H_2O(g)$$
Atoms: $12\,C + 12\,H + 30\,O \rightarrow 12\,C + 12\,H + 30\,O$

The equation is now balanced.

(d) The unbalanced reaction is
$$C_8H_{18}(\ell) + O_2(g) \rightarrow CO_2(g) + H_2O(g)$$
Atoms: $8\,C + 18\,H + 2\,O \rightarrow 1\,C + 2\,H + 3\,O$

We can start by balancing the C atoms, as they appear in only one reactant and product, by placing an 8 in front of CO_2 on the right-hand side.
$$C_8H_{18}(\ell) + O_2(g) \rightarrow 8\,CO_2(g) + H_2O(g)$$
Atoms: $8\,C + 18\,H + 2\,O \rightarrow 8\,C + 2\,H + 17\,O$

Next we can balance the H atoms by placing a 9 in front of H_2O on the right-hand side.
$$C_8H_{18}(\ell) + O_2(g) \rightarrow 8\,CO_2(g) + 9\,H_2O(g)$$
Atoms: $8\,C + 18\,H + 2\,O \rightarrow 8\,C + 18\,H + 25\,O$

Finally we can balance the O atoms by placing 25/2 in front of O_2 on the left-hand side.
$$C_8H_{18}(\ell) + 25/2\,O_2(g) \rightarrow 8\,CO_2(g) + 9\,H_2O(g)$$
Atoms: $8\,C + 18\,H + 25\,O \rightarrow 8\,C + 18\,H + 25\,O$

To eliminate the fractional coefficients we multiply all the coefficients by 2.
$$2\,C_8H_{18}(\ell) + 25\,O_2(g) \rightarrow 16\,CO_2(g) + 18\,H_2O(g)$$
Atoms: $16\,C + 36\,H + 50\,O \rightarrow 16\,C + 36\,H + 50\,O$

The equation is now balanced.

Think about It
The higher the carbon content of the hydrocarbon, the greater the moles of CO_2 released per mole of the hydrocarbon.

7.25. Collect and Organize
For the combustion of several gaseous hydrocarbons for which we are given the structures, we are to complete the equations and balance the equations.

Analyze
In the combustion of hydrocarbons, the only products are carbon dioxide and water. To balance the reactions we will use the three steps described in the textbook.

Solve

(a) The unbalanced reaction is
$$C_2H_4(g) + O_2(g) \rightarrow CO_2(g) + H_2O(g)$$
Atoms: $2\,C + 4\,H + 2\,O \rightarrow 1\,C + 2\,H + 3\,O$

We can start by balancing the C atoms, as they appear in only one reactant and product, by placing a 2 in front of CO_2 on the right-hand side.
$$C_2H_4(g) + O_2(g) \rightarrow 2\,CO_2(g) + H_2O(g)$$
Atoms: $2\,C + 4\,H + 2\,O \rightarrow 2\,C + 2\,H + 5\,O$

Next we can balance the H atoms by placing a 2 in front of H_2O on the right-hand side.
$$C_2H_4(g) + O_2(g) \rightarrow 2\,CO_2(g) + 2\,H_2O(g)$$
Atoms: $2\,C + 4\,H + 2\,O \rightarrow 2\,C + 4\,H + 6\,O$

Finally we can balance the O atoms by placing a 3 in front of O_2 on the left-hand side.
$$C_2H_4(g) + 3\,O_2(g) \rightarrow 2\,CO_2(g) + 2\,H_2O(g)$$
Atoms: $2\,C + 4\,H + 6\,O \rightarrow 2\,C + 4\,H + 6\,O$

The equation is now balanced.

(b) The unbalanced reaction is
$$C_3H_6(g) + O_2(g) \rightarrow CO_2(g) + H_2O(g)$$
Atoms: $3\,C + 6\,H + 2\,O \rightarrow 1\,C + 2\,H + 3\,O$

We can start by balancing the C atoms, as they appear in only one reactant and product, by placing a 3 in front of CO_2 on the right-hand side.
$$C_3H_6(g) + O_2(g) \rightarrow 3\,CO_2(g) + H_2O(g)$$
Atoms: $3\,C + 6\,H + 2\,O \rightarrow 3\,C + 2\,H + 7\,O$

Next we can balance the H atoms by placing a 3 in front of H_2O on the right-hand side.
$$C_3H_6(g) + O_2(g) \rightarrow 3\,CO_2(g) + 3\,H_2O(g)$$
Atoms: $3\,C + 6\,H + 2\,O \rightarrow 3\,C + 6\,H + 9\,O$

Finally we can balance the O atoms by placing 9/2 in front of O_2 on the left-hand side.
$$C_3H_6(g) + 9/2\,O_2(g) \rightarrow 3\,CO_2(g) + 3\,H_2O(g)$$
Atoms: $3\,C + 6\,H + 9\,O \rightarrow 3\,C + 6\,H + 9\,O$

To eliminate the fractional coefficients we multiply all the coefficients by 2.
$$2\,C_3H_6(g) + 9\,O_2(g) \rightarrow 6\,CO_2(g) + 6\,H_2O(g)$$
Atoms: $6\,C + 12\,H + 18\,O \rightarrow 6\,C + 12\,H + 18\,O$

The equation is now balanced.

(c) The unbalanced reaction is
$$C_4H_{10}(g) + O_2(g) \rightarrow CO_2(g) + H_2O(g)$$
Atoms: $4\,C + 10\,H + 2\,O \rightarrow 1\,C + 2\,H + 3\,O$

We can start by balancing the C atoms, as they appear in only one reactant and product, by placing a 4 in front of CO_2 on the right-hand side.
$$C_4H_{10}(g) + O_2(g) \rightarrow 4\,CO_2(g) + H_2O(g)$$
Atoms: $4\,C + 10\,H + 2\,O \rightarrow 4\,C + 2\,H + 9\,O$

Next we can balance the H atoms by placing a 5 in front of H_2O on the right-hand side.
$$C_4H_{10}(g) + O_2(g) \rightarrow 4\,CO_2(g) + 5\,H_2O(g)$$
Atoms: $4\,C + 10\,H + 2\,O \rightarrow 4\,C + 10\,H + 13\,O$

Finally we can balance the O atoms by placing 13/2 in front of O_2 on the left-hand side.
$$C_4H_{10}(g) + 13/2\,O_2(g) \rightarrow 4\,CO_2(g) + 5\,H_2O(g)$$

Atoms: $4\,C + 10\,H + 13\,O \rightarrow 4\,C + 10\,H + 13\,O$

To eliminate the fractional coefficients we multiply all the coefficients by 2.

$$2\,C_4H_{10}(g) + 13\,O_2(g) \rightarrow 8\,CO_2(g) + 10\,H_2O(g)$$

Atoms: $8\,C + 20\,H + 26\,O \rightarrow 8\,C + 20\,H + 26\,O$

The equation is now balanced.

(d) The unbalanced reaction is

$$C_4H_8(g) + O_2(g) \rightarrow CO_2(g) + H_2O(g)$$

Atoms: $4\,C + 8\,H + 2\,O \rightarrow 1\,C + 2\,H + 3\,O$

We can start by balancing the C atoms, as they appear in only one reactant and product, by placing a 4 in front of CO_2 on the right-hand side.

$$C_4H_8(g) + O_2(g) \rightarrow 4\,CO_2(g) + H_2O(g)$$

Atoms: $4\,C + 8\,H + 2\,O \rightarrow 4\,C + 2\,H + 9\,O$

Next we can balance the H atoms by placing a 4 in front of H_2O on the right-hand side.

$$C_4H_8(g) + O_2(g) \rightarrow 4\,CO_2(g) + 4\,H_2O(g)$$

Atoms: $4\,C + 8\,H + 2\,O \rightarrow 4\,C + 8\,H + 12\,O$

Finally we can balance the O atoms by placing a 6 in front of O_2 on the left-hand side.

$$C_4H_8(g) + 6\,O_2(g) \rightarrow 4\,CO_2(g) + 4\,H_2O(g)$$

Atoms: $4\,C + 8\,H + 12\,O \rightarrow 4\,C + 8\,H + 12\,O$

The equation is now balanced.

Think about It
Be careful in counting the atoms from a ball-and-stick structure. It is easy to miss atoms and arrive at the wrong molecular formula.

7.27. **Collect and Organize**
To balance the chemical equations we use the three steps described in the textbook.

Analyze
To balance each equation we first write the unbalanced equation by using the chemical formulas of the reactants and products and take inventory of the atoms in the reactants and products. Next, we balance an element that is present in only one reactant and product, again taking the inventory of atoms. Finally, we balance the other elements present by placing coefficients in front of the species in the reaction so that the number of the atoms for each element is equal on both sides of the equation. If any fractional coefficients are present, we multiply the entire equation through to eliminate all fractions.

Solve
(a) For the reaction of sulfur dioxide with oxygen to form sulfur trioxide, the unbalanced reaction is

$$SO_2(g) + O_2(g) \rightarrow SO_3(g)$$

Atoms: $1\,S + 4\,O \rightarrow 1\,S + 3\,O$

The sulfur atoms are already balanced. To balance the O atoms, therefore, we place $\frac{1}{2}$ as the coefficient before O_2 on the left-hand side of the equation.

$$SO_2(g) + \tfrac{1}{2}\,O_2(g) \rightarrow SO_3(g)$$

Atoms: $1\,S + 3\,O \rightarrow 1\,S + 3\,O$

To eliminate the fractional coefficients we multiply all the coefficients by 2.

$$2\,SO_2(g) + O_2(g) \rightarrow 2\,SO_3(g)$$

Atoms: $1\,S + 6\,O \rightarrow 2\,S + 6\,O$

The equation is now balanced.

(b) For the reaction of hydrogen sulfide with oxygen to form sulfur dioxide and water, the unbalanced reaction is

$$H_2S(g) + O_2(g) \rightarrow SO_2(g) + H_2O(g)$$
Atoms: $2\,H + 1\,S + 2\,O \rightarrow 2\,H + 1\,S + 3\,O$

To balance the O atoms, therefore, we place $\frac{3}{2}$ as the coefficient before O_2 on the left-hand side of the equation.

$$H_2S(g) + 3/2\,O_2(g) \rightarrow SO_2(g) + H_2O(g)$$
Atoms: $2\,H + 1\,S + 3\,O \rightarrow 2\,H + 1\,S + 3\,O$

To eliminate the fractional coefficients we multiply all the coefficients by 2.

$$2H_2S(g) + 3\,O_2(g) \rightarrow 2\,SO_2(g) + 2\,H_2O(g)$$
Atoms: $4\,H + 2\,S + 6\,O \rightarrow 4\,H + 2\,S + 6\,O$

The equation is now balanced.

(c) For the reaction of hydrogen sulfide with sulfur dioxide to form sulfur and water, the unbalanced reaction is

$$H_2S(g) + SO_2(g) \rightarrow S_8(s) + H_2O(g)$$
Atoms: $2\,H + 2\,S + 2\,O \rightarrow 2\,H + 8\,S + 1\,O$

We can best start by balancing the oxygen atoms, as they appear in only one reactant and product, by placing a 2 in front of H_2O on the products side.

$$H_2S(g) + SO_2(g) \rightarrow S_8(s) + 2\,H_2O(g)$$
Atoms: $2\,H + 2\,S + 2\,O \rightarrow 4\,H + 8\,S + 2\,O$

To balance the H atoms, therefore, we place 2 as the coefficient before H_2S on the left-hand side of the equation.

$$2\,H_2S(g) + SO_2(g) \rightarrow S_8(s) + 2\,H_2O(g)$$
Atoms: $4\,H + 3\,S + 2\,O \rightarrow 4\,H + 8\,S + 2\,O$

To balance the sulfur atoms, we place a coefficient of $\frac{3}{8}$ in front of S_8 on the products side.

$$2\,H_2S(g) + SO_2(g) \rightarrow 3/8\,S_8(s) + 2\,H_2O(g)$$
Atoms: $4\,H + 3\,S + 2\,O \rightarrow 4\,H + 3\,S + 2\,O$

To eliminate the fractional coefficients we multiply all the coefficients by 8.

$$16\,H_2S(g) + 8\,SO_2(g) \rightarrow 3\,S_8(s) + 16\,H_2O(g)$$
Atoms: $32\,H + 24\,S + 16\,O \rightarrow 32\,H + 24\,S + 16\,O$

The equation is now balanced.

Think about It
Part c has large coefficients because of the formation of S_8, the most stable elemental form of sulfur.

7.29. **Collect and Organize**
We compare two valid ways to write a balanced equation for the combustion of ethane, and we decide whether the form of the balanced equation matters when calculating the amount of product formed from a given amount of a reactant.

Analyze
A balanced chemical reaction has the same number of a particular kind of atom (element) in the reactants as in the products.

Solve
Both equations give the same numerical answer for the amount of CO_2 produced in the reaction for a given amount of C_2H_6 because in both the molar ratio of CO_2 to C_2H_6 is 2:1.

Think about It
When we use balanced equations for stoichiometric calculations, the ratio of reactants and products to each other is important, not the actual numerical value of the coefficients.

7.31. **Collect and Organize**
We need to convert the given mass of carbon by which emissions would be reduced first to moles of carbon, then to the mass of carbon dioxide.

Analyze
We can convert the mass of carbon to moles by dividing by the average molar mass of carbon after converting the mass of carbon to grams from kilograms (1000 g = 1 kg). Because 1 mol of carbon dioxide contains 1 mol of carbon, the moles of carbon are equal to the moles of carbon dioxide. To find the mass of CO_2 in grams, we need only multiply the moles of CO_2 by the molar mass of CO_2 and then convert that mass (which will be in grams) to kilograms of CO_2.

Solve

(a) 5.4×10^9 kg C $\times \dfrac{1000 \text{ g}}{1 \text{ kg}} \times \dfrac{1 \text{ mol C}}{12.01 \text{ g}} = 4.5 \times 10^{11}$ mol C = mol CO_2

(b) 4.5×10^{11} mol $CO_2 \times \dfrac{44.01 \text{ g}}{1 \text{ mol } CO_2} \times \dfrac{1 \text{ kg}}{1000 \text{ g}} = 2.0 \times 10^{10}$ kg CO_2

Think about It
The mass of CO_2 emissions that would be reduced is greater than the mass of carbon burned. The molar mass of carbon dioxide is greater, so the mass of a certain molar amount of carbon dioxide is greater than that of the same molar amount of carbon.

7.33. **Collect and Organize**
To calculate the amount of CO_2 produced from the decomposition of 25.0 g of $NaHCO_3$ we need the balanced chemical equation to use in calculating the molar ratio of the CO_2 produced from a given mass of $NaHCO_3$.

Analyze
We know that the reactant for the balanced equation is $NaHCO_3$ and that the products are Na_2CO_3, H_2O, and CO_2. After we balance the equation, we can use the ratio of $NaHCO_3$ to CO_2 to find the moles of CO_2 from the moles of $NaHCO_3$ (found from the mass by dividing by the molar mass, 84.01 g/mol). From the moles of CO_2, we can find the mass of CO_2 produced by using 44.01 g/mol for the molar mass of CO_2.

Solve
(a) The unbalanced reaction is

$$NaHCO_3(s) \rightarrow CO_2(g) + H_2O(g) + Na_2CO_3(s)$$

Atoms: $1 \text{ Na} + 1 \text{ H} + 1 \text{ C} + 3 \text{ O} \rightarrow 2 \text{ Na} + 2 \text{ H} + 2 \text{ C} + 6 \text{ O}$

We notice here that the number of atoms in the products is always twice that in the reactants.
We can best start balancing the atoms by placing a 2 in front of $NaHCO_3$ on the left-hand side.

$$2 NaHCO_3(s) \rightarrow CO_2(g) + H_2O(g) + Na_2CO_3(s)$$

Atoms: $2 \text{ Na} + 2 \text{ H} + 2 \text{ C} + 6 \text{ O} \rightarrow 2 \text{ Na} + 2 \text{ H} + 2 \text{ C} + 6 \text{ O}$

The equation is now balanced.

(b) $25.0 \text{ g } NaHCO_3 \times \dfrac{1 \text{ mol } NaHCO_3}{84.01 \text{ g}} \times \dfrac{1 \text{ mol } CO_2}{2 \text{ mol } NaHCO_3} \times \dfrac{44.01 \text{ g } CO_2}{1 \text{ mol}} = 6.55 \text{ g } CO_2$

Think about It
The mass of CO_2 produced is quite a bit less than the 25 g of $NaHCO_3$ decomposed not only because the molar mass of CO_2 is lower than that of $NaHCO_3$ but also because for every 1 mol of $NaHCO_3$ decomposed, only ½ mol of CO_2 is produced.

7.35. **Collect and Organize**

We use stoichiometric relationships to calculate the amount of a reactant, $NaAlO_2$, required to produce a given amount of cryolite, Na_3AlF_6.

Analyze

First we need to calculate the moles of Na_3AlF_6 present in 1.00 kg by using 1000 g = 1 kg and the molar mass of Na_3AlF_6 (209.94 g/mol). From that and the 3:1 ratio of $NaAlO_2$ to Na_3AlF_6 in the balanced equation, we can calculate the moles of $NaAlO_2$ required. Finally, we use the molar mass of $NaAlO_2$ (81.97 g/mol) to convert the moles into mass.

Solve

$$1.00 \text{ kg } Na_3AlF_6 \times \frac{1000 \text{ g}}{1 \text{ kg}} \times \frac{1 \text{ mol } Na_3AlF_6}{209.94 \text{ g}} \times \frac{3 \text{ mol } NaAlO_2}{1 \text{ mol } Na_3AlF_6} \times \frac{81.97 \text{ g } NaAlO_2}{1 \text{ mol}} = 1170 \text{ g, or } 1.17 \text{ kg}$$

Think about It

In this reaction we need three times more moles of the reactant $NaAlO_2$ to yield 1 mol of product, Na_3AlF_6. Be careful here. The mass of $NaAlO_2$ required is not three times the mass of the product; the molar relationship is the important factor.

7.37. **Collect and Organize**

We have to determine first the moles of each reactant we have and then calculate the moles and mass of oxygen that 85 g of KO_2 would theoretically produce.

Analyze

We are given the balanced chemical equation for the reaction. For every 4 mol of KO_2 used, 3 mol of O_2 is produced. The molar mass of KO_2 computed from the molar masses of the elements in the periodic table is 71.10 g/mol, and for O_2, the molar mass is 32.00 g/mol.

Solve

The theoretical yield of oxygen from KO_2 is

$$85 \text{ g } KO_2 \times \frac{1 \text{ mol } KO_2}{71.10 \text{ g}} \times \frac{3 \text{ mol } O_2}{4 \text{ mol } KO_2} \times \frac{32.00 \text{ g } O_2}{1 \text{ mol } O_2} = 29 \text{ g } O_2$$

Think about It

Not only was KO_2 present in lower gram masses in the reaction, but it also has a significantly larger molar mass. This means that it is present in the least amount for this reaction. Be careful, though; you must also consider the molar ratio of the reactants to products in the balanced equation.

7.39. **Collect and Organize**

We are given balanced chemical reactions for converting UO_2 into UF_6 to enrich the uranium for use as a nuclear fuel. We are asked to find the mass of HF in the first reaction that will convert 5.00 kg of UO_2 to UF_4. In the second part, we calculate how much final product (UF_6) can be produced from a given mass of starting material, UO_2.

Analyze

For part a we need to find the moles of UO_2 used (from the molar mass of UO_2, 270.03 g/mol) and then use the stoichiometric ratio of UO_2 to HF (1:4) in the balanced equation to find the moles of HF required. From that we can determine the mass of HF needed by using the molar mass of HF (20.01 g/mol). For part b we first find the moles of UO_2 in 850.0 g by using the molar mass. Because 1 mol of UF_4 is produced for every mole of UO_2 reacted and 1 mol of UF_4 is used for every mole of UF_6 produced (ratio of 1:1:1), the moles of UO_2 equals the moles of UF_6 produced. From that result, we can then find the mass of UF_6 produced by using the molar mass of UF_6 (352.02 g/mol).

Solve

(a) $5.00 \text{ kg } UO_2 \times \dfrac{1000 \text{ g}}{1 \text{ kg}} \times \dfrac{1 \text{ mol } UO_2}{270.03 \text{ g}} \times \dfrac{4 \text{ mol HF}}{1 \text{ mol } UO_2} \times \dfrac{20.01 \text{ g}}{1 \text{ mol HF}} = 1480 \text{ g, or } 1.48 \text{ kg HF}$

(b) $850.0 \text{ g } UO_2 \times \dfrac{1 \text{ mol } UO_2}{270.03 \text{ g}} \times \dfrac{1 \text{ mol } UF_6}{1 \text{ mol } UO_2} \times \dfrac{352.02 \text{ g}}{1 \text{ mol } UF_6} = 1110 \text{ g, or } 1.11 \text{ kg } UF_6$

Think about It

Because UF_6 has a higher molar mass, the reaction produces more uranium product (in terms of mass) than the mass of the original reactant. Even though the molar mass of UF_6 is high, it is a volatile liquid and can be "distilled" in large columns to separate the isotopes. The lighter isotope, U-235, is not as heavy as the U-238 isotope and therefore can be enriched at the top of the column.

7.41. Collect and Organize

In converting chalcopyrite ($CuFeS_2$) to copper, we have to take into account that 1 mol of copper atoms is in the formula for this mineral.

Analyze

The problem asks how much copper could be produced from 1.00 kg of the mineral and looks like many other stoichiometry problems. We will have to use the molar mass of the mineral (183.52 g/mol) to find the moles of the mineral. From there, knowing that 1 mol of copper atoms is in 1 mol of the mineral, we can use the molar mass of copper (63.55 g/mol) to calculate the amount of copper that would be produced.

Solve

$$1.00 \text{ kg } CuFeS_2 \times \dfrac{1000 \text{ g}}{1 \text{ kg}} \times \dfrac{1 \text{ mol}}{183.52 \text{ g}} \times \dfrac{1 \text{ mol Cu}}{1 \text{ mol } CuFeS_2} \times \dfrac{63.55 \text{ g Cu}}{1 \text{ mol}} = 346 \text{ g Cu}$$

Think about It

Our calculation tells us that the ore is 34.6% Cu by mass.

7.43. Collect and Organize

We are asked to distinguish between *empirical formula* and *molecular formula*.

Analyze

An empirical formula gives the simplest whole-number ratio of atoms of the elements in a molecule, whereas a molecular formula gives the actual number of atoms in a molecule.

Solve

An empirical formula is concerned with the lowest whole-number ratios of atoms in a substance. A molecular formula is concerned with the actual numbers of each kind of atom that compose one molecular unit of the substance.

Think about It

Sometimes the molecular formula is equivalent to the empirical formula when the atoms in the molecular formula are in their lowest whole-number ratios.

7.45. Collect and Organize

We are asked whether the atom in a molecular formula with the largest molar mass is always the element present in the highest percentage by mass.

Analyze

The percent composition of a substance is the mass of each element in the compound divided by the molar mass of the compound. In calculating the percent mass for each element, we need to take into account how many atoms of that element are present in the molecular formula.

Solve

No, lighter elements may be present in sufficient quantities to be of a greater percentage of the mass than a heavier element.

Think about It

A good example is SiO_2. Silicon is the heavier element (28 g/mol), but the presence of two oxygen atoms (16 g/mol × 2) gives 53% O by mass but only 47% Si by mass.

7.47. Collect and Organize

To calculate the percent composition for the elements in each compound we divide the molar mass of each element from the periodic table by the molar mass for the compound and convert to a percentage.

Analyze

All the chemical formulas are given for the compounds. Assume that we have 1 mol of each compound. We first compute the molar mass. Then, to find the percentage of each element, divide the mass of each element present in the compound, taking into account the presence of multiple atoms of the element if appropriate, by the molar mass of the compound and multiply by 100.

Solve

(a) Molar mass of Na_2O = 61.98 g/mol.

$$\% \text{ Na} = \frac{(22.99 \times 2) \text{ g Na}}{61.98 \text{ g}} \times 100 = 74.19\% \text{ Na}$$

$$\% \text{ O} = \frac{16.00 \text{ g O}}{61.98 \text{ g}} \times 100 = 25.81\% \text{ O}$$

(b) Molar mass of NaOH = 40.00 g/mol.

$$\% \text{ Na} = \frac{22.99 \text{ g Na}}{40.00 \text{ g}} \times 100 = 57.48\% \text{ Na}$$

$$\% \text{ O} = \frac{16.00 \text{ g O}}{40.00 \text{ g}} \times 100 = 40.00\% \text{ O}$$

$$\% \text{ H} = \frac{1.01 \text{ g H}}{40.00 \text{ g}} \times 100 = 2.52\% \text{ H}$$

(c) Molar mass of $NaHCO_3$ = 84.01 g/mol.

$$\% \text{ Na} = \frac{22.99 \text{ g Na}}{84.01 \text{ g}} \times 100 = 27.37\% \text{ Na}$$

$$\% \text{ H} = \frac{1.01 \text{ g H}}{84.01 \text{ g}} \times 100 = 1.20\% \text{ H}$$

$$\% \text{ C} = \frac{12.01 \text{ g C}}{84.01 \text{ g}} \times 100 = 14.30\% \text{ C}$$

$$\% \text{ O} = \frac{(16.00 \times 3) \text{ g O}}{84.01 \text{ g}} \times 100 = 57.13\% \text{ O}$$

(d) Molar mass of Na_2CO_3 = 106.0 g/mol.

$$\% \text{ Na} = \frac{(22.99 \times 2) \text{ g Na}}{106.0 \text{ g}} \times 100 = 43.38\% \text{ Na}$$

$$\% \text{ C} = \frac{12.01 \text{ g C}}{106.0 \text{ g}} \times 100 = 11.33\% \text{ C}$$

$$\% \text{ O} = \frac{(16.00 \times 3) \text{ g O}}{106.0 \text{ g}} \times 100 = 45.28\% \text{ O}$$

Think about It

For all these common salts of sodium, the percentage of sodium is different. This is due not only to the different atom ratios of sodium present in the compound but also to the different molar masses of the compounds.

7.49. **Collect and Organize**

We cannot tell simply by looking at the chemical formula which compound has the greatest percentage of carbon by mass. We have to find the percent composition of hydrogen and carbon in each and then compare the compounds' percent carbon (% C).

Analyze

For each compound, assume that we have 1 mol of the substance and then compute the molar mass. For the percentage of carbon, divide the mass of all the carbon present in 1 mol by the molar mass and multiply by 100 to find the percentage.

Solve

(a) Naphthalene, $C_{10}H_8$:

$$\% \text{ C} = \frac{(12.01 \times 10) \text{ g C}}{128.2 \text{ g}} \times 100 = 93.69\% \text{ C}$$

(b) Chrysene, $C_{18}H_{12}$:

$$\% \text{ C} = \frac{(12.01 \times 18) \text{ g C}}{228.3 \text{ g}} \times 100 = 94.70\% \text{ C}$$

(c) Pentacene, $C_{22}H_{14}$:

$$\% \text{ C} = \frac{(12.01 \times 22) \text{ g C}}{278.4 \text{ g}} \times 100 = 94.91\% \text{ C}$$

(d) Pyrene, $C_{16}H_{10}$:

$$\% \text{ C} = \frac{(12.01 \times 16) \text{ g C}}{202.3 \text{ g}} \times 100 = 95.00\% \text{ C}$$

Pyrene, $C_{16}H_{10}$, has the highest % C by mass of all these hydrocarbons.

Think about It

These compounds all have relatively close percent compositions, which is not obvious by looking only at their chemical formulas.

7.51. **Collect and Organize**

We have to determine the percentage of O by mass to determine which compounds have greater than 50% oxygen by mass.

Analyze

To determine the percentage of O by mass in each compound, we assume that we have 1 mol of the substance. We then have to divide the mass of oxygen present by the molar mass of each compound.

Solve

The % O by mass in N_2O is

$$\% \text{ O} = \frac{16.00 \text{ g O}}{44.01 \text{ g}} \times 100 = 36.35\% \text{ O}$$

The % O by mass in NO is

$$\% \text{ O} = \frac{16.00 \text{ g O}}{30.01 \text{ g}} \times 100 = 53.32\% \text{ O}$$

The % O by mass in N_2O_3 is

$$\% \text{ O} = \frac{(16.00 \times 3) \text{ g O}}{76.01 \text{ g}} \times 100 = 63.15\% \text{ O}$$

The % O by mass in NO_2 is

$$\% \text{ O} = \frac{(16.00 \times 2) \text{ g O}}{46.01 \text{ g}} \times 100 = 69.55\% \text{ O}$$

On a mass basis, NO, N_2O_3, and NO_2 have greater than 50% oxygen.

Think about It

Because of the lower molar mass of nitrogen, the mass percentages of the elements in NO are not equal; rather, NO has a lower mass percentage of nitrogen than the mass percentage of oxygen.

7.53. Collect and Organize

We are asked to compare empirical formulas for a variety of hydrocarbons to see whether any are identical.

Analyze

The empirical formula is the lowest whole-number ratio of atoms in a compound. To compare these compounds, then, we need to first write the empirical formula (lowest whole-number ratio) for each. Since many of these compounds have even numbers of carbon and hydrogen atoms, we can reduce the molecular formula by dividing by 2 until we obtain a formula that can no longer be reduced to a lower whole-number ratio.

Solve

(a) Naphthalene, $C_{10}H_8$
   Empirical formula = C_5H_4

(b) Chrysene, $C_{18}H_{12}$
   Empirical formula = C_9H_6

(c) Anthracene, $C_{14}H_{10}$
   Empirical formula = C_7H_5

(d) Pyrene, $C_{16}H_{10}$
   Empirical formula = C_8H_5

(e) Benzoperylene, $C_{22}H_{12}$
   Empirical formula = $C_{11}H_6$

(f) Coronene, $C_{24}H_{12}$
   Empirical formula = C_2H

All these have different empirical formulas.

Think about It

Even though it is not true for the compounds in this problem, some compounds can have the same empirical formula.

7.55. Collect and Organize

For surgical-grade titanium we are to determine the empirical formula for the alloy given the percentages of titanium, aluminum, and vanadium it contains.

Analyze

The empirical formula is the lowest whole-number ratio of atoms in a compound. If we assume 100 g of surgical-grade titanium, we have 64.39 g of Ti, 24.19 g of Al, and 11.42 g of V in the sample. After we calculate the moles of each element by dividing the mass by the molar mass, we divide the molar amounts obtained by the smallest molar amount to find the lowest whole-number ratio of the elements.

Solve

$$\text{mol Ti} = \frac{64.39 \text{ g}}{47.87 \text{ g/mol}} = 1.345 \text{ mol Ti}$$

$$\text{mol Al} = \frac{24.19 \text{ g}}{26.98 \text{ g/mol}} = 0.8966 \text{ mol Al}$$

$$\text{mol V} = \frac{11.42 \text{ g}}{50.94 \text{ g/mol}} = 0.2242 \text{ mol V}$$

Dividing by the smallest molar amount (0.2242), we get a titanium–aluminum–vanadium ratio of 6:4:1. Therefore, the empirical formula for zircon is Ti_6Al_4V.

Think about It

This titanium alloy is useful as a surgical alloy because it resists corrosion, is lightweight and strong, and is biocompatible.

7.57. Collect and Organize

Given that a substance is 43.64% P and 56.36% O with a molar mass of 284 g/mol, we are to determine its empirical and molecular formulas.

Analyze

The percentage of P and O add up to 100%, so no other elements are present in this substance. To determine the empirical formula we assume 100 g of the compound; we have 43.64 g of P and 56.36 g of O. After we calculate the moles of each element by dividing the mass by the molar mass, we divide the molar amounts obtained by the smallest molar amount to find the lowest whole-number ratio of the elements (the empirical formula). We can obtain the molecular formula by comparing the molar mass of the empirical formula with the known molar mass of the substance.

Solve

(a) Assuming 100 g of product,

$$43.64 \text{ g P} \times \frac{1 \text{ mol}}{30.974 \text{ g}} = 1.409 \text{ mol P}$$

$$56.36 \text{ g O} \times \frac{1 \text{ mol}}{15.999 \text{ g}} = 3.523 \text{ mol O}$$

This is a 1:2.5 molar ratio of P to O, or a 2:5 ratio, so the empirical formula is P_2O_5.
(b) The molar mass of this empirical formula is 141.95, which is half of the known molar mass, so the molecular formula is P_4O_{10}.

Think about It

This question reflects how we would experimentally determine the formula for a new compound.

7.59. **Collect and Organize**

We use the percent composition of the asbestos mineral chrysotile to determine the empirical formula.

Analyze

If we assume 100 g of chrysotile, the percent composition (26.31% Mg, 20.27% Si, 1.45% H, and the rest O) gives us the grams of each element. We can convert these to moles of each element via the molar masses of the elements from the periodic table. The empirical formula will be the lowest whole-number ratio of the moles of the elements in the chrysotile.

Solve

Oxygen is the only element not specified with a mass percentage. Therefore, we can determine oxygen's percentage by

$$100 - (26.31 + 20.27 + 1.45) = 51.97\%$$

The following give the moles of each element:

$$26.31 \text{ g Mg} \times \frac{1 \text{ mol}}{24.31 \text{ g}} = 1.082 \text{ mol Mg}$$

$$20.27 \text{ g Si} \times \frac{1 \text{ mol}}{28.09 \text{ g}} = 0.7216 \text{ mol Si}$$

$$1.45 \text{ g H} \times \frac{1 \text{ mol}}{1.01 \text{ g}} = 1.44 \text{ mol H}$$

$$51.97 \text{ g O} \times \frac{1 \text{ mol}}{16.00} = 3.248 \text{ mol O}$$

Dividing these by the smallest molar amount (0.7216) gives a magnesium–silicon–hydrogen–oxygen ratio of 1.5:1:2:4.5. Multiplying these by 2 gives a whole-number ratio of 3 Mg : 2 Si : 4 H : 9 O for an empirical formula of $Mg_3Si_2H_4O_9$.

Think about It

The trick here is to recognize that the mass percentage of oxygen was not given in the original statement of the problem. Be sure to determine the moles for each element present in the compound.

7.61. Collect and Organize

From the percent composition of a compound containing copper, chlorine, and oxygen, we are to determine the formula. We have to convert the mass to moles and then find the lowest whole-number molar ratio for the elements in the compound.

Analyze

If we assume 100 g of the compound, the percentage of each element (24.2% Cu, 27.0% Cl, 48.8% O) gives us the mass of the elements in that 100 g amount. We can convert those masses into moles by using the molar masses of the elements from the periodic table. Then we compare the moles to find the molar ratio.

Solve

$$24.2 \text{ g Cu} \times \frac{1 \text{ mol}}{63.55 \text{ g}} = 0.381 \text{ mol Cu}$$

$$27.0 \text{ g Cl} \times \frac{1 \text{ mol}}{35.45 \text{ g}} = 0.762 \text{ mol Cl}$$

$$48.8 \text{ g O} \times \frac{1 \text{ mol}}{16.00 \text{ g}} = 3.05 \text{ mol O}$$

Dividing each mole amount by the smallest mole amount (0.381) gives a ratio of 1 Cu : 2 Cl : 8 O. The empirical formula for the compound therefore is $CuCl_2O_8$.

Think about It

Here, the molar ratio, upon dividing the moles in 100 g of the substance, comes out to a whole-number ratio. We did not have to multiply to obtain whole numbers for this compound.

7.63. Collect and Organize

We consider why combustion analysis must be carried out in excess amounts of oxygen.

Analyze

In combustion analysis, compounds (usually organic) are burned in oxygen and the masses of recovered CO_2 and H_2O produced in the reaction are related to the percentages of C and H in the original compound.

Solve

The excess of oxygen is required in combustion analysis to ensure the complete reaction of the hydrogen and carbon to form water and carbon dioxide.

Think about It

Combustion in an atmosphere deficient in oxygen gives CO instead of CO_2 as the main gaseous carbon product.

7.65. Collect and Organize

We are asked whether combustion analysis can ever give the true molecular formula for a compound.

Analyze

Combustion analysis gives us the percent mass of C, H, and (by calculation of the missing mass for some compounds) O in the compound, from which we can derive the empirical formula.

Solve

Yes, the combustion analysis can give the true molecular formula for a compound, but only if the empirical formula is the same as the molecular formula and only if the compound contains only C, H, and O.

Think about It

We can confirm the molar mass of a compound by other methods such as boiling point elevation, freezing point depression, or osmotic pressure.

7.67. Collect and Organize

From the data obtained from the combustion analysis for a compound containing carbon, hydrogen, and oxygen, we are asked to determine the mass of carbon and hydrogen in the given mass of the compound and to find the mass and moles of oxygen. From there we can determine the molar ratios of C, H, and O.

Analyze

We can calculate the moles and masses of C and H directly from the combustion analysis results. The oxygen content will be the difference in the mass of the carbon plus hydrogen in the compound and the mass of the 0.100 g sample. We can then determine the moles of oxygen by using the molar mass of oxygen from the periodic table, and we can find the ratio of carbon to hydrogen to oxygen to determine the empirical formula.

Solve

$$0.1783 \text{ g CO}_2 \times \frac{1 \text{ mol CO}_2}{44.01 \text{ g}} \times \frac{1 \text{ mol C}}{1 \text{ mol CO}_2} = 4.051 \times 10^{-3} \text{ mol C}$$

$$4.051 \times 10^{-3} \text{ mol C} \times \frac{12.011 \text{ g C}}{1 \text{ mol}} = 4.866 \times 10^{-2} \text{ g C}$$

$$0.0734 \text{ g H}_2\text{O} \times \frac{1 \text{ mol H}_2\text{O}}{18.02 \text{ g}} \times \frac{2 \text{ mol H}}{1 \text{ mol H}_2\text{O}} = 8.147 \times 10^{-3} \text{ mol H}$$

$$8.147 \times 10^{-3} \text{ mol H} \times \frac{1.008 \text{ g H}}{1 \text{ mol}} = 8.212 \times 10^{-3} \text{ g H}$$

$$\text{Total mass of C and H} = 4.866 \times 10^{-2} \text{ g} + 8.212 \times 10^{-3} \text{ g} = 5.687 \times 10^{-2} \text{ g}$$

$$\text{Mass of O present} = 0.100 \text{ g} - 0.05687 \text{ g} = 0.043 \text{ g O}$$

$$\text{Moles of O in compound} = 0.043 \text{ g O} \times \frac{1 \text{ mol}}{15.999 \text{ g}} = 2.7 \times 10^{-3} \text{ mol O}$$

Dividing the moles of C, H, and O by the smallest molar amount (2.7×10^{-3} mol) gives a ratio of 1.5 C : 3 H : 1 O. Multiplying this through by 2 to obtain whole-number ratios, we get an empirical formula of $C_3H_6O_2$.

Think about It

This problem involves an additional step to determine the mass of carbon and hydrogen present so that we can calculate the mass (and therefore the moles) of oxygen in the compound.

7.69. Collect and Organize

From the combustion data of a given mass of a compound containing only hydrogen and carbon and the molar mass of the compound, we are to determine the empirical and molecular formulas.

Analyze

This compound contains only hydrogen and carbon. The water (135.0 mg) resulted from the combustion of the hydrogen, and the carbon dioxide (440.0 mg) resulted from the combustion of the carbon. First, we determine the mass of hydrogen and oxygen present in the water and the carbon dioxide. From those results, we determine the mass percentage of the hydrogen and carbon in the compound (we know the original mass of the sample used in the analysis, 135.0 mg). From the mass percentage, we can find moles and the mole ratio of carbon and hydrogen in the compound and from there determine the empirical and molecular formulas (knowing the molar mass of the compound is 270 g/mol).

Solve

The mass and percentage of carbon and hydrogen in the compound are

$$440.0 \text{ mg CO}_2 \times \frac{1 \text{ g}}{1000 \text{ mg}} \times \frac{1 \text{ mol CO}_2}{44.01 \text{ g}} \times \frac{1 \text{ mol C}}{1 \text{ mol CO}_2} = 0.009998 \text{ mol C}$$

$$135.0 \text{ mg H}_2\text{O} \times \frac{1 \text{ g}}{1000 \text{ mg}} \times \frac{1 \text{ mol H}_2\text{O}}{18.02 \text{ g}} \times \frac{2 \text{ mol H}}{1 \text{ mol H}_2\text{O}} = 0.01498 \text{ mol H}$$

Dividing 0.01498 mol H by 0.009998 mol C gives a ratio of 1 C : 1.499 H. Multiplying by 2 to obtain a whole-number ratio gives an empirical formula of C_2H_3. The molar mass of this empirical formula is 27.05 g/mol. The molar mass of the compound is 270 g/mol. This is 10 times the molar mass of the empirical formula. Therefore, the molecular formula is $C_{20}H_{30}$.

Think about It
The empirical formula is derived from the molar ratio of the elements in the compound. Because combustion analysis gives us the amount of carbon and hydrogen in the compound, we need only relate the moles of CO_2 and H_2O to the C and H present in the compound.

7.71. Collect and Organize
Given that a reaction starts with equal masses of iron and sulfur, we consider the mass of iron(II) sulfide that can be produced in the reaction.

Analyze
The elements react to give a molar ratio of 1 Fe : 1 S. Because these elements have different molar masses (Fe = 55.845 and S = 32.065 g/mol), an equal mass of S contains more moles of sulfur than the same mass of iron contains moles of iron.

Solve
Excess sulfur is present at the end of the reaction, so the mass of FeS produced is (c) less than the sum of the masses of Fe and S to start.

Think about It
The limiting reactant here is iron.

7.73. Collect and Organize
We are to distinguish between *theoretical yield* and *percent yield*.

Analyze
The theoretical yield is calculated based on the amounts of reactants used in a chemical reaction. The percent yield takes into account the actual experimental yield.

Solve
Theoretical yield is the greatest amount of a product possible from a reaction and assumes that the reaction runs to completion. The percent yield is the observed experimental yield divided by the theoretical yield and multiplied by 100.

Think about It
The actual yields are almost always less than the theoretical yield because of side reactions, incomplete reactions, and loss during purification steps. The percent yields for most reactions are less than 100%.

7.75. Collect and Organize
We are to provide two reasons why the actual yield for a reaction is usually less than the theoretical yield.

Analyze
The actual yield is determined experimentally, and the theoretical yield assumes that all the limiting reactant is chemically transformed into product.

Solve
The observed, or actual, yield for a reaction is usually less than the theoretical yield because reactions do not always go to completion; the reaction may be slow or may have, for a portion of the reaction, given different products from those expected.

Think about It

Chemists try hard to maximize yields for important products by changing the chemical reaction path of the synthesis or by changing the conditions (temperature, pressure, solvent, etc.) under which the reaction is run.

7.77. Collect and Organize

We have to determine the maximum amount of hollandaise sauce that can be made with the ingredients on hand.

Analyze

The ingredient that would produce the least amount of the sauce will be the limiting ingredient; therefore, that amount is the largest possible amount of sauce that can be made.

Solve

Because the sauce requires $^1/_2$ c (cup) butter, $^1/_2$ c water, 4 egg yolks, and the juice of one lemon, we can determine how many cups of sauce could be made from the ingredients on hand.

Two cups of butter would be enough to prepare 4 c of sauce.
Unlimited amounts of hot water are enough to prepare an unlimited amount of sauce.
Twelve eggs is enough to prepare 3 c of sauce.
Four lemons is enough to prepare 4 c of sauce.

The limiting ingredient is eggs; all the other ingredients are in sufficient supply to make 4 c of hollandaise sauce. With the limited number of eggs, we can make 3 c of sauce.

Think about It

The most sauce that we can make is limited by the ingredient most limited in supply. This is true for chemical reactions as well, although we are thinking in moles, not cups of butter or number of eggs.

7.79. Collect and Organize

If 75 metric tons of coal is contaminated with 3.0% sulfur by mass, we are asked to calculate the efficiency of the power plant SO_2 capture scrubber when 3.9 metric tons of SO_2 is captured from this 75 tons burned. We are also to calculate how much SO_2 escapes.

Analyze

We first must calculate the mass of sulfur in the coal and then convert that into how much SO_2 is produced upon combustion. The balanced equation for the production of SO_2 from S is

$$S(s) + O_2(g) \rightarrow SO_2(g)$$

From the difference between the amount of SO_2 captured and that produced, we can determine the efficiency of the scrubbers and how much SO_2 escaped.

Solve

$$75 \text{ metric tons} \times \frac{1000 \text{ kg}}{1 \text{ metric ton}} \times \frac{1000 \text{ g}}{\text{kg}} \times 0.03 = 2.25 \times 10^6 \text{ g of S in the coal}$$

$$2.25 \times 10^6 \text{ g S} \times \frac{1 \text{ mol}}{32.065 \text{ g}} \times \frac{1 \text{ mol SO}_2}{1 \text{ mol S}} \times \frac{64.064 \text{ g}}{1 \text{ mol}} \times \frac{1 \text{ kg}}{1000 \text{ g}} \times \frac{1 \text{ metric ton}}{1000 \text{ kg}} = 4.5 \text{ metric tons SO}_2$$

$$\text{efficiency} = \frac{3.9 \text{ metric tons captured}}{4.5 \text{ metric tons produced}} \times 100 = 87\%$$

amount of SO_2 escaped = 4.5 – 3.9 = 0.60 metric tons

Think about It

The efficiency of the scrubbers is relatively high, but still a lot of SO_2 escapes into the atmosphere in this example. SO_2 is one of the gases that mix with water vapor in the atmosphere to acidify rain.

7.81. Collect and Organize

To begin this problem we first write the balanced chemical equation for the reaction of ammonia (NH_3) with hydrogen chloride (HCl). From the information given (3.0 g of ammonia and 5.0 g of hydrogen chloride), we are asked to determine the limiting reactant, predict the theoretical yield, and calculate the amount of excess reactant after completion.

Analyze
First we need to write the balanced chemical equation for the reaction of ammonia with hydrogen chloride. We need the molar masses of the reactants to compute the moles of each present. The molar mass of NH_3 is 17.03 g/mol, and for HCl the molar mass is 36.46 g/mol.

Solve
(a) The balanced chemical equation is

$$NH_3(g) + HCl(g) \rightarrow NH_4Cl(s)$$

(b) The moles of NH_3 present at the start of the reaction:
$$3.0 \text{ g } NH_3 \times \frac{1 \text{ mol}}{17.03 \text{ g}} = 0.18 \text{ mol } NH_3$$

The moles of HCl present at the start of the reaction:
$$5.0 \text{ g HCl} \times \frac{1 \text{ mol}}{36.46 \text{ g}} = 0.14 \text{ mol HCl}$$

Comparing these two mole amounts and considering that 1 mol of NH_3 reacts with 1 mol of HCl in the balanced equation, we see that HCl is the limiting reactant.

(c) The amount of NH_4Cl theoretically formed in the reaction is
$$0.14 \text{ mol HCl} \times \frac{1 \text{ mol } NH_4Cl}{1 \text{ mol HCl}} \times \frac{53.5 \text{ g}}{1 \text{ mol}} = 7.33 \text{ g } NH_4Cl \text{ produced}$$

(d) We know that in the reaction, 0.14 mol of NH_3 is used up, and therefore

$$0.18 \text{ mol} - 0.14 \text{ mol} = 0.04 \text{ mol of } NH_3$$

will be left over. We can convert this excess of NH_3 in moles to grams with the molar mass of NH_3.
$$0.04 \text{ mol } NH_3 \times \frac{17.03 \text{ g}}{1 \text{ mol } NH_3} = 0.7 \text{ g } NH_3$$

Thus, 0.7 g of NH_3 remains at the end of the reaction.

Think about It
Although a larger gram amount of HCl was present in the reaction, it proved to be the limiting reactant.

7.83. Collect and Organize
For the production of syngas, a mixture of CO and H_2, from C and H_2O, we are asked to write a balanced reaction and to determine the percent yield of a reaction that uses 66 kg of carbon to produce 6.8 kg of H_2.

Analyze
We can use the three-step method to balance the equation for the production of syngas. Next we will calculate the theoretical yield of H_2 from 66 kg of carbon by using the molar masses of C and H_2 and the ratio of C to H_2 from the balanced chemical equation. We can calculate percent yield by dividing the actual yield (6.8 kg) by the theoretical yield and multiplying by 100.

Solve
(a) The unbalanced chemical equation is

$$C(s) + H_2O(\ell) \rightarrow CO(g) + H_2(g)$$

Atoms: $\quad 1\,C + 2\,H + 1\,O \rightarrow 1\,C + 2\,H + 1\,O$

The equation is already balanced.

(b)

$$66 \text{ kg C} \times \frac{1000 \text{ g}}{\text{kg}} \times \frac{1 \text{ mol C}}{12.011 \text{ g}} \times \frac{1 \text{ mol H}_2}{1 \text{ mol C}} \times \frac{2.016 \text{ g H}_2}{1 \text{ mol}} \times \frac{1 \text{ kg}}{1000 \text{ kg}} = 11 \text{ kg}$$

$$\% \text{ yield} = \frac{6.8 \text{ kg}}{11 \text{ kg}} \times 100 = 61\%$$

Think about It

The hydrogen in this reaction can be used as a fuel, perhaps in a hydrogen–oxygen fuel cell.

7.85. **Collect and Organize**

We first have to balance the equation for the conversion of glucose into ethanol. We need the molar ratio of the reactant to the ethanol product to determine the theoretical yield of ethanol for the fermentation of 100.0 g of glucose that produces 50.0 mL of ethanol.

Analyze

First, we have to write the balanced equation for the process for part a. For part b, we need the molar masses of $C_6H_{12}O_6$ (180.16 g/mol) and C_2H_5OH (46.07 g/mol). We need the density of the ethanol (0.789 g/mL) to convert the grams of ethanol produced theoretically in the reaction to milliliters to compute the percent yield for the reaction, which is given by

$$\% \text{ yield} = \frac{\text{observed experimental yield}}{\text{theoretical yield}} \times 100$$

Solve

(a) The balanced equation is

$$C_6H_{12}O_6(aq) \rightarrow 2 \, C_2H_5OH(\ell) + 2 \, CO_2(g)$$

(b) The theoretical yield of C_2H_5OH is

$$100.0 \text{ g C}_6\text{H}_{12}\text{O}_6 \times \frac{1 \text{ mol C}_6\text{H}_{12}\text{O}_6}{180.16 \text{ g}} \times \frac{2 \text{ mol C}_2\text{H}_5\text{OH}}{1 \text{ mol C}_6\text{H}_{12}\text{O}_6} \times \frac{46.07 \text{ g C}_2\text{H}_5\text{OH}}{1 \text{ mol}} \times \frac{1 \text{ mL C}_2\text{H}_5\text{OH}}{0.789 \text{ g}} = 64.82 \text{ mL C}_2\text{H}_5\text{OH}$$

The percent yield for this reaction is

$$\% \text{ yield} = \frac{50.0 \text{ mL}}{64.82 \text{ mL}} \times 100 = 77.1\%$$

Think about It

The conversion of glucose by fermentation into ethanol is fairly efficient.

7.87. **Collect and Organize**

Hydroxyapatite is composed of calcium, phosphorus, oxygen, and hydrogen. We are asked to systematically name the compound and to find its mass percentage of calcium. We are also asked to think about how the mass percentage of calcium changes when F replaces OH in the compound.

Analyze

We use the naming rules to systematically name the hydroxyapatite. We can calculate the mass percentage of calcium by dividing the mass of calcium present (assuming 1 mol of the substance) by the total mass of the compound, taking into account that five Ca atoms are present in the molecular formula.

Solve

(a) Hydroxyapatite would be named calcium triphosphate hydroxide.
(b) If we assume 1 mol of hydroxyapatite with a molar mass of 502.31 g/mol and use the mass of calcium of 40.078 g/mol, the mass percentage of calcium in hydroxyapatite is

$$\frac{(40.08 \times 5) \text{ g}}{502.31 \text{ g}} \times 100 = 39.89\% \text{ Ca}^{2+}$$

(c) The mass percentage in $Ca_5(PO_3)_4F$ is

$$\frac{(40.08 \times 5) \text{ g}}{504.30 \text{ g}} \times 100 = 39.74\% \text{ Ca}^{2+}$$

The mass percentage of calcium decreases, but only slightly.

Think about It
The strengthening of the structure of hydroxyapatite when OH^- is replaced by fluoride happens in our teeth when we drink fluoridated water and use fluoride toothpaste.

7.89. Collect and Organize
For 5.1 metric tons of bauxite ore that is 86% aluminum oxide (Al_2O_3), we are to calculate the percent yield of the recovery if 2.3 metric tons was extracted from this ore.

Analyze
First we will use the percent composition of the ore (86%) to find the mass of Al_2O_3 in the 5.1 metric tons. Then to determine the theoretical amount of Al in the bauxite, we will convert the mass of Al_2O_3 to moles. One mole of Al_2O_3 has 2 mol of Al, which we can then convert into the mass of aluminum expected from the bauxite (the theoretical "yield"). The percent yield is the actual yield of 2.3 metric tons over the calculated theoretical yield multiplied by 100.

Solve
The amount of aluminum in the ore is
$$5.1 \text{ metric tons} \times 0.86 = 4.39 \text{ metric tons}$$
The theoretical amount of aluminum in the ore is
$$4.39 \text{ metric tons} \times \frac{1000 \text{ kg}}{\text{metric ton}} \times \frac{1000 \text{ g}}{\text{kg}} \times \frac{\text{mol Al}_2\text{O}_3}{101.96 \text{ g}} \times \frac{2 \text{ mol Al}}{1 \text{ mol Al}_2\text{O}_3} \times \frac{26.982 \text{ g}}{\text{mol}} \times \frac{1 \text{ kg}}{1000 \text{ g}} \times \frac{1 \text{ metric ton}}{1000 \text{ kg}}$$
$$= 2.32 \text{ metric tons}$$
The percent yield is
$$\frac{2.3 \text{ metric tons}}{2.32 \text{ metric tons}} \times 100 = 99\%$$

Think about It
The extraction of aluminum from bauxite is near 100%, but the process is energy intensive and therefore costly.

7.91. Collect and Organize
We are given balanced chemical equations for the extraction of gold from veins in rocks. We are asked to calculate the amounts of reactants for the process and to find the size of a block made from the gold product.

Analyze
We need the molar masses of Au (196.97 g/mol), NaCN (49.01 g/mol), $NaAu(CN)_2$ (271.99 g/mol), and Zn (65.38 g/mol). We use the density of gold (19.3 g/cm³) to calculate the size of the block of gold for part c.

Solve
(a) If the ore is 0.009% gold by mass, then the mass of gold in 1 metric ton (1000 kg) is
$$1000 \text{ kg} \times \frac{1000 \text{ g}}{1 \text{ kg}} \times 0.00009 = 90 \text{ g Au}$$
The amount of NaCN required to extract the gold is
$$90 \text{ g Au} \times \frac{1 \text{ mol Au}}{196.97} \times \frac{8 \text{ mol NaCN}}{4 \text{ mol Au}} \times \frac{49.01 \text{ g NaCN}}{1 \text{ mol}} = 45 \text{ g NaCN}$$
(b) We can solve for the amount of Zn required by starting with the amount of Au.
$$90 \text{ g Au} \times \frac{1 \text{ mol Au}}{196.97} \times \frac{4 \text{ mol NaAu(CN)}_2}{4 \text{ mol Au}} \times \frac{1 \text{ mol Zn}}{2 \text{ mol NaAu(CN)}_2} \times \frac{65.38 \text{ g Zn}}{1 \text{ mol}} = 15 \text{ g Zn}$$

(c) The amount of gold recovered from the ore is 90 g. We use the density of gold to find the size of the block of gold for this mass.

$$90 \text{ g Au} \times \frac{1 \text{ cm}^3}{19.3 \text{ g}} = 4.66 \text{ cm}^3$$

Think about It
This problem assumes that the processing steps all go to completion (100% yield).

7.93. **Collect and Organize**
For this problem we must use percent compositions of the compounds that form upon heating $UO_x(NO_3)_y(H_2O)_z$ to ultimately determine the values of x, y, and z.

Analyze
We need the molar masses of uranium (238.03 g/mol) and oxygen (16.00 g/mol) to determine the molar ratios of U to O in the oxides. We also are given that the charge on uranium in the oxides may range from 3+ to 6+.

Solve
(a) If U_aO_b is 83.22% U, then it is 16.78% O. Assuming 100 g of the compound, and using the molar masses of these elements, we obtain their molar ratios:

$$83.22 \text{ g U} \times \frac{1 \text{ mol U}}{238.03 \text{ g}} = 0.3496 \text{ mol U}$$

$$16.78 \text{ g O} \times \frac{1 \text{ mol O}}{16.00 \text{ g}} = 1.049 \text{ mol O}$$

Multiplying these molar amounts by 3 gives a whole-number ratio, for an empirical formula of UO_3 for this oxide. In this formula $a = 1$ and $b = 3$ with a charge on the U of 6+ (since O is 2–).
(b) If U_cO_d is 84.8% U, then it is 15.2% O. Assuming 100 g of the compounds, and using the molar masses of these elements, we obtain their molar ratios:

$$84.8 \text{ g U} \times \frac{1 \text{ mol U}}{238.03 \text{ g}} = 0.356 \text{ mol U}$$

$$15.2 \text{ g O} \times \frac{1 \text{ mol O}}{16.00 \text{ g}} = 0.950 \text{ mol O}$$

Dividing these molar amounts by the lowest number of moles (0.356) gives a ratio of 1 U to 2.67 O. To reach a whole-number ratio, we multiply by 3 to get U_3O_8, in which $c = 3$ and $d = 8$. The charge on the U atoms is 5.33+ which indicates mixed oxidation states for the uranium cations in this ore.
(c) Upon gentle heating, $UO_x(NO_3)_y(H_2O)_z$ loses water according to the following equation:

$$UO_x(NO_3)_y(H_2O)_z \rightarrow UO_x(NO_3)_y + z \text{ H}_2O$$

More heating of $UO_x(NO_3)_y$ gives the reaction

$$UO_x(NO_3)_y \rightarrow U_nO_m + \text{nitrogen oxides}$$

Putting these equations together,

$$UO_x(NO_3)_y(H_2O)_z \rightarrow UO_x(NO_3)_y + z \text{ H}_2O \rightarrow U_nO_m + \text{nitrogen oxides}$$

The continued heating of the compound indicates that at the end of the reaction, we have U_3O_8 (part b). The balanced reaction then is

$$3 \text{ UO}_x(NO_3)_y(H_2O)_z \rightarrow 3 \text{ UO}_x(NO_3)_y + 3z \text{ H}_2O \rightarrow U_3O_8 + \text{nitrogen oxides}$$

The amount in moles of H_2O present on the basis of 0.742 g of U_3O_8 is

$$0.742 \text{ g } U_3O_8 \times \frac{1 \text{ mol}}{842 \text{ g}} \times \frac{3z \text{ mol } H_2O}{1 \text{ mol } U_3O_8} \times \frac{18.02 \text{ g } H_2O}{1 \text{ mol}} = 0.0476z \text{ g } H_2O$$

The mass of water lost in this process is $1.328 - 1.042 = 0.286 \text{ g } H_2O$. The moles of water lost is therefore

$$0.0476z = 0.286$$
$$z = 6$$

The amount in moles of $UO_x(NO_3)_y$ from the 0.742 g of U_3O_8 is

$$0.742 \text{ g } U_3O_8 \times \frac{1 \text{ mol}}{842 \text{ g}} \times \frac{3 \text{ mol } UO_x(NO_3)_y}{1 \text{ mol } U_3O_8} = 0.00264 \text{ mol } UO_x(NO_3)_y$$

Because we know the mass of $UO_x(NO_3)_y$, for this number of moles, the molar mass of $UO_x(NO_3)_y$ is

$$\frac{1.042 \text{ g}}{0.00264 \text{ mol}} = 395 \text{ g/mol}$$

This molar mass is expressed by

$$395 \text{ g/mol} = 238 \text{ g/mol} + [(x + 3y)(16.00 \text{ g/mol})] + y(14.00 \text{ g/mol})$$
$$157 \text{ g/mol} = 16x + 62y$$

We know that the total charge on $UO_x(NO_3)_y$ is 0 (it is a neutral compound). This can be expressed as

$$-2(x) + -1(y) + c = 0$$

where x = number of O^{2-} ions, y = number of NO_3^- ions, and c = charge on U in the molecular formula. We are given that c could be 3+, 4+, 5+, or 6+. When $c = 6$, $-2x - y = -6$, or $2x + y = 6$. Rearranging this gives $y = 6 - 2x$, which when substituted into $157 \text{ g/mol} = 16x + 62y$, gives

$$157 \text{ g/mol} = 16x + 62(6 - 2x)$$
$$157 \text{ g/mol} = -108x + 372$$
$$-215 \text{ g/mol} = -108x$$
$$2 = x$$

and then

$$y = 6 - 2x = 2$$

If $c = 5+$, $4+$, or $3+$, the solution does not work. The formula for $UO_x(NO_3)_y(H_2O)_z$ is $UO_2(NO_3)_2(H_2O)_6$.

Think about It
The value of the charge on U in part b must mean that it is a mixed-oxidation-state compound. Here one-third of the U atoms have a 6+ charge and two-thirds of the U atoms have a 5+ charge.

7.95. Collect and Organize
We are to compare the chemical formulas of xylose ($C_5H_{10}O_5$) and methyl galacturonate ($C_7H_{12}O_7$) to determine whether they have the same empirical formula, and we are asked to write equations for their combustion reactions.

Analyze
For two compounds to have the same empirical formula, they must have the same lowest whole-number ratio of the elements that compose them. To write a combustion reaction, recall that the other reactant is oxygen (O_2) and the products are water (H_2O) and carbon dioxide (CO_2).

Solve

(a) These two compounds do not have the same empirical formula. Each is already in its lowest whole-number ratio of the elements, and the formulas are not identical.

(b) The combustion of xylose is given by

$$C_5H_{10}O_5(s) + 5\ O_2(g) \rightarrow 5\ CO_2(g) + 5\ H_2O(\ell)$$

The combustion of methyl galacturonate is given by

$$2\ C_7H_{12}O_7(s) + 13\ O_2(g) \rightarrow 14\ CO_2(g) + 12\ H_2O(\ell)$$

Think about It

The higher the carbon content of the reactant undergoing combustion, the more moles of CO_2 produced.

7.97. Collect and Organize

We are given the balanced equation in which formaldehyde (HCO_2H) is prepared from CO_2 and H_2S in the presence of FeS. First, we identify the ions that make up FeS and FeS_2 and name these iron compounds. Next, we calculate the amount of HCO_2H produced when 1.00 g of FeS, 0.50 g of H_2S, and 0.50 g of CO_2 are used in the reaction that gives 50% yield. This is a limiting reactant problem, and we must identify the limiting reactant.

Analyze

To solve the limiting reactant–percent yield problem, we need the molar masses of FeS (87.91 g/mol), H_2S (34.08 g/mol), CO_2 (44.01 g/mol), and HCO_2H (46.03 g/mol). We have to determine the theoretical yield and then consider that the reaction goes only to 50% yield.

Solve

(a and b) FeS is iron(II) sulfide with Fe^{2+} and S^{2-}; FeS_2 is iron(IV) sulfide with Fe^{4+} and S^{2-} from your knowledge so far in this course with Fe^{4+} and S^{2-}. Actually, this compound is Fe^{2+} with S_2^{2-} and is named iron(II) persulfide.

(c) The amount of HCO_2H that could be produced from each of the starting materials is as follows:

$$1.00\ \text{g FeS} \times \frac{1\ \text{mol}}{87.91\ \text{g}} \times \frac{1\ \text{mol HCO}_2\text{H}}{1\ \text{mol FeS}} \times \frac{46.03\ \text{g}}{1\ \text{mol}} = 0.524\ \text{g HCO}_2\text{H could be produced from 1.00 g FeS}$$

$$0.50\ \text{g H}_2\text{S} \times \frac{1\ \text{mol}}{34.08\ \text{g}} \times \frac{1\ \text{mol HCO}_2\text{H}}{1\ \text{mol H}_2\text{S}} \times \frac{46.03\ \text{g}}{1\ \text{mol}} = 0.68\ \text{g HCO}_2\text{H could be produced from 0.50 g H}_2\text{S}$$

$$0.50\ \text{g CO}_2 \times \frac{1\ \text{mol}}{44.01\ \text{g}} \times \frac{1\ \text{mol HCO}_2\text{H}}{1\ \text{mol CO}_2} \times \frac{46.03\ \text{g}}{1\ \text{mol}} = 0.52\ \text{g HCO}_2\text{H could be produced from 0.50 g CO}_2$$

Because the smallest amount (CO_2 and FeS nearly tie as limiting reactant) is the theoretical yield if the reaction proceeds completely (100% yield), this reaction, which goes only to 50% completion, yields 0.52 g/2 = 0.26 g of HCO_2H.

Think about It

At first this problem looks difficult because we are told the reaction gives only a 50% yield. We did not need to account for that until the end, however, and the problem is primarily a limiting reactant problem.

7.99. Collect and Organize

We are asked to balance the reactions of (a) FeO with water to form Fe_3O_4 and H_2 and then (b) the same reaction except that when CO_2 is present the reaction gives CH_4 in place of H_2.

Analyze

To balance each equation we first write the unbalanced equation by using the chemical formulas of the reactants and products. Next, we balance an element that is present in only one reactant and product. Finally, we balance the other elements present by placing coefficients in front of the species in the reaction so that the number of the atoms for each element is equal on both sides of the equation. If any fractional coefficients are present, we multiply the entire equation through to eliminate all fractions.

Solve

(a) For the reaction of FeO with H_2O to produce Fe_3O_4 and H_2, the unbalanced reaction is

$$FeO(s) + H_2O(\ell) \rightarrow Fe_3O_4(s) + H_2(g)$$

Atoms: $1\ Fe + 2\ O + 2\ H \rightarrow 3\ Fe + 4\ O + 2\ H$

To balance the Fe atoms we place 3 as the coefficient before FeO on the left-hand side of the equation.

$$3\ FeO(s) + H_2O(\ell) \rightarrow Fe_3O_4(s) + H_2(g)$$

Atoms: $3\ Fe + 4\ O + 2\ H \rightarrow 3\ Fe + 4\ O + 2\ H$

The equation is now balanced.

(b) For the reaction of FeO with water in the presence of CO_2 to give Fe_3O_4 and CH_4, the unbalanced reaction is

$$FeO(s) + H_2O(\ell) + CO_2(g) \rightarrow Fe_3O_4(s) + CH_4(g)$$

Atoms: $1\ Fe + 4\ O + 2\ H + 1\ C \rightarrow 3\ Fe + 4\ O + 4\ H + 1\ C$

To balance the H atoms we place 2 as the coefficient before H_2O on the left-hand side of the equation.

$$FeO(s) + 2\ H_2O(\ell) + CO_2(g) \rightarrow Fe_3O_4(s) + CH_4(g)$$

Atoms: $Fe + 5\ O + 4\ H + 1\ C \rightarrow 3\ Fe + 4\ O + 4\ H + 1\ C$

We will need to balance the O and Fe atoms together. To do so we place 12 as the coefficient before FeO on the left-hand side of the equation and a 4 as the coefficient before Fe_3O_4 on the right-hand side of the equation.

$$12\ FeO(s) + 2\ H_2O(\ell) + CO_2(g) \rightarrow 4\ Fe_3O_4(s) + CH_4(g)$$

Atoms: $12\ Fe + 16\ O + 4\ H + 1\ C \rightarrow 12\ Fe + 16\ O + 4\ H + 1\ C$

The equation is now balanced.

Think about It

Balancing the equation in part b is tricky and requires a little insight and trial and error. Here, when we balance two species at once, the other coefficients fall into place.

7.101. **Collect and Organize**

The alternative fuel E-85 is 85% (by volume) ethanol, and we are to determine how many moles of ethanol is in 1 gal of the fuel and how many moles of CO_2 would be produced if that ethanol were combusted.

Analyze

(a) If we first convert 1 gal to milliliters (1 gal = 3785 mL), we can find the milliliters of ethanol in the fuel by multiplying by 0.85 (the percent ethanol by volume in the fuel). From the milliliters of ethanol, we can calculate the mass of ethanol by multiplying by the density (0.79 g/mL). From the mass and the molar mass of ethanol (46.07 g/mol), we can determine the moles of ethanol in 1 gal of the fuel.

(b) When ethanol burns completely, it produces CO_2 and H_2O. The balanced equation for the burning of ethanol is

$$C_2H_5OH(\ell) + 3\ O_2(g) \rightarrow 2\ CO_2(g) + 3\ H_2O(\ell)$$

From the stoichiometry of 1 ethanol to 2 carbon dioxide, we obtain the moles of CO_2 produced in the reaction.

Solve

(a)

$$(3785\ mL \times 0.85) \times \frac{0.79\ g}{mL} \times \frac{1\ mol}{46.07\ g} = 55\ mol\ ethanol$$

(b)

$$55\ mol\ ethanol \times \frac{2\ mol\ CO_2}{1\ mol\ ethanol} = 1.1 \times 10^2\ mol\ CO_2$$

Think about It

We could do the calculation for (a) all in one step, without separately calculating the milliliters of ethanol, the mass, and then the moles.

7.103. **Collect and Organize**

From the mass of the salt before and after dehydration (0.6240 and 0.5471 g, respectively) and the known ratio of M to Cl to H_2O in the compound as given by the molecular formula, $MCl_2 \cdot 2H_2O$, we are to determine the identity (through calculation of the molar mass) of M.

Analyze

From the difference of the masses, we can obtain the mass of water lost and from that value calculate the moles of water lost. The moles of water lost equals the moles of Cl in the compound and is twice the moles of M in the compound. From the moles of Cl, we can find the mass of Cl in the sample. The mass of M in the sample is the total mass of the sample minus the combined masses of the water and the chlorine. Once we know the mass of M, we can divide by the moles of M in the sample found earlier to determine the molar mass of M, which identifies the metal.

Solve

$$\text{moles of water in sample} = (0.6240 \text{ g} - 0.5471 \text{ g}) \times \frac{1 \text{ mol } H_2O}{18.02 \text{ g}} = 4.27 \times 10^{-3} \text{ mol}$$

From the formula we also know that $\text{mol Cl} = 4.27 \times 10^{-3}$ mol and $\text{mol M} = 2.14 \times 10^{-3}$ mol. Therefore, the molar mass of M is

$$\text{mass of Cl in sample} = 4.27 \times 10^{-3} \text{ mol} \times \frac{35.453 \text{ g}}{1 \text{ mol Cl}} = 0.151 \text{ g}$$

$$\text{total mass of } H_2O \text{ and Cl} = 0.0769 \text{ g} + 0.151 \text{ g} = 0.228 \text{ g}$$

$$\text{mass of M in sample} = 0.6240 \text{ g} - 0.228 \text{ g} = 0.396 \text{ g}$$

$$\text{molar mass of M} = \frac{0.396 \text{ g}}{2.14 \times 10^{-3} \text{ mol}} = 185 \text{ g/mol}$$

The identity of M is Re.

Think about It

This problem relies heavily on our being able to relate the moles of atoms in a compound's formula to each other.

7.105. **Collect and Organize**

To determine the percent yield of ammonia in the reaction described, we need a balanced chemical equation for the reaction of 6.04 kg of H_2 with N_2 to give 28.0 kg of NH_3. We have excess N_2 in the reaction, so the theoretical yield is based solely on the moles of H_2 present at the beginning of the reaction.

Analyze

The balanced equation for the reaction is

$$N_2(g) + 3 H_2(g) \rightarrow 2 NH_3(g)$$

Solve

The theoretical yield of ammonia in this reaction is

$$6.04 \text{ kg } H_2 \times \frac{1000 \text{ g}}{1 \text{ kg}} \times \frac{1 \text{ mol } H_2}{2.016 \text{ g}} \times \frac{2 \text{ mol } NH_3}{3 \text{ mol } H_2} \times \frac{17.03 \text{ g } NH_3}{1 \text{ mol}} = 34{,}015 \text{ g, or } 34.0 \text{ kg } NH_3$$

The percent yield is

$$\frac{28.0 \text{ kg}}{34.0 \text{ kg}} \times 100 = 82.4\%$$

Think about It

In this reaction hydrogen is the limiting reactant because the problem states that the reaction is run with an excess of nitrogen.

7.107. **Collect and Organize**

Sulfur dioxide can be trapped to form calcium sulfate before it enters the atmosphere. We are to write the balanced equation for the process and calculate the mass of calcium sulfate produced from each ton (t) of SO_2.

Analyze

(a) The reactants and products for the "scrubbing" of SO_2 in an unbalanced equation are

$$SO_2(g) + CaO(s) + O_2(g) \rightarrow CaSO_4(s)$$

(b) We use the stoichiometric relationship of SO_2 to $CaSO_4$ in the balanced equation to calculate how much calcium sulfate is produced.

Solve

(a) $2\ SO_2(g) + 2\ CaO(s) + O_2(g) \rightarrow 2\ CaSO_4(s)$

(b) $1.00\ t\ SO_2 \times \dfrac{1000\ kg}{1\ t} \times \dfrac{1000\ g}{1\ kg} \times \dfrac{1\ mol\ SO_2}{64.06\ g} \times \dfrac{2\ mol\ CaSO_4}{2\ mol\ SO_2} \times \dfrac{136.14\ g}{1\ mol\ CaSO_4} \times \dfrac{1\ kg}{1000\ g} \times \dfrac{1\ t}{1000\ kg} = 2.13\ t$

Think about It

The calcium sulfate produced could find use as a desiccant as well as in cement, plaster, and blackboard chalk.

7.109. **Collect and Organize**

Using the percent composition of a mineral, we are to determine the formula.

Analyze

The percent composition is given in percentage by mass. If we assume 100 g of the mineral, 34.55 g of it is Mg, 19.96 g of it is Si, and 45.49 g of it is O. Using the molar masses of these elements, we can calculate the moles that these masses represent for each element and then find the whole-number ratio of the elements in the compound to give the formula of the mineral.

Solve

$$34.55\ g\ Mg \times \dfrac{1\ mol}{24.31\ g} = 1.421\ mol\ Mg$$

$$19.96\ g\ Si \times \dfrac{1\ mol}{28.09\ g} = 0.7106\ mol\ Si$$

$$45.49\ g\ O \times \dfrac{1\ mol}{16.00\ g} = 2.843\ mol\ O$$

This gives a molar ratio of Mg:Si:O of 2:1:4; the formula for the mineral is Mg_2SiO_4.

Think about It

The SiO_4^{4-} ion is the silicate ion, and this mineral's name is therefore magnesium silicate.

CHAPTER 8 | Aqueous Solutions: Chemistry of the Hydrosphere

8.1. Collect and Organize

This question asks us to differentiate between a strong binary acid and a weak binary acid through which we are specifically to identify the acid that is weak. A binary acid is an acid containing hydrogen and another element, such as HCl. A strong acid completely dissociates, meaning that all binary molecules of HX are present in solution as H^+ and X^-. A weak acid does not completely dissociate, meaning that some of the HX molecules are in the form of H^+ and X^- and some are present in the form HX.

Analyze

From Figure P8.1, the red spheres are attached to three white spheres and have a positive charge, so these must represent the H_3O^+ that results from the dissociation of the binary acids. The green, yellow, and magenta spheres carrying a negative charge must represent the Xs in the binary acids HX. If the X^- are free in solution and surrounded only by water molecules and not combined with H^+ (a white atom), then that HX must be a strong acid. If, however, HX is found in the solution as a molecule along with H^+ and X^-, then that HX must be a weak acid.

Solve

All the green and magenta spheres are present in solution as ions, not in combination with H^+ as HX. Therefore, HX (green) and HX (magenta) must both be strong acids. HX (yellow), however, is represented as two HX molecules and three X^- (yellow) ions. Because only some of the HX (yellow) has dissociated, HX (yellow) is the weak acid.

Think about It

The extent to which a weak acid may be dissociated can vary. If this were a strong weak acid, perhaps only one HX (yellow) molecule would be represented in Figure P8.1 along with four X^- (yellow) anions.

8.3. Collect and Organize

From Figure P8.3 we are asked to identify which ions are represented by the green and blue spheres at the equivalence point for a titration of sulfuric acid (H_2SO_4) with sodium hydroxide (NaOH).

Analyze

At the equivalence point the moles of acid (H_2SO_4) have reacted with the stoichiometric number of moles of base (NaOH). The reaction that describes this titration reaction is

$$H_2SO_4(aq) + 2\,NaOH(aq) \rightarrow Na_2SO_4(aq) + H_2O(\ell)$$

Solve

All sodium salts are soluble in water and therefore Na_2SO_4 will be present in solution as Na^+ and SO_4^{2-} ions. The Na^+ cations will have water molecules surrounding them, with the O atoms oriented toward them, whereas the SO_4^{2-} anions will have water molecules surrounding them, with the H atoms oriented toward them. Therefore, the blue spheres are the Na^+ cations and the green spheres are the SO_4^{2-} anions.

Think about It

The stoichiometries of the ions in solution are correct; we see twice as many Na^+ ions as SO_4^{2-} ions, as should be the case for the ions dissociated from Na_2SO_4.

8.5. Collect and Organize

Using Figure P8.5 we are to identify the oxidation change that occurs for the nitrogen atom in the reaction.

Analyze

The figure represents the following chemical equation

$$2\,NO + O_2 \rightarrow 2\,NO_2$$

Solve

The oxidation state for O in NO and NO_2 is –2. Therefore, the oxidation state of N in NO is +2 and in NO_2 the oxidation state for N is +4. Therefore, the N atom in this reaction is oxidized from +2 to +4, for an oxidation state change of 2.

Think about It

Because this is a redox reaction, something must be reduced. Here, O_2 changes its oxidation state from 0 to –2.

8.7. **Collect and Organize**

We are to rank the molecules of N and O in Figure P8.7 in order of decreasing oxidation state of the nitrogen atom.

Analyze

In each of these species the oxygen atom has an oxidation state of –2. From that we can determine the oxidation state of the nitrogen atoms.

Solve

(a) The formula for this species is N_2O_5. With five O atoms, each with a –2 oxidation state, both N atoms must have an oxidation state of +5.
(b) The formula for this species is N_2O_4. With four O atoms at a –2 oxidation state, both N atoms must have an oxidation state of +4.
(c) The formula for this species is NO. With the O atom at a –2 oxidation state, the N atom must have an oxidation state of +2.
(d) The formula for this species is N_2O_3. With three O atoms at a –2 oxidation state, both N atoms must have an oxidation state of +3.
(e) The formula for this species is NO_2. With two O atoms at a –2 oxidation state, the N atom must have an oxidation state of +4.
The species in order of decreasing (less positive) oxidation state:

$$\text{(a) } N_2O_5 > \text{(b) } N_2O_4 = \text{(e) } NO_2 > \text{(d) } N_2O_3 > \text{(c) } NO$$

Think about It

That the oxidation state of N in N_2O_4 is the same as that in NO_2 makes sense because these two compounds have the same empirical formula.

8.9. **Collect and Organize**

For the titration of sulfuric acid with barium hydroxide, we are asked to write the overall equation and then consider how the conductivity of the solution would change during the titration.

Analyze

The reaction in the titration is an acid–base neutralization reaction. Therefore, the products are water and a salt ($BaSO_4$, which is insoluble). To think about how the conductivity changes, we need the ionic equation. Conductivity will be high for the solution when many ions are present in solution. When no ions are present, the conductivity is that of pure water (zero on our graph).

Solve

(a) Overall equation for the titration is

$$H_2SO_4(aq) + Ba(OH)_2(aq) \rightarrow BaSO_4(s) + 2\ H_2O(\ell)$$

(b) The ionic equation is

$$2\ H^+(aq) + SO_4^{2-}(aq) + Ba^{2+}(aq) + 2\ OH^-(aq) \rightarrow BaSO_4(s) + 2\ H_2O(\ell)$$

Before the titration begins, we have only a solution of H_2SO_4, which is ionized in solution to $2\ H^+(aq)$ and SO_4^{2-} (aq). The conductivity of this solution is high (and above that of pure water). As the titration proceeds, the conductivity will decrease because of the formation of low-solubility $BaSO_4$ and nonionized H_2O. At the equivalence point all the H_2SO_4 has reacted; only $BaSO_4$ and H_2O are present, and therefore the conductivity will be zero (that of pure water). As we titrate with $Ba(OH)_2$ beyond the equivalence point, the conductivity will increase because of the presence of excess Ba^{2+} and OH^- ions. The graph that shows the change is (c).

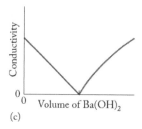

(c)

Think about It

Before the equivalence point, conductivity is due to unreacted H_2SO_4, but after the equivalence point the conductivity is due to excess $Ba(OH)_2$.

8.11. **Collect and Organize**

The molarity of a solution is the moles of solute in 1 L of solution. For each part of this problem, we are given the moles of solute in a volume (in milliliters) of solution. Molarity is abbreviated as *M* (for example, 2.00 *M*).

Analyze

To find the molarity, we need only divide the moles of solute by the volume of solution in liters. To get the volume in liters, we simply divide the milliliters of solution by 1000 or, even more simply, move the decimal three places to the left (for example, 100.0 mL = 0.1000 L).

Solve

(a) $\dfrac{0.56 \text{ mol}}{0.1000 \text{ L}} = 5.6 \ M \ BaCl_2$

(b) $\dfrac{0.200 \text{ mol}}{0.2000 \text{ L}} = 1.00 \ M \ Na_2CO_3$

(c) $\dfrac{0.325 \text{ mol}}{0.2500 \text{ L}} = 1.30 \ M \ C_6H_{12}O_6$

(d) $\dfrac{1.48 \text{ mol}}{0.2500 \text{ L}} = 5.92 \ M \ KNO_3$

Think about It

These calculations can be done quickly if you recognize, for example, that 100 mL is 1/10 of a liter. Therefore, the molarity of the solution will be 10 times the number of moles.

8.13. **Collect and Organize**

The molarity of ions in a solution is found similarly to the molarity of a solute: divide the moles of the ion present by the volume of the solution.

Analyze

In this problem, all the volumes are given in milliliters. To convert these volumes to liters, we move the decimal three places to the left (for example, 100.0 mL = 0.1000 L). The quantity of ions is given in grams. To find moles of solute we use the molar mass of each ion (recall that the mass of missing or added electrons is negligible).

Solve

(a) $\dfrac{0.29 \text{ mol NaNO}_3}{\text{L}} \times \dfrac{1 \text{ mol Na}^+}{\text{mol NaNO}_3} = 0.29 \ M \ \text{Na}^+$

(b) $\dfrac{0.33 \text{ g NaCl} \times \dfrac{1 \text{ mol NaCl}}{58.44 \text{ g}} \times \dfrac{1 \text{ mol Na}^+}{1 \text{ mol NaCl}}}{0.025 \text{ L}} = 0.23 \ M \ \text{Na}^+$

(c) $\dfrac{0.88 \text{ mol Na}_2\text{SO}_4}{\text{L}} \times \dfrac{2 \text{ mol Na}^+}{\text{mol Na}_2\text{SO}_4} = 1.76 \, M \text{ Na}^+$

(d) $\dfrac{0.46 \text{ g Na}_3\text{PO}_4 \times \dfrac{1 \text{ mol Na}_3\text{PO}_4}{163.94 \text{ g}} \times \dfrac{3 \text{ mol Na}^+}{1 \text{ mol Na}_3\text{PO}_4}}{0.100 \text{ L}} = 0.084 \, M \text{ Na}^+$

Think about It

Calculating molarity given a mass of a solute involves first calculating moles of solute with the molar mass.

8.15. **Collect and Organize**

We are asked to calculate the grams of a solute needed to prepare a solution of a specific concentration.

Analyze

First we can find the moles of solute needed for the solution by multiplying the molarity by the volume (in liters). Once we have moles, we can use the molar mass of the solute to calculate the mass of solute needed.

Solve

(a) $1.000 \text{ L} \times \dfrac{0.200 \text{ mol}}{1 \text{ L}} \times \dfrac{58.44 \text{ g}}{1 \text{ mol}} = 11.7 \text{ g NaCl}$

(b) $0.2500 \text{ L} \times \dfrac{0.125 \text{ mol}}{1 \text{ L}} \times \dfrac{159.61 \text{ g}}{1 \text{ mol}} = 4.99 \text{ g CuSO}_4$

(c) $0.5000 \text{ L} \times \dfrac{0.400 \text{ mol}}{1 \text{ L}} \times \dfrac{32.04 \text{ g}}{1 \text{ mol}} = 6.41 \text{ g CH}_3\text{OH}$

Think about It

This is a practical calculation for preparing solutions when we know that we want to have a solution with a particular concentration.

8.17. **Collect and Organize**

From the concentration of ions, we are asked to calculate the total mass of the ions in 2.75 L of river water.

Analyze

We first have to convert the millimolar (mM) concentrations of each ion to molar (1000 mM = 1 M) by moving the decimal three places to the left (for example, 0.100 mM = 1.00×10^{-4} M). From the molar concentration of each ion we can find the moles (and subsequently the mass) of each through multiplying the molarity by the volume (2.75 L). Finally, we need to add all the masses of the ions together.

Solve

Mass of Ca^{2+}: $2.75 \text{ L} \times \left(\dfrac{8.20 \times 10^{-4} \text{ mol}}{\text{L}} \right) \times \left(\dfrac{40.08 \text{ g}}{1 \text{ mol}} \right) = 0.0904 \text{ g}$

Mass of Mg^{2+}: $2.75 \text{ L} \times \left(\dfrac{4.30 \times 10^{-4} \text{ mol}}{\text{L}} \right) \times \left(\dfrac{24.31 \text{ g}}{1 \text{ mol}} \right) = 0.0287 \text{ g}$

Mass of Na$^+$: $2.75 \text{ L} \times \left(\dfrac{3.00 \times 10^{-4} \text{ mol}}{\text{L}} \right) \times \left(\dfrac{22.99 \text{ g}}{1 \text{ mol}} \right) = 0.0190 \text{ g}$

Mass of K$^+$: $2.75 \text{ L} \times \left(\dfrac{2.00 \times 10^{-2} \text{ mol}}{\text{L}} \right) \times \left(\dfrac{39.10 \text{ g}}{1 \text{ mol}} \right) = 2.15 \text{ g}$

Mass of Cl$^-$: $2.75 \text{ L} \times \left(\dfrac{2.50 \times 10^{-4} \text{ mol}}{\text{L}} \right) \times \left(\dfrac{35.45 \text{ g}}{1 \text{ mol}} \right) = 0.0244 \text{ g}$

Mass of SO_4^{2-}: $2.75 \text{ L} \times \left(\dfrac{3.80 \times 10^{-4} \text{ mol}}{\text{L}} \right) \times \left(\dfrac{96.06 \text{ g}}{1 \text{ mol}} \right) = 0.100 \text{ g}$

Mass of HCO_3^-: $2.75 \text{ L} \times \left(\dfrac{1.82 \times 10^{-3} \text{ mol}}{\text{L}} \right) \times \left(\dfrac{61.02 \text{ g}}{1 \text{ mol}} \right) = 0.305 \text{ g}$

Total mass of ions: $0.0904 + 0.0287 + 0.0190 + 2.15 + 0.0244 + 0.100 + 0.305 = 2.72 \text{ g}$

Think about It
The mass of the ions dissolved in natural water is sometimes called "total dissolved solids."

8.19. **Collect and Organize**
For each pesticide we are given the volume and concentration of the solution. From this information we can find the moles of pesticide by multiplying the volume by the concentration.

Analyze
We have to watch our units here for concentration and volume. We need to use the fact that 1000 mL = 1 L and 1000 mmol = 1 mol.

Solve

(a) $0.400 \text{ L} \times \dfrac{0.024 \text{ mol}}{\text{L}} = 9.6 \times 10^{-3} \text{ mol, or } 9.6 \text{ mmol lindane}$

(b) $1.65 \text{ L} \times \dfrac{4.73 \times 10^{-4} \text{ mol}}{\text{L}} = 7.80 \times 10^{-4} \text{ mol, or } 0.780 \text{ mmol dieldrin}$

(c) $25.8 \text{ L} \times \dfrac{3.4 \times 10^{-3} \text{ mol}}{\text{L}} = 8.8 \times 10^{-2} \text{ mol, or } 88 \text{ mmol DDT}$

(d) $154 \text{ L} \times \dfrac{2.74 \times 10^{-2} \text{ mol}}{\text{L}} = 4.22 \text{ mol aldrin}$

Think about It
Converting milliliters to liters, liters to milliliters, millimoles to moles, and moles to millimoles by moving the decimal is convenient, but be sure that you do not mistakenly move it in the wrong direction (for example, saying that 2.56 mmol = 2560 mol would be wrong).

8.21. **Collect and Organize**
The table gives information on both sample size and the mass of DDT in each groundwater sample. To compare the DDT amounts among samples, we are asked to calculate the DDT in millimoles per liter.

Analyze
We have to first compute the millimoles of DDT in each sample by dividing the mass (in milligrams) by the molar mass of DDT ($C_{14}H_9Cl_5$, 354.49 mg/mmol). To find the concentration in each sample, we divide this result by the volume of the sample in liters.

Solve

Sample from the orchard: $\dfrac{0.030 \text{ mg} \times \left(\dfrac{1 \text{ mmol}}{354.49 \text{ mg}} \right)}{0.2500 \text{ L}} = 3.4 \times 10^{-4} \text{ mmol/L}$

Sample from the residential area: $\dfrac{0.035 \text{ mg} \times \left(\dfrac{1 \text{ mmol}}{354.49 \text{ mg}} \right)}{1.750 \text{ L}} = 5.6 \times 10^{-5} \text{ mmol/L}$

Sample from the residential area after storm: $\dfrac{0.57 \text{ mg} \times \left(\dfrac{1 \text{ mmol}}{354.49 \text{ mg}}\right)}{0.0500 \text{ L}} = 3.2 \times 10^{-2} \text{ mmol/L}$

Think about It

With all the concentrations of DDT in the samples now expressed in millimoles per liter (mM), we can make comparisons. The orchard is a little less contaminated than the residential area. The big surprise is that after a storm the groundwater contains nearly 600 times more DDT than before the storm.

8.23. Collect and Organize

We are given the concentration of zinc ion in the sewer effluent in milligrams per liter and asked to express this in molarity, which is moles per liter.

Analyze

Because we are given milligrams of Zn^{2+} we first have to convert that mass to grams (divide by 1000) and then compute the moles from the molar mass of Zn^{2+} (65.41 g/mol). This will be the moles of Zn^{2+} in 1 L.

Solve

$$\frac{10 \text{ mg Zn}^{2+}}{1 \text{ L}} \times \frac{1 \text{ g}}{1000 \text{ mg}} \times \frac{1 \text{ mol}}{65.38 \text{ g}} = 1.5 \times 10^{-4} \, M \text{ Zn}^{2+}$$

Think about It

This problem is made even shorter when you are comfortable in immediately stating that 10 mg = 0.010 g Zn.

8.25. Collect and Organize

We are asked to decide whether the solubility of the substance would allow us to prepare a 1.0 M solution.

Analyze

If the mass of solute needed to prepare a 1.0 M solution is greater than the solubility limit, we will not be able to prepare the solution in 1.0 M concentration. We must use comparable units in making the comparisons. The solubility of these compounds could be expressed in grams per milliliter. For a 1.0 M solution of each, we need to weigh out 1 molar mass of the substance and dissolve it in 1000 mL. If we express that value in grams per milliliter, we will have the direct comparisons.

Solve

(a) $CuSO_4 \cdot 5 \, H_2O$ has a molar mass of 249.68 g/mol. For a 1.0 M solution, 249.68 g would be dissolved in 1 L, or 1000 mL. This is 0.25 g/mL. This is slightly higher than the solubility (0.231 g/mL).
(b) $AgNO_3$ has a molar mass of 169.87 g/mol. For a 1.0 M solution, 169.87 g would be dissolved in 1 L, or 1000 mL. This is 0.17 g/mL. This is lower than the solubility (1.22 g/mL).
(c) $Fe(NO_3)_2 \cdot 6 \, H_2O$ has a molar mass of 287.94 g/mol. For a 1.0 M solution, 287.94 g would be dissolved in 1 L, or 1000 mL. This is 0.29 g/mL. This is lower than the solubility (1.13 g/mL).
(d) $Ca(OH)_2$ has a molar mass of 74.092 g/mol. For a 1.0 M solution, 74.092 g would be dissolved in 1 L, or 1000 mL. This is 0.07 g/mL. This is lower than the solubility (0.185 g/mL).
Therefore, we would be able to prepare 1.0 M solutions for substances (b)–(d) but not for (a) $CuSO_4 \cdot 5H_2O$.

Think about It

Finding the common units to make the comparison in the question is important. We could have expressed the concentration in moles per liter and converted the solubility data from grams per milliliter to moles per liter. As long as the units are comparable, we will arrive at the same answer.

8.27. Collect and Organize

We need to use the density of the coastal water given (1.02 g/mL) to calculate the volume of water for the concentration (1.09 g Mg^{2+}/kg). We also need to convert grams of Mg^{2+} into moles by using the molar mass.

Analyze

Using unit conversions, we can solve this in a single step. We can use the density to find the mass in kilograms of coastal seawater directly because the density of 1.02 g/mL = 1.02 kg/L. Then we convert the grams of Mg^{2+} to moles by using the molar mass of Mg^{2+} (24.305 g/mol).

Solve

$$\frac{1.09 \text{ g } Mg^{2+}}{1 \text{ kg}} \times \frac{1.02 \text{ kg}}{1 \text{ L}} \times \frac{1 \text{ mol}}{24.305 \text{ g}} = 4.57 \times 10^{-2} \text{ } M \text{ } Mg^{2+}$$

Think about It

Recognizing the relationships of kilograms to grams and milliliters to liters made this problem quick to solve.

8.29. **Collect and Organize**

In diluting a solution, the final concentration is less than the original concentration. Each solution is diluted to 25.0 mL.

Analyze

For each dilution, we can use Equation 8.6:

$$V_{initial} \times M_{initial} = V_{final} \times M_{final}$$

Since we are calculating the final concentration, C_{final}, we can rearrange the equation to

$$M_{final} = \frac{V_{initial} \times M_{initial}}{V_{final}}$$

Solve

(a) When 1.00 mL of 0.452 M Na^+ is diluted to 25.0 mL, we have $V_{initial}$ = 1.00 mL, $M_{initial}$ = 0.452 M, and V_{final} = 25.0 mL. The final concentration after diluting will be

$$M_{final} = \frac{1.00 \text{ mL} \times 0.452 \text{ } M}{25.0 \text{ mL}} = 1.81 \times 10^{-2} \text{ } M \text{ } Na^+$$

(b) When 2.00 mL of 3.4 mM LiCl is diluted to 25.0 mL, the final concentration will be

$$M_{final} = \frac{2.00 \text{ mL} \times 3.4 \text{ m}M}{25.0 \text{ mL}} = 2.7 \times 10^{-1} \text{ m}M \text{ LiCl}$$

(c) When 5.00 mL of 6.42×10^{-2} mM Zn^{2+} is diluted to 25.0 mL, the final concentration after diluting will be

$$M_{final} = \frac{5.00 \text{ mL} \times 6.42 \times 10^{-2} \text{ m}M}{25.0 \text{ mL}} = 1.28 \times 10^{-2} \text{ m}M \text{ } Zn^{2+}$$

Think about It

The milliliter volume units for these calculations do not need to be converted to another unit. As long as $V_{initial}$ and V_{final} are in the same units, the units will cancel in the calculations.

8.31. **Collect and Organize**

This "dilution" question is reversed: the concentration of Na^+ increases as the water in the puddle evaporates during the summer day. Given the initial concentration of Na^+ (0.449 M) and the percent evaporation, we are asked to find the final concentration of Na^+.

Analyze

We first have to compute volumes from the percent volume of the puddle after evaporation. If we assume a 1000 mL puddle, a reduction of the puddle volume to 23% would mean that 230 mL of the water in the puddle remains. Rearranging the dilution equation for the final concentration gives

$$M_{final} = \frac{V_{initial} \times M_{initial}}{V_{final}}$$

Solve

Here, $V_{\text{initial}} = 1000$ mL, $M_{\text{initial}} = 0.449$ M, and $V_{\text{final}} = 230$ mL. The final concentration of Na^+ in the puddle after evaporation is

$$M_{\text{final}} = \frac{1000 \text{ mL} \times 0.449 \text{ } M}{230 \text{ mL}} = 1.95 \text{ } M$$

Think about It

The concentration of the Na^+ in the puddle increased, as we would expect.

8.33. Collect and Organize

Given the size and amount of API in an adult dose of a cough suppressant, we are to determine the concentration and calculate the volume of the adult cough syrup needed to prepare a syrup of lower strength for children.

Analyze

The concentration of the cough suppressant in each syrup is calculated by dividing the milligrams of API by the volume of the dose. We can then use the dilution equation to determine how much of the adult syrup to dilute to obtain the children's syrup.

Solve

The adult dose concentration is

$$\frac{35 \text{ mg}}{20.0 \text{ mL}} = 1.75 \text{ mg/mL, or } 1.8 \text{ mg/mL (to two significant figures)}$$

The children's dose concentration is

$$\frac{4.00 \text{ mg}}{10.0 \text{ mL}} = 0.400 \text{ mg/mL}$$

For the child-strength cough syrup, the volume of adult syrup needed is

$$V_{\text{adult}} = \frac{V_{\text{child}} \times M_{\text{child}}}{M_{\text{adult}}} = \frac{0.400 \text{ mg/mL} \times 100.0 \text{ mL}}{1.75 \text{ mg/mL}} = 23 \text{ mL}$$

Think about It

This answer makes sense because the child-strength cough syrup is about 1/4 the strength of the adult cough syrup.

8.35. Collect and Organize / Analyze

Electricity can conduct through a solution if it contains mobile ions.

Solve

Table salt produces Na^+ and Cl^- ions in solution when it dissolves. Sugar does not dissociate into ions because it is not a salt. Ions are required to conduct electricity. Sugar, therefore, is not a good conductor of electricity in solution, but table salt (NaCl) in solution is.

Think about It

A solution that conducts electricity is called an electrolyte, and one that does not conduct electricity is a nonelectrolyte.

8.37. Collect and Organize

Electricity can be conducted through a liquid if mobile ions are present.

Analyze

Liquid methanol does not contain any ions because it does not dissociate. Molten sodium hydroxide, by contrast, contains mobile Na^+ and OH^- ions.

Solve

The lack of ions in methanol means that the liquid is nonconductive. Molten NaOH, however, has freely moving Na^+ and OH^- ions, which can conduct electricity.

Think about It

Solid NaOH, however, is a poor conductor because the ions are locked into position in the structure of the solid.

8.39. Collect and Organize

The ability to conduct electricity rises with the presence of more ions in solution.

Analyze

All the solutions contain salts, but they have different numbers of ions in their formula units and different concentrations. For each salt, we have to determine the number of ions (in terms of molarity).

Solve

(a) $1.0\ M$ NaCl contains $1.0\ M\ Na^+ + 1.0\ M\ Cl^- = 2.0\ M$ ions.
(b) $1.2\ M$ KCl contains $1.2\ M\ K^+ + 1.2\ M\ Cl^- = 2.4\ M$ ions.
(c) $1.0\ M\ Na_2SO_4$ contains $2.0\ M\ Na^+ + 1.0\ M\ SO_4^{2-} = 3.0\ M$ ions.
(d) $0.75\ M$ LiCl contains $0.75\ M\ Li^+ + 0.75\ M\ Cl^- = 1.5\ M$ ions.
Therefore, the order of the solutions in decreasing ability to conduct electricity is
$$\text{(c) } 1.0\ M\ Na_2SO_4 > \text{(b) } 1.2\ M\ KCl > \text{(a) } 1.0\ M\ NaCl > \text{(d) } 0.75\ M\ LiCl$$

Think about It

Although the Na_2SO_4 and NaCl solutions are both $1\ M$ in salt concentration, the solution of Na_2SO_4 is more conductive because it contains $3\ M$ ions versus NaCl's $2\ M$ ions.

8.41. Collect and Organize

The concentration of Na^+ ions in each solution depends on the concentration of the solution as well as the number of sodium ions in the chemical formula of the salt. The concentration of all these salt solutions is $0.025\ M$.

Analyze

If a substance has one Na^+ in its formula, then the concentration of Na^+ ions in a solution of that salt is equal to the concentration of the substance in solution. But if, for example, two Na^+ ions are in the salt's formula, the concentration of Na^+ ions in the solution is twice the concentration of the salt.

Solve

(a) $0.025\ M$ NaBr is $0.025\ M\ Na^+$.
(b) $0.025\ M\ Na_2SO_4$ is $2 \times 0.025\ M = 0.050\ M\ Na^+$.
(c) $0.025\ M\ Na_3PO_4$ is $3 \times 0.025\ M = 0.075\ M\ Na^+$.

Think about It

Salts dissociate into their constituent ions, and so a solution may become more concentrated in a particular ion than the original concentration of salt.

8.43. Collect and Organize

We are to identify the property that makes an acid an acid.

Analyze

Acids complement bases and their reactions involve the exchange of protons (H^+) between the acid and the base.

Solve

Acids transfer H^+ to a base, and in water they increase the concentration of H^+ in solution.

Think about It

In aqueous solution, the base can be H_2O so that when the acid transfers its H^+ to water, H_3O^+ is produced.

8.45. Collect and Organize
In the context of acid–base reactions, we are asked to name two strong acids and two weak acids.

Analyze
A strong acid is one that completely dissociates into $H^+ + A^-$ in solution. A weak acid only partially dissociates and gives a mixture of H^+, A^-, and HA in solution.

Solve
Strong acids include HCl, HNO_3, $HClO_4$, H_2SO_4, HI, and HBr; weak acids include CH_3COOH, HCOOH, HF, and H_3PO_4.

Think about It
Strong bases include NaOH and KOH; weak bases include NH_3 and anions of weak acids such as the acetate ion, CH_3COO^-.

8.47. Collect and Organize
We are to identify the property that makes a base a base.

Analyze
Bases complement acids, and their reactions involve the exchange of protons (H^+) between the acid and the base.

Solve
Bases accept H^+ from an acid, and in water they increase the concentration of OH^- in solution.

Think about It
In aqueous solution, the acid can be H_2O so that when the base accepts H^+ from water, OH^- is produced.

8.49. Collect and Organize / Analyze
In the context of acid–base reactions, we are asked to name two strong bases and two weak bases. A strong base is one that completely dissociates into OH^- in solution. A weak base only partially dissociates and gives a mixture of B^+, OH^-, and BOH in solution.

Solve
Strong bases include NaOH, KOH, CsOH, LiOH, RbOH, $Ba(OH)_2$, $Sr(OH)_2$, and $Ca(OH)_2$; weak bases include NH_3, CH_3NH_2, and C_5H_5N.

Think about It
Strong acids include HBr and HNO_3; weak acids include acetic acid and formic acid.

8.51. Collect and Organize
In each part of this problem, we identify the acid (proton donor) and base (proton acceptor). To write the net ionic equations we have to identify the spectator ions and remove them from the ionic equation.

Analyze
For each reaction, write the species present in aqueous solution (showing dissociation). From these species, you can identify the acid and base. Then eliminate any spectator ions in the ionic equation to give the net ionic equation.

Solve
(a) Ionic and net ionic equation:
$$2\,H^+(aq) + SO_4^{2-}(aq) + Ca^{2+}(aq) + 2\,OH^-(aq) \rightarrow CaSO_4(s) + 2\,H_2O(\ell)$$
The acid is H_2SO_4; the base is $Ca(OH)_2$.
(b) Ionic and net ionic equation:
$$PbCO_3(s) + 2\,H^+(aq) + SO_4^{2-}(aq) \rightarrow PbSO_4(s) + CO_2(g) + H_2O(\ell)$$
$PbCO_3$ is the base; sulfuric acid is the acid.

(c) Ionic equation:
$$Ca^{2+}(aq) + 2\ OH^-(aq) + 2\ CH_3COOH(aq) \rightarrow Ca^{2+}(aq) + 2\ CH_3COO^-(aq) + 2\ H_2O(\ell)$$
Calcium is a spectator ion. $Ca(OH)_2$ is the base; CH_3COOH is the acid.
Net ionic equation:
$$OH^-(aq) + CH_3COOH(aq) \rightarrow CH_3COO^-(aq) + H_2O(\ell)$$

Think about It
Reactions (a) and (c) are neutralization reactions, whereas reaction (b) is an acid–base reaction that also forms a precipitate ($PbSO_4$) and a gas (CO_2).

8.53. Collect and Organize
We need to write molecular formulas for the reactants from the chemical names, determine the formulas for the products, write a balanced molecular equation, and then write the net ionic equation.

Analyze
All the reactions involve an acid–base reaction in which a proton is transferred from the acid to the base. We can use the rules of Chapter 4 to write the formulas from the chemical names. In the net ionic equation, we must eliminate all spectator ions.

Solve
(a) Molecular equation:
$$Mg(OH)_2(s) + H_2SO_4(aq) \rightarrow MgSO_4(aq) + 2\ H_2O(\ell)$$
Ionic and net ionic equations:
$$Mg(OH)_2(s) + 2\ H^+(aq) + SO_4^{2-}(aq) \rightarrow Mg^{2+}(aq) + SO_4^{2-}(aq) + 2\ H_2O(\ell)$$
$$Mg(OH)_2(s) + 2\ H^+(aq) \rightarrow Mg^{2+}(aq) + 2\ H_2O(\ell)$$
(b) Molecular equation:
$$MgCO_3(s) + 2\ HCl(aq) \rightarrow MgCl_2(aq) + H_2CO_3(aq)$$
The carbonic acid reacts in solution to give CO_2 and H_2O, so the ionic and net ionic equations are as follows:
$$MgCO_3(s) + 2\ H^+(aq) + 2\ Cl^-(aq) \rightarrow Mg^{2+}(aq) + 2\ Cl^-(aq) + H_2O(\ell) + CO_2(g)$$
$$MgCO_3(s) + 2\ H^+(aq) \rightarrow Mg^{2+}(aq) + H_2O(\ell) + CO_2(g)$$
(c) Molecular equation:
$$NH_3(g) + HCl(g) \rightarrow NH_4Cl(s)$$
This is also the net ionic equation because these species are not in aqueous solution and cannot form ions.

Think about It
Species that are solids or gases do not appear as ionic species. Only soluble species dissolved in water appear with the designation "(aq)" in the ionic equations.

8.55. Collect and Organize
We are given that lead(II) carbonate ($PbCO_3$) and lead(II) hydroxide [$Pb(OH)_2$] dissolve in acidic solutions (containing H_3O^+).

Analyze
To write the net ionic equations, we need to determine the acid–base reaction that might be occurring. Here the acid is in solution as H_3O^+, which we can write as $H^+(aq)$. This species must react with the anions of the solid salts (CO_3^{2-} and OH^-).

Solve
Lead(II) carbonate:
$$PbCO_3(s) + 2\ H^+(aq) \rightarrow Pb^{2+}(aq) + H_2CO_3(aq)$$
Carbonic acid reacts in solution to give $H_2O(\ell)$ and $CO_2(g)$:
$$PbCO_3(s) + 2\ H^+(aq) \rightarrow Pb^{2+}(aq) + CO_2(g) + H_2O(\ell)$$
Lead(II) hydroxide:
$$Pb(OH)_2(s) + 2\ H^+(aq) \rightarrow Pb^{2+}(aq) + 2\ H_2O(\ell)$$

Think about It

Both solids, by reacting with acid to form either CO_2 with water or just water, dissolve the solid, releasing toxic Pb^{2+} ions into the water.

8.57. Collect and Organize

Solutions that contain a solute may be classified as unsaturated, saturated, or supersaturated. We are to distinguish saturated from supersaturated solutions.

Analyze

More of the solute can dissolve in an unsaturated solution, but a saturated solution contains all the solute it can hold in the solution.

Solve

A saturated solution contains the maximum concentration of a solute. A supersaturated solution temporarily contains more than the maximum concentration of a solute at a given temperature.

Think about It

A supersaturated solution eventually precipitates out some solute (until it reaches the point of saturation).

8.59. Collect and Organize

We are to define a precipitation reaction.

Analyze

A precipitation reaction is distinct from an acid–base or redox reaction. A precipitation reaction must have the appearance of a solid product when two homogeneous solutions are mixed.

Solve

A precipitation reaction occurs when two solutions are mixed to form an insoluble compound.

Think about It

It is possible to have reactions that are both acid–base or redox reactions in combination with a precipitation reaction. As long as the reaction produces an insoluble product, it is a precipitation reaction.

8.61. Collect and Organize

We are asked to compare a saturated solution with a concentrated solution.

Analyze

A saturated solution is one in which no more solute can dissolve. A concentrated solution is one that contains a large amount of solute.

Solve

A saturated solution may not be a concentrated solution if the solute is only sparingly or slightly soluble in the solution. Then the solution is a saturated dilute solution.

Think about It

Be careful when using the terms *unsaturated/saturated* and *dilute/concentrated*, which have precise meanings in chemistry.

8.63. Collect and Organize

We can use the rules in Table 8.3 to predict solubility. All the compounds listed in the problem are ionic salts and are being dissolved in water.

Analyze

Soluble salts include those of the alkali metals and the ammonium cation and those with the acetate or nitrate anion. Exceptions exist to the general solubility of halide salts (Ag^+, Cu^+, Hg_2^{2+}, and Pb^{2+} halides are insoluble) and sulfates (Ba^{2+}, Ca^{2+}, Hg_2^{2+}, Pb^{2+}, and Sr^{2+} sulfates are insoluble). All other salts are insoluble except the hydroxides of Ba^{2+}, Ca^{2+}, and Sr^{2+}.

Solve
(a) Barium sulfate is insoluble.
(b) Barium hydroxide is soluble.
(c) Lanthanum nitrate is soluble.
(d) Sodium acetate is soluble.
(e) Lead hydroxide is insoluble.
(f) Calcium phosphate is insoluble.

Think about It
Knowing well the few simple rules of solubility can help us easily predict which salts dissolve in water and which do not.

8.65. Collect and Organize
We are to write balanced molecular and net ionic equations for any precipitation reactions. For each reaction, we have to determine whether the mix of cations and anions present in solution results in an insoluble salt.

Analyze
We use the solubility rules in Table 8.3 to determine which, if any, species precipitates when the two solutions are mixed. The net ionic equation can be written from the ionic equation by eliminating any of the spectator ions, those ions not involved in forming the insoluble precipitate.

Solve
(a) The reactants in aqueous solution are Pb^{2+}, NO_3^-, Na^+, and SO_4^{2-}. If $Pb(NO_3)_2$ and Na_2SO_4 switched anionic partners we would form $PbSO_4$ and $NaNO_3$. Of these two salts, $PbSO_4$ is insoluble. The ionic equation describing this reaction is
$$Pb^{2+}(aq) + 2\ NO_3^-(aq) + 2\ Na^+(aq) + SO_4^{2-}(aq) \rightarrow PbSO_4(s) + 2\ Na^+(aq) + 2\ NO_3^-(aq)$$
The balanced reaction is
$$Pb(NO_3)_2(aq) + Na_2SO_4(aq) \rightarrow PbSO_4(s) + 2\ NaNO_3(aq)$$
The net ionic equation is
$$Pb^{2+}(aq) + SO_4^{2-}(aq) \rightarrow PbSO_4(s)$$
(b) The reactants in aqueous solution are Ni^{2+}, Cl^-, NH_4^+, and NO_3^-. If $NiCl_2$ and NH_4CO_3 switched anionic partners we would form $Ni(NO_3)_2$ and NH_4Cl. Both salts are soluble; therefore, no precipitation reaction occurs.
(c) The reactants in aqueous solution are Fe^{2+}, Cl^-, Na^+, and S^{2-}. If $FeCl_2$ and Na_2S switched anionic partners we would form FeS and NaCl. Of these two salts, FeS is insoluble. The ionic equation describing this reaction is
$$Fe^{2+}(aq) + 2\ Cl^-(aq) + 2\ Na^+(aq) + S^{2-}(aq) \rightarrow FeS(s) + 2\ Na^+(aq) + 2\ Cl^-(aq)$$
The balanced reaction is
$$FeCl_2(aq) + Na_2S(aq) \rightarrow FeS(s) + 2\ NaCl(aq)$$
The net ionic equation is
$$Fe^{2+}(aq) + S^{2-}(aq) \rightarrow FeS(s)$$
(d) The reactants in aqueous solution are Mg^{2+}, SO_4^{2-}, Ba^{2+}, and Cl^-. If $MgSO_4$ and $BaCl_2$ switched anionic partners we would form $MgCl_2$ and $BaSO_4$. Of these two salts, $BaSO_4$ is insoluble. The ionic equation describing this reaction is
$$Mg^{2+}(aq) + SO_4^{2-}(aq) + Ba^{2+}(aq) + 2\ Cl^-(aq) \rightarrow Mg^{2+}(aq) + 2\ Cl^-(aq) + BaSO_4(s)$$
The balanced reaction is
$$MgSO_4(aq) + BaCl_2(aq) \rightarrow MgCl_2(aq) + BaSO_4(s)$$
The net ionic equation is
$$Ba^{2+}(aq) + SO_4^{2-}(aq) \rightarrow BaSO_4(s)$$

Think about It
The net ionic equation for a precipitation reaction describes the formation of the insoluble salt from the aqueous cations and anions.

8.67. Collect and Organize
The compound that precipitates first from an evaporating solution will be the least soluble.

Analyze
The potential salts that could form are all salts of Ca^{2+}: $CaCl_2$, $CaCO_3$, and $Ca(NO_3)_2$. The solubility rules state that nitrate and chloride salts are soluble for Ca^{2+} but imply that the carbonate salt of calcium is insoluble.

Solve
The most insoluble salt, $CaCO_3$, precipitates first from the evaporating solution.

Think about It
Calcium carbonate may not have precipitated from the original, more dilute solution because $CaCO_3$, being somewhat soluble, had not yet become concentrated enough to be a saturated solution. Once the saturation point is reached through evaporation, the salt will precipitate.

8.69. **Collect and Organize**

To determine how much $MgCO_3$ precipitates in this reaction, we have to determine whether Na_2CO_3 or $Mg(NO_3)_2$ is the limiting reactant. The net ionic reaction for the reaction is

$$Mg^{2+}(aq) + CO_3^{2-}(aq) \rightarrow MgCO_3(s)$$

Analyze
From the given volumes of each reactant and its concentration, we first need to calculate the moles of Mg^{2+} and CO_3^{2-} present in the mixed solution. These react in a 1:1 molar ratio to form $MgCO_3$. By comparison of the moles of Mg^{2+} and CO_3^{2-} we can determine the limiting reactant. Because 1 mol of $MgCO_3$ will form from 1 mol of either Mg^{2+} or CO_3^{2-}, the moles of the limiting reactant must equal the moles of $MgCO_3$ formed. From the moles of $MgCO_3$ formed, we can calculate the mass formed by using the molar mass of $MgCO_3$ (84.31 g/mol).

Solve

$$\text{mol } CO_3^{2-} = 10.0 \text{ mL } Na_2CO_3 \times \frac{0.200 \text{ mol}}{1000 \text{ mL}} \times \frac{1 \text{ mol } CO_3^{2-}}{1 \text{ mol } Na_2CO_3} = 2.00 \times 10^{-3} \text{ mol}$$

$$\text{mol } Mg^{2+} = 5.00 \text{ mL } Mg(NO_3)_2 \times \frac{0.0500 \text{ mol}}{1000 \text{ mL}} \times \frac{1 \text{ mol } Mg^{2+}}{1 \text{ mol } Mg(NO_3)_2} = 2.50 \times 10^{-4} \text{ mol}$$

The limiting reactant is $Mg(NO_3)_2$ and 2.50×10^{-4} mol of $MgCO_3$ will form.
The mass of $MgCO_3$ produced is

$$2.50 \times 10^{-4} \text{ mol} \times \frac{84.31 \text{ g}}{1 \text{ mol}} = 2.11 \times 10^{-2} \text{ g } MgCO_3$$

Think about It
In every stoichiometric equation, the moles of the reactants are important. For species in solution, the moles can be found by multiplying the volume of the solution by the concentration, just as finding moles from a mass of substance involves dividing the mass of substance by the molar mass.

8.71. **Collect and Organize**

From the balanced equation, 1 mol of O_2 is required to react with 4 mol of $Fe(OH)^+$, the Fe(II) species. Knowing the volume and concentration of Fe(II), we are asked to find the grams of O_2 needed to form the insoluble $Fe(OH)_3$ product.

Analyze
We can find the moles of $Fe(OH)^+$ in solution by multiplying the volume of the Fe(II) solution (75 mL) by its concentration (0.090 M). The number of moles of O_2 required in the reaction is 1/4 of the moles of $Fe(OH)^+$ present. From moles of O_2 we can use the molar mass of O_2 (32.00 g/mol) to calculate the grams of O_2 needed.

Solve

$$\text{mol Fe(OH)}^+ = 75 \text{ mL} \times \frac{0.090 \text{ mol}}{1000 \text{ mL}} = 6.75 \times 10^{-3} \text{ mol}$$

$$\text{mass of O}_2 = 6.75 \times 10^{-3} \text{ mol Fe(OH)}^+ \times \frac{1 \text{ mol O}_2}{4 \text{ mol Fe(OH)}^+} \times \frac{32.00 \text{ g O}_2}{1 \text{ mol}} = 5.4 \times 10^{-2} \text{ g}$$

Think about It

Because the molar ratio of Fe(OH)$^+$ to O$_2$ is 1:4, we require fewer moles of O$_2$ in this reaction than we have of the Fe(II) species.

8.73. Collect and Organize

To remove 90% of the phosphate from the 4.5×10^6 L of drinking water, we first have to determine the moles of PO$_4^{3-}$ present and then multiply by 0.90 to obtain the amount of PO$_4^{3-}$ that needs to be removed. The balanced equation tells us that 5 mol of Ca(OH)$_2$ is required to react with 3 mol of PO$_4^{3-}$. From that information, we can calculate the amount of Ca(OH)$_2$ needed.

Analyze

We can find the moles of PO$_4^{3-}$ in the water from the volume of water and the concentration of PO$_4^{3-}$. Because that concentration is given as 25 mg/L, we need to use the molar mass of PO$_4^{3-}$ (94.97 g/mol) to calculate moles per liter. We then must multiply this amount by 0.90 (so that 90% of the phosphates are removed). Because the molar ratio for the reaction between PO$_4^{3-}$ and Ca(OH)$_2$ is 3:5, we see that the moles of Ca(OH)$_2$ needed is 5/3 times the moles of phosphate in the water. Once we know moles of Ca(OH)$_2$, we can use the molar mass (74.09 g/mol) to calculate the mass of Ca(OH)$_2$ required.

Solve

$$\text{mol PO}_4^{3-} = 4.5 \times 10^6 \text{ L} \times \frac{25 \text{ mg}}{\text{L}} \times \frac{1 \text{ g}}{1000 \text{ mg}} \times \frac{1 \text{ mol}}{94.97 \text{ g}} = 1185 \text{ mol}$$

$$90\% \text{ of the phosphate} = 1184.6 \text{ mol} \times 0.90 = 1066 \text{ mol}$$

$$\text{mass of Ca(OH)}_2 \text{ required} = 1066 \text{ mol PO}_4^{3-} \times \frac{5 \text{ mol Ca(OH)}_2}{3 \text{ mol PO}_4^{3-}} \times \frac{74.09 \text{ g}}{1 \text{ mol}} = 1.3 \times 10^5 \text{ g, or 130 kg}$$

Think about It

When doing any stoichiometry problem, convert the mass or volume given to moles.

8.75. Collect and Organize

We are to define the connection between losses or gains of electrons and changes in oxidation numbers.

Analyze

Oxidation numbers are assigned to atoms in compounds on the basis of the number of electrons they formally bring to the species. The loss of electrons (oxidation) means that the oxidation number becomes more positive. The gain of electrons (reduction) means that the oxidation number becomes more negative.

Solve

The number of electrons gained or lost is directly related to the change in oxidation number of a species. If a species loses two electrons, the oxidation number of one of the atoms in the species will increase by 2 (for example, from +1 to +3).

Think about It

Oxidation numbers can help us decide which species is oxidized and which is reduced in a redox reaction.

8.77. Collect and Organize

The charges of all the ions are shown as superscripts for the species. We are to determine the sum of oxidation numbers for each species.

Analyze

Because the sum of the oxidation numbers of the atoms must equal the total charge on the polyatomic ion, the sum of the oxidation numbers for each species is simply the charge on the species.

Solve

(a) –1 for OH^-
(b) +1 for NH_4^+
(c) –2 for SO_4^{2-}
(d) –3 for PO_4^{3-}

Think about It

Recall that we can use the charge on a species to determine the oxidation state of an atom in the species that might have a variable oxidation state. For example, the oxidation state for S in SO_4^{2-} is +6 because the sum of the oxidation states of the four oxygen atoms is –8 ($4\ O^{2-}$) and the overall charge is 2– on the anion.

8.79. Collect and Organize

Both silver and gold are placed into sulfuric acid, but only silver dissolves. We are asked which metal is the better reducing agent.

Analyze

For the metals to dissolve, they must be oxidized from their metallic state to a soluble cation (Au^{3+} or Ag^+). When a metal is oxidized, it acts as a reducing agent. Here Au does not reduce sulfuric acid, but Ag does.

Solve

Because silver dissolves (is oxidized) in sulfuric acid but gold does not, silver is more easily oxidized and is therefore the stronger of the two metals as a reducing agent.

Think about It

Oxidation and reduction reactions always occur in pairs. If a substance is reduced, it acts as an oxidizing agent; if a substance is oxidized, it acts as a reducing agent.

8.81. Collect and Organize

For the C_nH_{2n+2} formula of alkanes, we are to describe how the oxidation state of carbon in the compounds changes as *n* (or the chain length) increases.

Analyze

We can look at this by considering the oxidation state changes for a short series: CH_4, C_2H_6, C_3H_8, and C_4H_{10}. Remember that carbon is slightly more electronegative than hydrogen, so in these compounds carbon will have a negative oxidation state.

Solve

The oxidation state of carbon in CH_4 is –4, for C_2H_6 it is –3, for C_3H_8 it is –8/3 (or –2.66), and for C_4H_{10} it is –10/4 (or –2.5). From this series we see that as *n* increases the oxidation state of the carbon atom in the alkanes increases (becomes less negative or more positive).

Think about It

For C_nH_{2n+2}, the oxidation state of the carbon atoms is $-(2n+2)/n$.

8.83. Collect and Organize

The oxidation number for chlorine in these species varies depending on the number of oxygens to which the Cl atom is bound and the overall charge on the species.

Analyze

The oxidation number for oxygen in these species is –2. For hydrogen it is +1. The oxidation number for chlorine in each species, therefore, must be positive and can be determined by

oxidation number on Cl = charge on species – [(number of O atoms) × (–2) + (number of H atoms) × (+1)]

Solve

(a) HClO: oxidation number on Cl = 0 – [1(–2) + 1(+1)] = +1
(b) $HClO_3$: oxidation number on Cl = 0 – [3(–2) + 1(+1)] = +5
(c) $HClO_4$: oxidation number on Cl = 0 – [4(–2) + 1(+1)] = +7

Think about It

You may also determine the oxidation number by considering the charge on each ion and then adding them to get the overall charge on the species. For example, in $HClO_3$ we have H^+, O^{2-}, O^{2-}, O^{2-}, and Cl^{n+} with the sum of +1, –2, –2, –2, and $n+$ equaling zero, so n must be 5.

8.85. **Collect and Organize**

For the dehydration reaction of glucose to form C and H_2O, we are asked to determine the moles of electrons transferred in the reaction.

Analyze

The moles of electrons transferred in this reaction will be a result of a redox reaction to form water and carbon.

Solve

We first need to determine the redox reaction for this dehydration of glucose. We should start by looking at the oxidation numbers of C, H, and O in the reactants and products and looking for changes. In glucose, $C_{12}H_{22}O_{11}$, the oxygen atoms will have an oxidation state of –2 (for 11 O atoms this is a total of –22), and the hydrogen atoms will have an oxidation state of +1 (for 22 H atoms this is a total of +22). This means that the carbon atoms in glucose have an oxidation state of 0. In water the oxidation state of H is +1 and of O is –2, and in carbon the oxidation state is 0. Therefore, no change in oxidation state has occurred and therefore no electrons transferred in this reaction.

Think about It

This molecule has the exactly correct stoichiometric amount of H and O to make H_2O.

8.87. **Collect and Organize**

To write the balanced equation to determine the moles of O_2 used in reaction with 1 mol of Fe_3O_4 to form Fe_2O_3, we have to identify the reactants and products and then balance the atoms.

Analyze

We are given the formulas for the reactant, Fe_3O_4, and the product, Fe_2O_3, so we can write the unbalanced equation for the conversion in the presence of oxygen and balance the reaction by inspection.

Solve

Write reactants and products in an unbalanced equation:
$$Fe_3O_4 + O_2 \rightarrow Fe_2O_3$$
Balance iron atoms:
$$2\,Fe_3O_4 + O_2 \rightarrow 3\,Fe_2O_3$$
Balance oxygen atoms:
$$2\,Fe_3O_4 + \tfrac{1}{2}\,O_2 \rightarrow 3\,Fe_2O_3$$
Eliminate the fractional coefficient:
$$4\,Fe_3O_4 + O_2 \rightarrow 6\,Fe_2O_3$$
For every mole of Fe_3O_4 reacted we would use 0.25 mol of O_2.

Think about It

In this reaction O_2 is the oxidizing agent.

8.89. **Collect and Organize**

For every species we are asked to find the oxidation number for each atom. From those oxidation numbers, we can see which species is oxidized and which species is reduced.

Analyze

All these reactions involve species of iron, silicon, oxygen, and hydrogen. Oxygen typically has an oxidation number of –2; hydrogen typically has an oxidation number of +1. Oxidation numbers of pure elements are zero. Iron is the atom most likely to have a variable oxidation number. Silicon's oxidation number is usually +4, consistent with its position in group 14 of the periodic table. Because all the compounds are neutral, the sum of the oxidation numbers for the atoms must be zero.

Solve

(a) Reactants   Products
   SiO_2: Si = +4, O = –2 Fe_2SiO_4: Fe = +2, Si = +4, O = –2
   Fe_3O_4: Fe = +8/3, O = –2 O_2: O = 0
   Notice that we compute an oxidation state for Fe in Fe_3O_4 as +8/3. Actually this compound consists of FeO (Fe^{2+}) and Fe_2O_3 (Fe^{3+}).
   Oxygen is oxidized (O^{2-} to O_2) and iron is reduced (Fe^{3+} to Fe^{2+}).

(b) Reactants   Products
   SiO_2: Si = +4, O = –2 Fe_2SiO_4: Fe = +2, Si = +4, O = –2
   Fe: Fe = 0
   O_2: O = 0
   Iron is oxidized (Fe^0 to Fe^{2+}) and oxygen is reduced (O_2 to O^{2-}).

(c) Reactants   Products
   FeO: Fe = +2, O = –2 $Fe(OH)_3$: Fe = +3, O = –2, H = +1
   O_2: O = 0
   H_2O: H = +1, O = –2
   Iron is oxidized (Fe^{2+} to Fe^{3+}) and oxygen is reduced (O_2 to O^{2-}).

Think about It

Molecular elemental oxygen is reduced in equations (b) and (c) and, therefore, acts as an oxidizing agent.

8.91. **Collect and Organize**

For the conversion of $FeCO_3$ to Fe_2O_3 and Fe_3O_4 in separate processes, we are to determine from balancing the redox equations how many moles of oxygen are consumed. We are to combine the reduction half-reaction of O_2 with an oxidation half-reaction and then balance it.

Analyze

We can assume that the carbon in $FeCO_3$ is converted into carbon dioxide in each process and that we are in an acidic environment for the conversions. We might be able to balance these reactions by inspection, but let's look at this from the half-reaction perspective. In the reduction half-reaction, O_2 is reduced to H_2O. In the oxidation half-reaction, $FeCO_3$ is oxidized to either Fe_2O_3 or Fe_3O_4. We will balance each half-reaction for atoms and then for charge. To combine them, we must balance the electrons produced in the oxidation reaction with the electrons gained in the reduction reaction. To do so we may have to multiply each half-reaction by a factor to give the same number of electrons in both.

Solve

(a) The reduction of oxygen involves 4 e^-, whereas the oxidation of $FeCO_3$ involves 2 e^-. To obtain a balanced overall equation, we must multiply the oxidation half-reaction by 2.

$$O_2 + 4\,H^+ + 4\,e^- \rightarrow 2\,H_2O$$
$$\underline{\left(2\,FeCO_3 + H_2O \rightarrow Fe_2CO_3 + 2\,CO_2 + 2\,H^+ + 2\,e^-\right) \times 2}$$
$$O_2 + 4\,H^+ + 4\,FeCO_3 + 2\,H_2O \rightarrow 2\,H_2O + 2\,Fe_2O_3 + 4\,CO_2 + 4\,H^+$$

After we cancel species that appear on both sides of the equation, this simplifies to

$$O_2(g) + 4\,FeCO_3(s) \rightarrow 2\,Fe_2O_3(s) + 4\,CO_2(g)$$

For every mole of $FeCO_3$ consumed in this process, 0.25 mole of oxygen is needed.

(b) The reduction of oxygen involves 4 e^-, whereas the oxidation of $FeCO_3$ involves 2 e^-. To obtain a balanced overall equation, we must multiply the oxidation half-reaction by 2.

$$O_2 + 4\,H^+ + 4\,e^- \rightarrow 2\,H_2O$$

$$\underline{\left(3\,FeCO_3 + H_2O \rightarrow Fe_3O_4 + 3\,CO_2 + 2\,H^+ + 2\,e^-\right) \times 2}$$

$$O_2 + 4\,H^+ + 6\,FeCO_3 + 2\,H_2O \rightarrow 2\,H_2O + 2\,Fe_3O_4 + 6\,CO_2 + 4\,H^+$$

After we cancel species that appear on both sides of the equation, this simplifies to

$$O_2(g) + 6\,FeCO_3(s) \rightarrow 2\,Fe_3O_4(s) + 6\,CO_2(g)$$

For every mole of $FeCO_3$ consumed in this process, 0.17 mole of oxygen is needed.

Think about It
Both redox reactions simplify to overall reactions that do not need acid as a reactant, even though the half-reactions do depend on having H^+ available for the reaction.

8.93. Collect and Organize
Ammonium ions (NH_4^+) are oxidized by oxygen gas to give nitrate ions (NO_3^-). We are asked to balance the reaction in acid solution.

Analyze
To balance the reaction, first write the unbalanced half-reactions. In each, balance all atoms except hydrogen and oxygen, and then use H_2O to balance oxygen and H^+ to balance hydrogen (in that order). Finally, balance charge with electrons. If the reactions have unequal numbers of electrons produced and consumed, multiply each half-reaction by a factor to give the same number of electrons in each. Then combine the half-reactions.

Solve
The oxidation of NH_4^+ involves eight electrons, whereas the reduction of O_2 requires four electrons. To obtain a balanced overall equation, we must multiply the reduction half-reaction by 2.

$$3\,H_2O + NH_4^+ \rightarrow NO_3^- + 10\,H^+ + 8\,e^-$$

$$\underline{\left(4\,e^- + 4\,H^+ + O_2 \rightarrow 2\,H_2O\right) \times 2}$$

$$3\,H_2O + NH_4^+ + 8\,H^+ + 2\,O_2 \rightarrow NO_3^- + 10\,H^+ + 4\,H_2O$$

After we cancel species that appear on both sides of the equation, this simplifies to

$$NH_4^+(aq) + 2\,O_2(g) \rightarrow NO_3^-(aq) + 2\,H^+(aq) + H_2O(\ell)$$

Think about It
This is an eight-electron oxidation in which the oxidation number of the nitrogen atom changes from -3 in NH_4^+ to $+5$ in NO_3^-.

8.95. Collect and Organize
We can balance the reaction by breaking it up into half-reactions. The problem does not specify whether the freshwater stream is acidic or basic; we assume acidic conditions here.

Analyze
The half-reactions involve the oxidation of manganese ($+2$ to $+4$) and the reduction of iron ($+3$ to $+2$). We use the steps for balancing atoms and electrons for acidic conditions.

Solve
The half-reactions are

$$Fe(OH)_2^+ \rightarrow Fe^{2+}$$

$$Mn^{2+} \rightarrow MnO_2$$

Balancing for oxygen and hydrogen by using H_2O and H^+ gives

$$2\,H^+ + Fe(OH)_2^{\,+} \rightarrow Fe^{2+} + 2\,H_2O$$

$$2\,H_2O + Mn^{2+} \rightarrow MnO_2 + 4\,H^+$$

Balancing for charge with electrons:

$$e^- + 2\,H^+ + Fe(OH)_2^{\,+} \rightarrow Fe^{2+} + 2\,H_2O$$

$$2\,H_2O + Mn^{2+} \rightarrow MnO_2 + 4\,H^+ + 2\,e^-$$

We have to multiply the reduction reaction by 2 to balance the electrons:

$$\left(e^- + 2\,H^+ + Fe(OH)_2^{\,+} \rightarrow Fe^{2+} + 2\,H_2O\right) \times 2$$

$$\underline{2\,H_2O + Mn^{2+} \rightarrow MnO_2 + 4\,H^+ + 2\,e^-}$$

$$4\,H^+ + 2\,Fe(OH)_2^{\,+} + 2\,H_2O + Mn^{2+} \rightarrow 2\,Fe^{2+} + 4\,H_2O + MnO_2 + 4\,H^+$$

This simplifies to

$$2\,Fe(OH)_2^{\,+}(aq) + Mn^{2+}(aq) \rightarrow 2\,Fe^{2+}(aq) + 2\,H_2O(\ell) + MnO_2(s)$$

Think about It
The assumption that this reaction can be balanced under acidic conditions is a good one since dissolved CO_2 in natural waters makes them slightly acidic because of the presence of carbonic acid, H_2CO_3.

8.97. Collect and Organize
Use the half-reaction method to balance the equation that describes the extraction of silver ores by cyanide.

Analyze
The reaction occurs in basic solution. We first balance it for acidic conditions and then add OH^- to both sides of the equation to give a basic solution. The oxidation reaction involves silver (0 to +1). The reduction reaction must involve oxygen. Most likely the product is H_2O, which gives an oxidation number change for oxygen of 0 to –2.

Solve
The half-reactions are

$$Ag + 2\,CN^- \rightarrow Ag(CN)_2^{\,-}$$

$$O_2 \rightarrow H_2O$$

Balancing for oxygen and hydrogen in acidic conditions:

$$Ag + 2\,CN^- \rightarrow Ag(CN)_2^{\,-}$$

$$4\,H^+ + O_2 \rightarrow 2\,H_2O$$

Balancing for charge with electrons:

$$Ag + 2\,CN^- \rightarrow Ag(CN)_2^{\,-} + e^-$$

$$4\,e^- + 4\,H^+ + O_2 \rightarrow 2\,H_2O$$

Adding the equations:

$$\left(Ag + 2\,CN^- \rightarrow Ag(CN)_2^{\,-} + e^-\right) \times 4$$

$$\underline{4\,e^- + 4\,H^+ + O_2 \rightarrow 2\,H_2O}$$

$$4\,Ag + 8\,CN^- + 4\,H^+ + O_2 \rightarrow 4\,Ag(CN)_2^{\,-} + 2\,H_2O$$

Adding 4 OH^- to both sides of the equation:

$$4\,OH^- + 4\,Ag + 8\,CN^- + 4\,H^+ + O_2 \rightarrow 4\,Ag(CN)_2^{\,-} + 2\,H_2O + 4\,OH^-$$

$$4\,H_2O + 4\,Ag + 8\,CN^- + O_2 \rightarrow 4\,Ag(CN)_2^{\,-} + 2\,H_2O + 4\,OH^-$$

$$2\,H_2O(\ell) + 4\,Ag(s) + 8\,CN^-(aq) + O_2(g) \rightarrow 4\,Ag(CN)_2^{\,-}(aq) + 4\,OH^-(aq)$$

Think about It
Always check your final equation for both charge and atom balance.

8.99. Collect and Organize

Use the half-reaction method to balance the reactions in acidic solutions.

Analyze

Balancing in acidic solutions involves writing the half-reactions, balancing the atoms, balancing the charge, and adding the half-reactions to obtain the overall redox equation.

Solve

(a) The half-reactions are

$$ClO_3^- \rightarrow ClO_2$$
$$SO_2 \rightarrow SO_4^{2-}$$

Balancing for O and H:

$$2\,H^+ + ClO_3^- \rightarrow ClO_2 + H_2O$$
$$2\,H_2O + SO_2 \rightarrow SO_4^{2-} + 4\,H^+$$

Balancing for charge:

$$e^- + 2\,H^+ + ClO_3^- \rightarrow ClO_2 + H_2O$$
$$2\,H_2O + SO_2 \rightarrow SO_4^{2-} + 4\,H^+ + 2\,e^-$$

Adding the half-reactions and simplifying:

$$2 \times \left(e^- + 2\,H^+ + ClO_3^- \rightarrow ClO_2 + H_2O \right)$$
$$2\,H_2O + SO_2 \rightarrow SO_4^{2-} + 4\,H^+ + 2\,e^-$$

$$\overline{4\,H^+ + 2\,ClO_3^- + 2\,H_2O + SO_2 \rightarrow 2\,ClO_2 + 2\,H_2O + SO_4^{2-} + 4\,H^+}$$

$$2\,ClO_3^-(aq) + SO_2(g) \rightarrow 2\,ClO_2(g) + SO_4^{2-}(aq)$$

(b) The half-reactions are

$$ClO_3^- \rightarrow ClO_2$$
$$2\,Cl^- \rightarrow Cl_2$$

Balancing for O and H:

$$2\,H^+ + ClO_3^- \rightarrow ClO_2 + H_2O$$
$$2\,Cl^- \rightarrow Cl_2$$

Balancing for charge:

$$e^- + 2\,H^+ + ClO_3^- \rightarrow ClO_2 + H_2O$$
$$2\,Cl^- \rightarrow Cl_2 + 2\,e^-$$

Adding the half-reactions:

$$2 \times \left(e^- + 2\,H^+ + ClO_3^- \rightarrow ClO_2 + H_2O \right)$$
$$2\,Cl^- \rightarrow Cl_2 + 2\,e^-$$

$$\overline{4\,H^+(aq) + 2\,ClO_3^-(aq) + 2\,Cl^-(aq) \rightarrow 2\,ClO_2(g) + 2\,H_2O(\ell) + Cl_2(g)}$$

(c) The half-reactions with balanced atoms (except H and O) are

$$ClO_3^- \rightarrow ClO_2$$
$$Cl_2 \rightarrow 2\,Cl^- + O_2$$

Balancing for O and H:

$$2\,H^+ + ClO_3^- \rightarrow ClO_2 + H_2O$$
$$Cl_2 + 2\,H_2O \rightarrow 2\,Cl^- + O_2 + 4\,H^+$$

Balancing for charge:

$$e^- + 2\,H^+ + ClO_3^- \rightarrow ClO_2 + H_2O$$

$$Cl_2 + 2\,H_2O \rightarrow 2\,Cl^- + O_2 + 4\,H^+ + 2\,e^-$$

Adding the half-reactions and simplifying:

$$2 \times \left(e^- + 2\,H^+ + ClO_3^- \rightarrow ClO_2 + H_2O\right)$$

$$\underline{Cl_2 + 2\,H_2O \rightarrow 2\,Cl^- + O_2 + 4\,H^+ + 2\,e^-}$$

$$2\,ClO_3^-(aq) + Cl_2(g) \rightarrow 2\,ClO_2(g) + 2\,Cl^-(aq) + O_2(g)$$

Think about It
For part c, we needed to complete the equation by recognizing that Cl_2 is reduced to Cl^- by water to produce O_2.

8.101. Collect and Organize
All the titrations involve a neutralization reaction. The moles of base (OH^-) required must equal the moles of acid (H^+) in the sample.

Analyze
First, we need to calculate the number of moles of acid from the volume and concentration of acid in the samples. Because the stoichiometry of the neutralization reaction is 1 mol OH^- : 1 mol H^+, the moles of base required is equal to the moles of H^+ in the sample. We can find the volume of base needed by dividing moles of OH^- required by the concentration of base used.

Solve

(a) $10.0 \text{ mL} \times \dfrac{0.0500 \text{ mol HCl}}{1000 \text{ mL}} \times \dfrac{1 \text{ mol H}^+}{1 \text{ mol HCl}} \times \dfrac{1 \text{ mol OH}^-}{1 \text{ mol H}^+} \times \dfrac{1000 \text{ mL}}{0.100 \text{ mol NaOH}} = 5.00 \text{ mL}$

(b) $25.0 \text{ mL} \times \dfrac{0.126 \text{ mol HNO}_3}{1000 \text{ mL}} \times \dfrac{1 \text{ mol H}^+}{1 \text{ mol HNO}_3} \times \dfrac{1 \text{ mol OH}^-}{1 \text{mol H}^+} \times \dfrac{1000 \text{ mL}}{0.100 \text{ mol NaOH}} = 31.5 \text{ mL}$

(c) $50.0 \text{ mL} \times \dfrac{0.215 \text{ mol H}_2SO_4}{1000 \text{ mL}} \times \dfrac{2 \text{ mol H}^+}{1 \text{ mol H}_2SO_4} \times \dfrac{1 \text{ mol OH}^-}{1 \text{ mol H}^+} \times \dfrac{1000 \text{ mL}}{0.100 \text{ mol NaOH}} = 215 \text{ mL}$

Think about It
Because sulfuric acid has two H^+ ions (it is a diprotic acid), we need twice as many moles of OH^- to neutralize it as for the same concentration of a monoprotic acid such as HNO_3.

8.103. Collect and Organize
Using the solubility of $Ca(OH)_2$ we first have to calculate the moles of $Ca(OH)_2$ in the solution; then we can find the volume of the $HCl(aq)$ solution to neutralize the $Ca(OH)_2$ solution.

Analyze
To find the moles of $Ca(OH)_2$ in the saturated solution, we first have to multiply the volume of the solution by the solubility of $Ca(OH)_2$. This gives the grams of $Ca(OH)_2$ in the solution, which we can then convert into moles by dividing the grams of $Ca(OH)_2$ by the molar mass of $Ca(OH)_2$. Because 2 moles of OH^- is in $Ca(OH)_2$, the moles of OH^- to neutralize must be twice the moles of $Ca(OH)_2$. We can then use the 1:1 molar ratio of OH^- to H^+ in the neutralization reaction and the concentration of the HCl solution to find the volume of HCl required to neutralize the $Ca(OH)_2$ solution.

Solve

Moles of $Ca(OH)_2$ in the saturated solution:

$$10.0 \text{ mL} \times \frac{0.185 \text{ g}}{100.0 \text{ mL}} \times \frac{1 \text{ mol}}{74.09 \text{ g}} = 2.50 \times 10^{-4} \text{ mol}$$

Volume (in milliliters) of HCl required to neutralize:

$$2.50 \times 10^{-4} \text{ mol } Ca(OH)_2 \times \frac{2 \text{ mol } OH^-}{1 \text{ mol } Ca(OH)_2} \times \frac{1 \text{ mol } H^+}{1 \text{ mol } OH^-} \times \frac{1 \text{ mol } HCl}{1 \text{ mol } H^+} \times \frac{1000 \text{ mL}}{0.00100 \text{ mol } HCl} = 500 \text{ mL}$$

Think about It

Calcium hydroxide is not very soluble in water, but this neutralization requires a large volume of HCl solution because the HCl solution is fairly dilute.

8.105. Collect and Organize

In the titration of 25.00 mL of seawater to determine the chloride concentration, 27.80 mL of 0.5000 M $AgNO_3$ is used to reach the equivalence point. From this information we are asked to determine the concentration of Cl^- in the seawater in units of millimolar and in grams per kilogram where the density of the seawater is 1.025 g/mL.

Analyze

The titration of Cl^- with Ag^+ to form the precipitate AgCl has the following balanced equation:

$$AgNO_3(aq) + Cl^-(aq) \rightarrow AgCl(s) + NO_3^-(aq)$$

To solve for the concentration of chloride ion in the seawater we will need to first find the moles of $AgNO_3$ used to reach the equivalence point. Because this is the moles of Cl^- in the 25.00 mL sample, we can calculate the concentration in moles per liter and then convert it to millimoles per liter and finally to grams of Cl^- per kilogram of seawater.

Solve

$$27.80 \text{ mL } AgNO_3 \times \frac{0.5000 \text{ mol } AgNO_3}{1000 \text{ mL}} \times \frac{1 \text{ mol } AgCl}{1 \text{ mol } AgNO_3} \times \frac{1 \text{ mol } Cl^-}{1 \text{ mol } AgCl} \times \frac{1}{0.02500 \text{ L}} = 0.5560 \text{ } M$$

$$\frac{0.5560 \text{ mol}}{L} \times \frac{1000 \text{ mmol}}{1 \text{ mol}} = 556.0 \text{ m}M$$

$$\frac{0.5560 \text{ mol}}{1000 \text{ mL}} \times \frac{1 \text{ mL}}{1.025 \text{ g}} \times \frac{1000 \text{ g}}{1 \text{ kg}} \times \frac{35.453 \text{ g } Cl^-}{1 \text{ mol}} = 19.23 \text{ g/kg}$$

Think about It

Although here the stoichiometry of the titration is simple (1:1), be careful to always consider the balanced equation because that simple ratio does not always apply.

8.107. Collect and Organize

Anion and cation exchangers swap unwanted cations and anions in water with other ions. We are asked to explain how they can deionize water.

Analyze

To deionize water (that is, remove all the cations and anions), we would have to swap the cations and anions with ones that, when combined, produce H_2O.

Solve

To deionize water, cations such as Na^+ and Ca^{2+} are exchanged for H^+ at cation-exchange sites. Anions such as Cl^- and SO_4^{2-} are exchanged for OH^- at anion-exchange sites. The released ions (H^+ and OH^-) at these sites combine to form H_2O.

Think about It

The electrical neutrality of the water is preserved. If we swap every Cl^- and Na^+ for OH^- and H^+ ions, we have kept the number of ions in the solution the same. However, because OH^- and H^+ combine to form neutral H_2O, we no longer have ions in the water; it is deionized.

8.109. Collect and Organize

We consider why using potassium ions in place of sodium ions in resins for ion exchange offers no advantage.

Analyze

Water softeners for water use resins with Na^+ for the exchange with harder cations such as Mg^{2+} and Ca^{2+}.

Solve

K^+ is in the same group in the periodic table and so probably would function the same as Na^+ in the resin, but potassium in the form of KCl is more expensive to use than the more abundant NaCl.

Think about It

Ion exchange and deionization preserves water's electrical neutrality. If we swap every Cl^- and Na^+ for OH^- and H^+ ions, we have kept the number of ions in the solution the same. However, because OH^- and H^+ combine to form neutral H_2O, we no longer have ions in the water; it is deionized.

8.111. Collect and Organize

In this precipitation titration, a known volume of barium nitrate is titrated into a solution of unknown sulfate concentration. We are asked to calculate how much sulfate is in the solution and express the concentration of sulfate in moles per liter (M).

Analyze

Using the concentration of the $Ba(NO_3)_2$ titrant and the volume of titrant used, we first find the moles of $Ba(NO_3)_2$ used in the titration. From the balanced equation

$$Ba(NO_3)_2 + SO_4^{2-} \rightarrow BaSO_4 + 2\,NO_3^-$$

we see that 1 mol $Ba(NO_3)_2$ reacts with 1 mol SO_4^{2-}. This 1:1 ratio means that the moles of titrant used equals the moles of SO_4^{2-} in the sample. To calculate concentration of SO_4^{2-} we divide the moles of SO_4^{2-} by the volume of the sample in liters.

Solve

$$3.19 \text{ mL } Ba(NO_3)_2 \times \frac{0.0250 \text{ mol } Ba(NO_3)_2}{1000 \text{ mL}} \times \frac{1 \text{ mol } SO_4^{2-}}{1 \text{ mol } Ba(NO_3)_2} \times \frac{1}{0.1000 \text{ L}} = 7.98 \times 10^{-4} \ M \ SO_4^{2-}$$

Think about It

Precipitation titrations give us the concentration of a species in solution and are accurate only when the salt formed has very low solubility. If we form a salt of marginal solubility, then we leave some of the species in solution and our calculation underestimates the concentration of the species in solution.

8.113. Collect and Organize

From the mass percent and density of concentrated HCl we are asked to determine the molarity of HCl. Then we are to calculate the amount needed to prepare a dilute solution from the concentrated HCl and figure out how much sodium bicarbonate is needed to neutralize a spill of concentrated HCl.

Analyze

This looks difficult, but we have all the information we need. Parts b and c depend on the answer to part a. For part a, if the solution is 36.0% by mass, then 100 g of concentrated HCl contains 36.0 g HCl. Using the molar mass of HCl (36.46 g/mol), we can convert the grams into moles. To obtain the volume of acid we divide the 100 g of acid by the density (1.18 g/mL). We now have moles of HCl and volume of HCl to compute the molarity. To determine the volume of concentrated HCl needed to prepare a more dilute solution of HCl in part b, we use Equation 8.6:

$$V_{initial} M_{initial} = V_{final} M_{final}$$

For part c we need the chemical equation that describes the neutralization:

$$NaHCO_3 + HCl \rightarrow NaCl + H_2O + CO_2$$

Solve

(a) Molarity of concentrated HCl solution:

$$36.0 \text{ g HCl solution} \times \frac{1 \text{ mol HCl}}{36.46 \text{ g}} = 0.987 \text{ mol HCl}$$

$$100 \text{ g solution} \times \frac{1 \text{ mL}}{1.18 \text{ g}} = 84.7 \text{ mL, or } 0.0847 \text{ L}$$

$$\text{Molarity HCl(conc)} = \frac{0.987 \text{ mol}}{0.0847 \text{ L}} = 11.7 \text{ } M$$

(b) Volume of HCl(conc) required to make 0.250 L of 2.00 M solution:

$$V_{initial} M_{initial} = V_{final} M_{final}$$

$$V_{initial} \times 11.7 \text{ } M = 250 \text{ mL} \times 2.00 \text{ } M$$

$$V_{initial} = 42.7 \text{ mL}$$

(c) Mass of $NaHCO_3$ required to neutralize the spill:

$$1.75 \text{ L HCl(conc)} \times \frac{11.7 \text{ mol}}{\text{L}} \times \frac{1 \text{ mol } NaHCO_3}{1 \text{ mol HCl}} \times \frac{84.01 \text{ } NaHCO_3}{1 \text{ mol}} = 1720 \text{ g, or } 1.72 \text{ kg}$$

Think about It

This problem puts together many of the chapter's topics, including the definition of molarity, the preparation of diluted solutions, and neutralization. It also involves concepts from previous chapters, including density and reaction stoichiometry.

8.115. Collect and Organize

This is a redox reaction, so we have to use the half-reaction method to first balance the equation. From the species involved we can then identify the oxidizing and reducing agents. Finally, we are asked to calculate the amount of $Na_2S_2O_4$ needed to remove a certain amount of CrO_4^{2-}.

Analyze

The redox reaction occurs in base. We can first balance the half-reactions in acid and then add sufficient OH^- to both sides of the equation to neutralize H^+. From the half-reactions and oxidation numbers we can identify the species that are oxidized and reduced and assign species as oxidizing or reducing agents. We need the balanced equations for the stoichiometry of reactants to calculate how much $Na_2S_2O_4$ is required to remove the CrO_4^{2-} from the wastewater. We also need the molar mass of $Na_2S_2O_4$.

Solve

(a) The reaction can be described in the following unbalanced equation:

$$S_2O_4^{2-}(aq) + CrO_4^{2-}(aq) \rightarrow SO_3^{2-}(aq) + Cr(OH)_3(s)$$

Balancing this by the half-reaction method in acidic solution first gives

$$\left(2 \text{ H}_2O + S_2O_4^{2-} \rightarrow 2 \text{ SO}_3^{2-} + 4 \text{ H}^+ + 2 \text{ e}^-\right) \times 3$$

$$\left(3 \text{ e}^- + 5 \text{ H}^+ + CrO_4^{2-} \rightarrow Cr(OH)_3 + H_2O\right) \times 2$$

$$\overline{6 \text{ H}_2O + 3 \text{ S}_2O_4^{2-} + 10 \text{ H}^+ + 2 \text{ CrO}_4^{2-} \rightarrow 6 \text{ SO}_3^{2-} + 12 \text{ H}^+ + 2 \text{ Cr(OH)}_3 + 2 \text{ H}_2O}$$

This simplifies to

$$4 \text{ H}_2O + 3 \text{ S}_2O_4^{2-} + 2 \text{ CrO}_4^{2-} \rightarrow 6 \text{ SO}_3^{2-} + 2 \text{ H}^+ + 2 \text{ Cr(OH)}_3$$

Placing in base we add OH^-:

$$2 \text{ OH}^- + 4 \text{ H}_2O + 3 \text{ S}_2O_4^{2-} + 2 \text{ CrO}_4^{2-} \rightarrow 6 \text{ SO}_3^{2-} + 2 \text{ H}^+ + 2 \text{ Cr(OH)}_3 + 2 \text{ OH}^-$$

Simplifying:

$$2 \text{ OH}^-(aq) + 2 \text{ H}_2O(\ell) + 3 \text{ S}_2O_4^{2-}(aq) + 2 \text{ CrO}_4^{2-}(aq) \rightarrow 6 \text{ SO}_3^{2-}(aq) + 2 \text{ Cr(OH)}_3(s)$$

(b) Because $S_2O_4^{2-}$ is the reactant in the oxidation half-reaction, we must look at $S_2O_4^{2-} \rightarrow SO_3^{2-}$. Here sulfur is oxidized from +3 to +4.

Because CrO_4^{2-} is the reactant in the reduction half-reaction, we must look at $CrO_4^{2-} \rightarrow Cr(OH)_3$. Here chromium is reduced from +6 to +3.

(c) The oxidizing agent is the species that is itself reduced: CrO_4^{2-}. The reducing agent is itself oxidized: $S_2O_4^{2-}$.

(d) The amount of $Na_2S_2O_4$ required is

$$100.0 \text{ L wastewater} \times \frac{0.00148 \text{ mol CrO}_4^{2-}}{1 \text{ L}} \times \frac{3 \text{ mol S}_2O_4^{2-}}{2 \text{ mol CrO}_4^{2-}} \times \frac{1 \text{ mol Na}_2S_2O_4}{1 \text{ mol S}_2O_4^{2-}} \times \frac{174.11 \text{ g}}{1 \text{ mol Na}_2S_2O_4} = 38.7 \text{ g}$$

Think about It

Be sure to always start with a balanced chemical equation before calculating the amount of reactants required or the amount of products in a reaction.

8.117. Collect and Organize

In this problem we examine the tarnishing of silver to Ag_2S and the conversion of Ag_2S back to Ag in the presence of aluminum metal. Both are redox reactions.

Analyze

We are given the chemical formulas for all the reactants and products with which to write the equations.

Solve

(a) The tarnishing of Ag occurs in the presence of H_2S and O_2 to form Ag_2S.

$$4 \text{ Ag} + 2 \text{ H}_2S + O_2 \rightarrow 2 \text{ Ag}_2S + 2 \text{ H}_2O$$

(b) The reaction of Ag_2S with Al and to remove tarnish is

$$\left(e^- + H^+ + Ag_2S \rightarrow 2 \text{ Ag} + HS^-\right) \times 3$$
$$\left(3 \text{ H}_2O + Al \rightarrow Al(OH)_3 + 3 \text{ H}^+ + 3 \text{ e}^-\right)$$
$$\overline{3 \text{ Ag}_2S + 3 \text{ H}_2O + Al \rightarrow 6 \text{ Ag} + 3 \text{ HS}^- + Al(OH)_3}$$

Think about It

Baking soda does not become involved in the reaction but makes the solution basic.

8.119. Collect and Organize

We are asked to predict the products of some reactions between various phosphorus, selenium, and boron oxides and water.

Analyze

When nonmetal oxides (acids and anhydrides) react with water, they give acidic solutions. For these reactions we need to simply add water to the reactant and write the formula of the acidic product. Using the naming rules from Chapter 2, we can name the acid product.

Solve

(a) $P_4O_{10} + 6 \text{ H}_2O \rightarrow 4 \text{ H}_3PO_4$ (phosphoric acid)

(b) $SeO_2 + H_2O \rightarrow H_2SeO_3$ (selenous acid)

(c) $B_2O_3 + 3 \text{ H}_2O \rightarrow 2 \text{ H}_3BO_3$ (boric acid)

Think about It

When we simply add water to the anhydride, an acid is formed from nonmetal oxides.

8.121. Collect and Organize

Both reactions described are redox reactions, and so we can use the half-reaction method to write and balance them.

Analyze

In the first reaction, ClO^- (with Cl^+) is combined with I^- to give Cl^- and I_2. Here, Cl is being reduced and I is being oxidized in acidic solution. In the second reaction, I_2 is titrated with $S_2O_3^{2-}$ (with S^{2+}) to give I^- and $S_4O_6^{2-}$ (with $S^{2.5+}$). Here, sulfur is being oxidized and I is being reduced.

Solve

First reaction, balancing the half-reactions and combining:

$$2\,e^- + 2\,H^+ + ClO^- \rightarrow Cl^- + H_2O$$
$$\underline{2\,I^- \rightarrow I_2 + 2\,e^-}$$
$$2\,H^+ + ClO^- + 2\,I^- \rightarrow Cl^- + H_2O + I_2$$

Second reaction, balancing the half-reactions and combining:

$$2\,e^- + I_2 \rightarrow 2\,I^-$$
$$\underline{2\,S_2O_3^{2-} \rightarrow S_4O_6^{2-} + 2\,e^-}$$
$$I_2 + 2\,S_2O_3^{2-} \rightarrow 2\,I^- + S_4O_6^{2-}$$

Overall equation:

$$2\,H^+(aq) + ClO^-(aq) + 2\,S_2O_3^{2-}(aq) \rightarrow Cl^-(aq) + H_2O(\ell) + S_4O_6^{2-}(aq)$$

Think about It

The second reaction does not require H^+ to balance the equation. This reaction, therefore, does not depend on the presence of acid to proceed and can take place in neutral solution.

8.123. Collect and Organize

Considering the values we are given for the stream contamination by perchlorate, the flow rate of the stream, and the advisory range for perchlorate in drinking water, we are asked to determine the amount of perchlorate that flows into Lake Mead and the volume of perchlorate-free water that would be needed to reduce concentrations from 700.0 to 4 µg/L. We also compare results from three labs on replicate samples of water for perchlorate and determine which lab gave the most precise results.

Analyze

(a) To write the formulas for sodium perchlorate and ammonium perchlorate we must write neutral chemical formulas using Na^+ with ClO_4^- and NH_4^+ with ClO_4^-. The cation and anion each have a charge of 1, so the cation and anion in each salt are present in a 1:1 ratio.

(b) To calculate how much ClO_4^- enters the lake from the stream we need to multiply the flow rate (after converting to liters per day) by the concentration of ClO_4^- in the stream (and convert micrograms into kilograms).

(c) In this part we can use Equation 8.6

$$V_{initial} \times M_{initial} = V_{final} \times M_{final}$$

where $M_{initial} = 700$ µg/L, and $M_{final} = 4$ µg/L, and $V_{initial}$ is 161×10^6 gal (volume that flows in the stream each day). V_{final} is the final total volume to reduce the concentration of ClO_4^- to 4 µg/L. The volume of lake water that must be mixed with the stream water will be $V_{final} - 161 \times 10^6$ gal.

(d) When we compare the sample data for Maryland, Massachusetts, and New Mexico, the most precise data for the replicate samples must have the narrowest range of values.

Solve

(a) Sodium perchlorate, $NaClO_4$
Ammonium perchlorate, NH_4ClO_4

(b) Perchlorate flow into Lake Mead each day

$$\frac{161 \times 10^6 \text{ gal}}{\text{day}} \times \frac{3.785 \text{ L}}{1 \text{ gal}} \times \frac{700 \text{ µg}}{L} \times \frac{1 \times 10^{-6} \text{ g}}{1 \text{ µg}} \times \frac{1 \times 10^{-3} \text{ kg}}{1 \text{ g}} = 427 \text{ kg}$$

(c) Using the dilution equation:

$$161 \times 10^6 \text{ gal} \times 700 \text{ } \mu g/L = 4 \text{ } \mu g/L \times V_{\text{final}}$$

$$V_{\text{final}} = 2.82 \times 10^{10} \text{ gal}$$

Volume of lake water required: 2.82×10^{10} gal $- 161 \times 10^6$ gal $= 2.80 \times 10^{10}$ gal

(d) The data for the samples from Maryland range from 0.9 to 1.4 µg/L, or a range of 0.5 µg/L; the data from Massachusetts range from 0.90 to 0.95 µg/L, or a range of 0.05 µg/L; and the data from New Mexico range from 1.1 to 1.3 µg/L, or a range of 0.2 µg/L. Because the range of data is lowest for the Massachusetts sample, this lab produced the most precise results.

Think about It
Looking closely at the dilution in part c, we see that the stream water must be diluted by

$$\frac{2.82 \times 10^{10} \text{ gal}}{161 \times 10^6 \text{ gal}} = 175$$

or nearly 200 times.

8.125. Collect and Organize
From the balanced equations that we write for the two fermentation steps for the conversion of sugar to acetic acid, we are to calculate how much acetic acid could be produced (with 100% theoretical yield) from 100 g of sugar.

Analyze
The first step in the fermentation of apple juice is an anaerobic process, so only the sugars are converted to ethanol and carbon dioxide. The acid fermentation of ethanol to give acetic acid and water, however, requires oxygen as a reactant. Oxidation states for the carbon atoms in both the reactants and products of these two fermentation reactions can be deduced using the typical oxidation states of H (+1) and O (–2). Because all the carbon species are neutral, the sum of the oxidation numbers must be zero. Therefore,

oxidation number on C = 0 – [number H atoms × (+1) + number of oxygen atoms × (–2)]

To calculate the maximum acetic acid produced from the fermentation of 100 g sugar, we first need to calculate the moles of sugar in 100 g by using the molar mass of CH_2O (30.03 g/mol). Then we use the molar ratios in the balanced equations to find the moles of acetic acid that can be produced (3:1 ratio for $CH_2O : C_2H_5OH$ and 1:1 ratio for $C_2H_3OH : HC_2H_3O_2$). Using the molar mass of acetic acid (60.05 g/mol), we can calculate the maximum mass of acetic acid that could be produced.

Solve
(a) The fermentation of the sugars is described by

$$3 \text{ } CH_2O \rightarrow CO_2 + C_2H_5OH$$

(b) The fermentation of ethanol is described by

$$C_2H_5OH + O_2 \rightarrow HC_2H_3O_2 + H_2O$$

(c) Oxidation states for carbon in reactants and products
CH_2O: C = 0 – [2(+1) + 1(–2)] = 0
CO_2: C = 0 – [2(–2)] = +4
C_2H_5OH: C = 0 – [6(+1) + 1(–2)] = –4 over two carbon atoms, so oxidation number on each carbon = –2
$HC_2H_3O_2$: C = 0 – [1(+1) + 3(+1) + 2(–2)] = 0

(d) The maximum amount of acetic acid that could be produced assumes that both fermentation reactions give 100% yield.

$$100 \text{ g } CH_2O \times \frac{1 \text{ mol } CH_2O}{30.03 \text{ g}} \times \frac{1 \text{ mol } C_2H_5OH}{3 \text{ mol } CH_2O} \times \frac{1 \text{ mol } HC_2H_3O_2}{1 \text{ mol } C_2H_5OH} \times \frac{60.05 \text{ g } HC_2H_3O_2}{1 \text{ mol}} = 66.7 \text{ g acetic acid}$$

Think about It
In the first step of the fermentation process the carbon of the sugar is being oxidized and reduced to CO_2 and C_2H_5OH, respectively. In the second step, ethanol is being oxidized and oxygen is being reduced.

8.127. Collect and Organize

For the two reactions that describe the formation of $CaSO_4$ (gypsum) we are asked to identify whether either is a redox reaction and to write a net ionic equation for the reaction of sulfuric acid with calcium carbonate for an alternate form of the equation.

Analyze

A redox reaction is indicated by a change in oxidation state in one of the elements in going from reactants to products in an equation. Net ionic equations are written from ionic equations by canceling any spectator ions that are present as both reactants and products.

Solve

(a) In the first reaction, the oxidation number of hydrogen stays the same (+1), but the oxidation number of S in H_2S (–2) increases to +6 in H_2SO_4. Coupled with this oxidation is the reduction of oxygen in O_2 (oxidation number = 0) to oxidation number –2 in H_2SO_4. Eight electrons are transferred in this reaction to oxidize S^{2-} to S^{6+}. In the second reaction, no oxidation numbers change (Ca = +2, C = +4, O = –2, H = +1, S = +6). This reaction is not a redox reaction and would be classified as an acid–base reaction instead.

(b) Ionic equation:

$$2\,H^+(aq) + SO_4^{2-}(aq) + CaCO_3(s) \rightarrow CaSO_4(s) + H_2O(\ell) + CO_2(g)$$

This is also the net ionic equation.

(c) The ionic equation would change slightly on the product side:

$$2\,H^+(aq) + SO_4^{2-}(aq) + CaCO_3(s) \rightarrow CaSO_4(s) + 2\,H^+(aq) + CO_3^{2-}(aq)$$

The net ionic equation would be

$$SO_4^{2-}(aq) + CaCO_3(s) \rightarrow CaSO_4(s) + CO_3^{2-}(aq)$$

Think about It

The decomposition of H_2CO_3 to CO_2 and H_2O is not a redox reaction because no atoms change oxidation number.

8.129. Collect and Organize

From four reactions involving the element calcium or its compounds, we are to find the redox reactions.

Analyze

In redox reactions, an element must undergo a change in oxidation number. By assigning oxidation numbers to the elements in each compound and then comparing products versus reactants, we can find the redox reactions.

Solve

(a) Reactant oxidation numbers: Ca = +2, C = +4, O = –2
   Product oxidation numbers: Ca = +2, C = +4, O = –2
   This is not a redox reaction.

(b) Reactant oxidation numbers: Ca = +2, O = –2, S = +4
   Product oxidation numbers: Ca = +2, O = –2, S = +4
   This is not a redox reaction.

(c) Reactant oxidation numbers: Ca = +2, Cl = –1
   Product oxidation numbers: Ca = 0, Cl = 0
   This is a redox reaction.

(d) Reactant oxidation numbers: Ca = 0, N = 0
   Product oxidation numbers: Ca = +2, N = –3
   This is a redox reaction.

Think about It

In redox reactions, both reduction and oxidation must be present. For example, in part c, calcium is reduced, whereas chlorine is oxidized.

CHAPTER 9 | Thermochemistry: Energy Changes in Chemical Reactions

9.1. Collect and Organize

From the depiction of a diesel engine piston (Figure P9.1), we are to describe how the internal energy of the trapped gases changes when the piston moves up.

Analyze

Here, the system we are considering is the gases. As the piston moves up, the gases in the cylinder are compressed.

Solve

Upon compression the molecules are squeezed together and the change in volume on the system is negative. Therefore, work is done on the system and $w = -P\Delta V$, where ΔV is negative, so w is positive and the internal energy change $E = q + w$ is positive. Here, the internal energy of the gases in the cylinder increases.

Think about It

If work is done by the system, in this situation where the gases expand, the internal energy of the gases in the cylinder decreases.

9.3. Collect and Organize

All the molecules shown in Figure P9.3 are hydrocarbons with either five or six carbon atoms. On the basis of differences in their structures, we are to predict which has the highest and which has the lowest fuel value.

Analyze

For hydrocarbons, as the hydrogen-to-carbon ratio decreases the fuel value also decreases. Therefore, we will distinguish between the hydrocarbon in this group that has the most and the least fuel value on the basis of the hydrogen-to-carbon ratio.

Solve

The hydrogen-to-carbon ratios of these hydrocarbons are as follows:
(a) C_6H_{14} H:C = 2.33:1
(b) C_6H_{12} H:C = 2:1
(c) C_5H_{12} H:C = 2.4:1
(d) C_6H_{14} H:C = 2.33:1
From these ratios, (c) C_5H_{12} has the highest fuel value and (b) C_6H_{12} has the lowest fuel value.

Think about It

Although structurally different, (a) and (d) have the same H:C ratio and therefore the same fuel value.

9.5. Collect and Organize

For the reaction depicted in Figure P9.4, we are to assign signs to the values ΔE, q, and w and then determine the percent yield of the reaction if each molecule represents 1 mol.

Analyze

From our answer to Problem 9.4, we know that the reaction is exothermic and is compressed in going from reactants to products. From the diagram we have 3 mol of N_2 and 9 mol of H_2 as reactants that form 4 mol of NH_3, with 3 mol of H_2 and 1 mol of N_2 remaining at the end of the reaction.

Solve

Because the reaction volume is less at the end of the reaction, the sign of w is positive, showing that work was done on the system. Because the reaction is exothermic, the sign of q is negative, showing flow of heat from the system to the surroundings. The change in E for the reaction is negative if the heat released by the reaction is greater than the work done on the system by the surrounding by decrease of volume. For the percent yield we consider the system compared to the balanced equation

$$N_2(g) + 3\,H_2(g) \rightarrow 2\,NH_3(g)$$

The 3 mol of N_2 present in the reaction mixture would be expected to use 9 mol of hydrogen (which we have exactly) and yield 6 mol of ammonia. Only 4 mol of ammonia is produced, so the percent yield of the reaction is

$$\frac{\text{experimental yield}}{\text{theoretical yield}} \times 100 = \frac{4\text{ mol NH}_3}{6\text{ mol NH}_3} \times 100 = 67\%$$

Think about It

A 100% yield for this reaction would have used up all the nitrogen and the hydrogen initially present in the reaction mixture.

9.7. **Collect and Organize**

The diagram in Figure P9.7 shows that the volume of the cylinder on the reactant side is greater than that on the product side. We are considering this reaction at constant temperature and pressure, and we are to write a balanced equation for the reaction, calculate the enthalpy of reaction for the formation of 1 mol of product, and determine the heat flow in the reaction in going from reactants to products.

Analyze

From the color scheme for the elements shown on the inside back cover of the textbook, the reactants are SO_2 and O_2 reacting to form SO_3. The reactant has six molecules of SO_2 and three molecules of O_2. These react to form six molecules of SO_3. The enthalpy of the reaction is calculated by subtracting the sum of the enthalpies of formation of the reactants (multiplied by the number of moles in the balanced equation for each product) from the sum of enthalpies of formation of the products (again multiplied by their molar amounts from the balanced equation).

Solve

(a) The balanced equation is

$$6\,SO_2(g) + 3\,O_2(g) \rightarrow 6\,SO_3(g)$$

or, more simply,

$$2\,SO_2(g) + O_2(g) \rightarrow 2\,SO_3(g)$$

(b) $\Delta H^\circ_{rxn} = \left[2\text{ mol }(\Delta H^\circ_f)SO_3(g) \right] - \left[2\text{ mol }(\Delta H^\circ_f)SO_2(g) + 1\text{ mol }(\Delta H^\circ_f)O_2(g) \right]$

$\Delta H^\circ_{rxn} = \left[2\text{ mol }SO_3 \times -395.7\text{ kJ/mol} \right] - \left[2\text{ mol }SO_2 \times -296.8\text{ kJ/mol} + 1\text{ mol }O_2 \times 0\text{ kJ/mol} \right]$

$= -197.8\text{ kJ/mol}$

This is for 2 mol of SO_3 formed; for 1 mol of SO_3, $\Delta H^\circ_{rxn} = -197.8$ kJ/mol $\div 2 = -98.9$ kJ/mol.

(c) Because this reaction is exothermic, heat flows out from the reaction mixture to the surroundings.

Think about It

The volume of the cylinder decreases because the reaction yields fewer product molecules than the number of reactant molecules.

9.9. **Collect and Organize**

Energy and work must be related since from our everyday experience we know that doing work takes energy.

Analyze

In this context, energy is defined as the capacity to do work. Work is defined as moving an object against a force over some distance. Energy is also thought to be a fundamental component of the universe. The Big Bang theory postulates that all matter originated from a burst of energy, and Albert Einstein proposed that $m = E/c^2$ (mass equals energy divided by the speed of light squared).

Solve

Energy is needed to do work, and doing work uses energy.

Think about It
A system with high energy has the potential to do a lot of work.

9.11. Collect and Organize / Analyze
We are to explain what is meant by a *state function*.

Solve
The value of a state function is independent of the path taken in reaching a particular state; only the initial and final values are important.

Think about It
Examples of state functions are internal energy and enthalpy, but not work and heat.

9.13. Collect and Organize
Potential energy can take several forms. We are to specifically describe the potential energy in 1 mol of acetylene (C_2H_2) gas.

Analyze
The basic definition of potential energy is the energy of position from PE = *mgh*. But potential energy is also present at the molecular level in the form of stored energy in the chemical bonds of a substance or its ability to transfer electrons.

Solve
The potential energy of a mole of acetylene consists of the energy stored in the chemical bonds. Specifically in acetylene it is the energy stored in the two C—H bonds and the C≡C bond. This energy is released when acetylene is combusted.

Think about It
Energy that we use for transportation and for electrical devices in the form of batteries derives from stored chemical potential energy.

9.15. Collect and Organize
Internal energy is the sum of the potential and kinetic energies of the components of a system.

Analyze
To increase kinetic energy, increase the motion of the molecules in the gas. To increase the potential energy, compress the gas to increase its pressure. It then can do work when it expands to its original volume.

Solve
We can increase the motion of the gas molecules by raising the temperature. To increase the pressure, we can compress the gas (decreasing the volume).

Think about It
Absolute internal energy is difficult to determine for a system, but changes in internal energy are easy to measure.

9.17. Collect and Organize / Analyze
We consider how pressure–volume (*P–V*) work can have energy units (joules).

Solve
P–V work (which would, at first glance, have units such as liter · atmospheres) has energy units because work is done by expending energy. *P–V* work is the energy expended or released in changing the volume against an outside pressure, so it may have units of energy.

Think about It

To convert liter · atmospheres to joules, we multiply by 101.325.

9.19. Collect and Organize

For the processes listed, we are asked to identify which are exothermic and which are endothermic.

Analyze

An exothermic process transfers energy from the system to the surroundings. Thus, something feels warm or hot in an exothermic process. An endothermic process transfers energy from the surroundings to the system. Thus, something feels cool or cold in an endothermic process.

Solve

(a) When molten aluminum solidifies, energy in the form of heat is released to the surroundings to cool the metal, so this process is exothermic.

(b) When rubbing alcohol evaporates from the skin, energy in the form of heat is absorbed by the alcohol from the skin (the surroundings) to evaporate the alcohol, so this process is endothermic.

(c) When fog forms, energy in the form of heat is released by the water vapor in the air to condense, so this process is exothermic.

Think about It

The opposite processes are the reverse: melting aluminum is endothermic, condensing alcohol is exothermic, and evaporating fog is endothermic.

9.21. Collect and Organize

Internal energy is defined as

$$\Delta E = q + w$$

where q = energy transferred and w = work done on a system $(-P\Delta V)$. Commonly, the energy transfer is caused by a temperature difference, so q is called "heat."

Analyze

When a process releases energy, the internal energy decreases and q is negative. The reverse is true (ΔE increases and q is positive) if the surroundings transfer energy to the system. If the volume of a system increases (ΔV is positive), then work is negative and the internal energy of the system decreases. The reverse is true (ΔE increases and w is positive) when the volume of the system decreases (for example, a gas is compressed).

Solve

When a liquid vaporizes at its boiling point, energy is absorbed from the surroundings. Thus, q is positive. The volume increases ($\Delta V > 0$), so work is done by the system on the surroundings and the sign of w is negative. More energy is transferred to the liquid than work done, so the sign of $q + w$ is positive; therefore, $\Delta E > 0$.

Think about It

Remember to focus on work and energy transfer from the system's point of view. This will help you be clear about the sign conventions as you learn more about thermochemistry.

9.23. Collect and Organize

The work being done is due to an expansion of the gas from 250.0 mL to 750.0 mL.

Analyze

Work is expressed as $-P\Delta V$. Here P is constant at 1.00 atm and the volume change is 500.0 mL, or 0.5000 L. We are to express work in both liter · atmospheres and joules. We can convert from one unit to another by using 101.325 J/L · atm.

Solve

$$w = -P\Delta V = (1.00 \text{ atm})(0.5000 \text{ L}) = -0.500 \text{ L} \cdot \text{atm}$$

In joules, this work is

$$-0.500 \text{ L} \cdot \text{atm} \times \frac{101.325 \text{ J}}{\text{L} \cdot \text{atm}} = -50.7 \text{ J}$$

Think about It

Because work was done by the system on the surroundings, the sign of work is negative.

9.25. **Collect and Organize**

For each part, we are to calculate internal energy (ΔE) from energy and work values.

Analyze

The formula for internal energy from energy transferred as heat and work is

$$\Delta E = q + w$$

We need only add the values of q and w given.

Solve

(a) $\Delta E = 100 \text{ J} + (-50 \text{ J}) = 50 \text{ J}$
(b) $\Delta E = 6.2 \times 10^3 \text{ J} + 0.7 \text{ L} \cdot \text{atm} = 6200 \text{ J} + (0.7 \text{ L} \cdot \text{atm} \times 101.325 \text{ J/ L} \cdot \text{atm}) = 6300 \text{ J}$, or 6.3 kJ
(c) $\Delta E = -615 \text{ kJ} + (-3.25 \text{ kWh}) = -615 \text{ kJ} + (-3.25 \text{ kWh} \times 3600 \text{ kJ/kWh}) = -12,300 \text{ kJ}$

Think about It

When adding q and w, be sure to add values with consistent units.

9.27. **Collect and Organize**

The change in internal energy for a system is

$$\Delta E = q + w$$

Analyze

The system releases energy to its surroundings, so q is negative. Because the system does work on the surroundings, w is negative.

Solve

$$\Delta E = q + w = -210 \text{ kJ} + (-65.5 \text{ kJ}) = -276 \text{ kJ}$$

Think about It

Be careful to always define the signs for q and w from the point of view of the system.

9.29. **Collect and Organize**

Work will be done by a system on the surroundings when the volume of the system shown in Figure P9.29 increases. For each reaction we are to determine for which one work is being done by the system on the surroundings and then determine the sign of w for that reaction.

Analyze

The volume of gas is proportional to the number of moles of gas (n) at constant temperature and pressure. Because both temperature and pressure are constant for each reaction, if n increases in going from reactants to products, the volume of the system increases and work is done by the system on the surroundings.

Solve

(a) In this reaction, 3 mol of gaseous reactants forms 3 mol of gaseous products. The Δn for the reaction is 0, so this reaction does not do work on the surroundings.
(b) In the reaction, 6 mol of gaseous reactants forms 7 mol of gaseous products. The Δn for the reaction is +1, so this reaction does work on the surroundings.

(c) In this reaction, 3 mol of gaseous reactants forms 2 mol of gaseous products. The Δn for the reaction is -1, so this reaction does not do work on the surroundings.

Reaction (b) does work on the surroundings. When work is done on the surroundings, the change in volume of the system is positive. Because $w = -P\Delta V$, the sign of w is negative for ΔV that is positive.

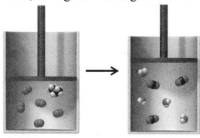

Think about It
Reaction c has $+w$ (from $-P\Delta V$, where $\Delta V = V_f - V_i$ and $V_i > V_f$, so ΔV is negative). This means that the surroundings did work on the system. The system was compressed.

9.31. Collect and Organize
We are asked to define a change in enthalpy.

Analyze
We can refer to the mathematical expression for the change in enthalpy (ΔH) to answer this question.
$$\Delta H = \Delta E + P\Delta V$$

Solve
By the equation above, a change in enthalpy is the sum of the change of internal energy and the product of the system's pressure and change in volume.

Think about It
Because $\Delta E = q + w$, internal energy changes may involve changes in energy or work or both.

9.33. Collect and Organize
We are asked why we assign a negative sign to ΔH for an exothermic process.

Analyze
In an exothermic process, the system transfers energy to the surroundings.

Solve
If the system transfers energy to the surroundings, its energy will be less after the process than at the start of the process, and q is negative. If the pressure is constant and only P–V work is done, then this q is ΔH, so ΔH must also be negative.

Think about It
The signs of thermodynamic quantities are always assigned from the point of view of the system. This approach can be confusing, as we are often observing the process from the point of view of the surroundings.

9.35. Collect and Organize
A drainpipe gets hot when Drano is added. We are asked what is the sign for ΔH for this process.

Analyze
Enthalpy is related to energy transferred as heat (q) by the equation
$$\Delta H = q_P$$

Solve

Because energy is released in the reaction between the Drano and the clog in the pipe, q is released from the system to the surroundings, so q is negative and therefore ΔH is also negative.

Think about It

All exothermic reactions have a negative ΔH.

9.37. Collect and Organize

If O_2 is the stable form of oxygen under standard conditions, it must have lower energy than other forms. The reaction describes breaking the oxygen–oxygen bond in O_2. We are asked what is the sign of ΔH.

Analyze

If a species is at low energy, then it must require an input of energy to take it out of its most stable form. Breaking the oxygen–oxygen bond, therefore, must require an input of energy.

Solve

The process of breaking the oxygen–oxygen bond is endothermic, and the sign of ΔH will be positive.

Think about It

Breaking of chemical bonds is always an endothermic process.

9.39. Collect and Organize

Compression of H_2 gas will give solid H_2. To predict the sign of the enthalpy change of this transformation, we have to consider the enthalpy of the phase change from gas to solid.

Analyze

To solidify substances, we must cool them to reduce their molecular motion.

Solve

To solidify hydrogen gas, we would remove energy from the gas, so the sign of q from the point of view of the system would be negative. Because $\Delta H = q_P$, the sign of ΔH is also negative.

Think about It

The reverse reaction, in which $H_2(s)$ sublimes into $H_2(g)$, is endothermic.

9.41. Collect and Organize

We look at the definitions and units of heat capacity and specific heat to differentiate these two terms.

Analyze

Heat capacity is the amount of energy needed to raise the temperature of an object by 1°C. Specific heat is the amount of energy needed to raise the temperature of 1 g of a substance by 1°C.

Solve

The difference in the terms lies in the specificity. Heat capacity does not take into account how much of a substance is present; it is defined for a given object. Specific heat is specified for 1 g of the substance.

Think about It

Specific heat for a substance is characteristic of that substance.

9.43. Collect and Organize

We consider why the heat of vaporization of water is so much greater than its heat of fusion.

Analyze

The enthalpy of fusion is the energy required to melt a solid substance. The enthalpy of vaporization is the energy required to vaporize the substance from a liquid to a gaseous state.

Solve

Melting and vaporizing are different processes, so we would not expect them to be the same. By melting ice we are giving the water molecules enough energy to temporarily break the hydrogen bonds between individual water molecules that are then re-formed with a neighboring water molecule. In vaporization, however, the strong hydrogen bonds between the water molecules are completely broken. Thus, vaporizing water requires much more energy.

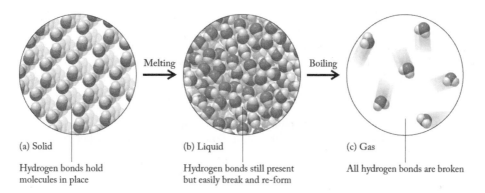

Think about It

Usually the enthalpy of vaporization is more endothermic than the enthalpy of fusion because in the phase change from liquid to gas, individual molecules must be completely separated from one another.

9.45. Collect and Organize

To compare the advantage of water-cooled engines over air-cooled engines, we have to compare the heat capacity of water with that of air.

Analyze

The specific heat capacity of water (4.18 J/g · °C) is higher than that of air (1.01 J/g · °C) at typical room conditions.

Solve

Water's high heat capacity compared with that of air means that water carries away more energy from the engine for every Celsius degree rise in temperature, so water is a good choice to cool automobile engines.

Think about It

On a volume basis, water has an even higher heat capacity than air does.

9.47. Collect and Organize

The amount of energy needed to raise the temperature of a substance depends on the substance's heat capacity and the change in temperature of the substance.

Analyze

The energy required to raise the temperature of a substance is related to the molar heat capacity by the equation

$$q = nc_P\Delta T$$

where q = energy, n = moles of the substance, c_P = molar heat capacity of the substance, and ΔT = difference in temperature, $T_f - T_i$.

Solve

$$q \text{ required} = \left(100.0 \text{ g} \times \frac{1 \text{ mol}}{18.02 \text{ g}}\right) \times \left(\frac{75.3 \text{ J}}{\text{mol} \cdot {}^\circ\text{C}}\right) \times \left(100.0\,{}^\circ\text{C} - 30.0\,{}^\circ\text{C}\right) = 29{,}300 \text{ J, or } 29.3 \text{ kJ}$$

Think about It
If the water were cooled from 100°C to 30°C, the sign of ΔT would be negative, and therefore q would be negative, showing that the system was cooled.

9.49. Collect and Organize
A heating curve plots temperature as a function of energy added to a substance.

Analyze
Methanol at −100°C is a solid. As energy is added, the solid methanol increases in temperature until it reaches its melting point, at which point the added energy does not change the temperature of the methanol until all the solid methanol has melted. Only when methanol is entirely liquid will added energy increase the temperature of the liquid until the boiling point of methanol is reached. During boiling, the temperature of the methanol does not change. Once the methanol is converted to gaseous form, added energy increases the temperature of the gaseous methanol.
Relevant equations for finding the energy required for each step are as follows:

$q = nc_P\Delta T$ for energy added to the solid, liquid, and gas phases, where $n = 1$ mol,
c_P = heat capacity for that phase, and ΔT = temperature change for that phase
$q = n\Delta H_{fus}$ energy for melting
$q = n\Delta H_{vap}$ energy for vaporization

Solve

Step in Heating Curve	T_i, °C	T_f, °C	q	Total q
Heating methanol ice	−100	−94	$q = 1$ mol × 48.7 J/mol · °C × 6°C = 0.292 kJ	0.29 kJ
Melting methanol ice	−94	−94	$q_{fus} = 1$ mol × 3.18 kJ/mol = 3.18 kJ	3.47 kJ
Warming liquid methanol	−94	65	$q = 1$ mol × 81.1 J/mol · °C × 159°C = 12.9 kJ	16.37 kJ
Boiling liquid methanol	65	65	$q_{vap} = 1$ mol × 35.3 kJ/mol = 35.3 kJ	51.67 kJ
Heating methanol gas	65	100	$q = 1$ mol × 43.9 J/mol · °C × 35°C = 1.54 kJ	53.21 kJ

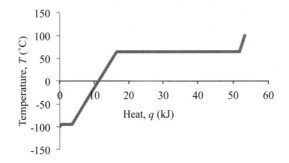

Think about It
Methanol has a wide temperature range as a liquid, making it useful as a solvent.

9.51. Collect and Organize
Sweating helps to cool athletes. During a workout, an athlete generates 233 kJ of energy. We are to calculate how much water the athlete would lose if all the energy is used to evaporate water.

Analyze
The energy generated by the athlete must vaporize the water, so the pertinent equation is

$$q = n\Delta H_{vap}$$

where ΔH_{vap} for water is 40.67 kJ/mol.

Solve

The amount of water in moles that 2000.0 kJ of energy would vaporize is

$$233 \text{ kJ} = n \times 43.5 \text{ kJ/mol}$$

$$n = 5.36 \text{ mol H}_2\text{O}$$

Converting this to mass,

$$5.36 \text{ mol} \times \frac{18.02 \text{ g H}_2\text{O}}{1 \text{ mol}} = 96.5 \text{ g H}_2\text{O}$$

Think about It

Since the density of water is 1.00 g/mL, the athlete would use 886 mL of water to dissipate the energy. To rehydrate, the athlete should drink about 1 L of water.

9.53. **Collect and Organize**

When the water is converted into steam, the skillet must lose energy to heat and boil the water away. We are asked to calculate the change in the temperature of the pan with a mass of 1.20 kg when all 10.0 mL water initially at 25°C is converted into steam at 100.0°C.

Analyze

The equation describing the energy exchange *between* the skillet and the water is

$$q_{\text{water gained}} = -q_{\text{skillet lost}}$$

where

$$q_{\text{water gained}} = nc_\text{p} \Delta T + n\Delta H_{\text{vap}}$$

$$q_{\text{skillet lost}} = nc_\text{p} \Delta T$$

Solve

$$q_{\text{water gained}} = -q_{\text{skillet lost}}$$

$$\left[10.0 \text{ g} \times \frac{1 \text{ mol}}{18.02 \text{ g}} \times \frac{75.3 \text{ J}}{\text{mol} \cdot °\text{C}} \times (100.0°\text{C} - 25.0°\text{C}) \right] + \left[10.0 \text{ g} \times \frac{1 \text{ mol}}{18.02 \text{ g}} \times \frac{40,670}{\text{mol} \cdot °\text{C}} \right]$$

$$= -\left(1200 \text{ g} \times \frac{1 \text{ mol Fe}}{55.845} \right) \times \frac{25.19 \text{ J}}{\text{mol} \cdot °\text{C}} \times \Delta T$$

$$\Delta T = -47.5°\text{C}$$

Think about It

Because the iron skillet has a moderately high molar heat capacity and contains much iron (in terms of moles), boiling the water into steam does not completely cool the skillet to room temperature.

9.55. **Collect and Organize**

To know why the calorimeter constant (that is, the heat capacity of the calorimeter) is important, we need to define the system and surroundings for the calorimetry experiment.

Analyze

The system in a calorimetry experiment is defined as the substance for which, for example, the heat capacity is being measured. The calorimeter is everything but the system (that is, the calorimeter is the surroundings).

Solve

Because energy is transferred between the system and the surroundings, the heat capacity of the calorimeter (the surroundings) is important because we need to know how much energy (generated or absorbed by the system) is required to change the temperature of the surroundings (the calorimeter) to calculate the heat capacity or final temperature of the system in an experiment.

Think about It

Calorimeter constants vary from calorimeter to calorimeter.

9.57. **Collect and Organize / Analyze**
The calorimeter constant is the heat capacity of the surroundings. In replacing water in a calorimeter with another liquid, we are changing the surroundings.

Solve
The heat capacity of the new liquid is different from that of water. The liquid is part of the calorimeter and therefore part of the surroundings. Yes, the calorimeter constant must be redetermined.

Think about It
If the system is expected to transfer a lot of energy to the calorimeter, then using a liquid with a higher heat capacity than water might be necessary.

9.59. **Collect and Organize**
Benzoic acid is often used to determine calorimeter constants. As mentioned in the text, when 1 g of it combusts, 26.38 kJ is released to the surroundings.

Analyze
The calorimeter constant is defined as

$$C_{calorimeter} = \frac{q}{\Delta T}$$

In the combustion of benzoic acid for this calorimeter, we use 5.000 g of benzoic acid and get a temperature change of 16.397°C.

Solve

$$C_{calorimeter} = \frac{\dfrac{26.38 \text{ kJ}}{\text{g benzoic acid}} \times 5.000 \text{ g}}{16.397 \,^{\circ}\text{C}} = 8.044 \, \frac{\text{kJ}}{^{\circ}\text{C}}$$

Think about It
Be sure to account for how many grams of benzoic acid is used in measuring the calorimeter constant.

9.61. **Collect and Organize**
In a bomb calorimeter $q_{system} = \Delta E_{comb}$, but since the *P–V* work is usually small, $\Delta E_{comb} \approx \Delta H_{comb}$. So we may assume that $\Delta H_{comb} = -q_{calorimeter}$ since $q_{rxn} = -q_{calorimeter}$.

Analyze
We can find ΔH_{comb} through

$$\Delta H_{comb} = -q_{calorimeter} = -C_{calorimeter} \Delta T$$

The ΔH_{comb} we find is for the combustion of 1.200 g of cinnamaldehyde. To find ΔH_{comb} in terms of kilojoules per mole, we need to divide the calculated ΔH_{comb} by the moles of cinnamaldehyde (C_9H_8O).

Solve

$$\Delta H_{comb} = -3.640 \text{ kJ/}^{\circ}\text{C} \times 12.79\,^{\circ}\text{C} = -46.56 \text{ kJ}$$

$$\text{molar } \Delta H_{comb} = \frac{-46.56 \text{ kJ}}{\left(1.200 \text{ g} \times \dfrac{1 \text{ mol}}{132.2 \text{ g}}\right)} = -5129 \, \frac{\text{kJ}}{\text{mol}}$$

Think about It
Expressing the enthalpies of reactions in terms of molar enthalpies allows us to compare reactions on a per-mole basis.

9.63. **Collect and Organize**
We are asked to work backward from the molar enthalpy of combustion of dimethyl phthalate to the final temperature of the calorimeter.

Analyze
First, we have to calculate ΔH_{comb} from the molar heat of combustion and the grams (which we convert into moles) of dimethyl phthalate ($C_{10}H_{10}O_4$). We can then find T_f by rearranging the equation for ΔH_{comb}.

$$\Delta H_{comb} = -C_{calorimeter}\,\Delta T$$

$$\Delta T = \frac{\Delta H_{comb}}{C_{cal}} = T_f - T_i$$

Solve
The ΔH_{comb} for 1.00 g of dimethyl phthalate is

$$1.00 \text{ g} \times \frac{1 \text{ mol}}{194.19 \text{ g}} \times \frac{4685 \text{ kJ}}{1 \text{ mol}} = 24.13 \text{ kJ}$$

The change in the temperature of the calorimeter is

$$\Delta T_f = \frac{24.13 \text{ kJ}}{7.854 \text{ kJ/°C}} = 3.072\,°C$$

Think about It
Although the molar ΔH_{comb} is large for dimethyl phthalate, this experiment combusts so little dimethyl phthalate that the change in temperature is small.

9.65. **Collect and Organize**
For the reaction of 0.243 g of Mg with 100.0 mL of 1.00 M HCl, we are to calculate the enthalpy of the reaction, knowing the temperature change of the solution and given the specific heat and density of the solution.

Analyze
All the energy from the reaction is transferred to the solution. We can find this heat from the equation

$$q_{solution} = mc_p\Delta T$$

Because all this heat came from the reaction of 0.243 g of Mg, the enthalpy of the reaction is

$$\Delta H_{rxn} = \frac{q_{rxn}}{\text{mol of Mg}}$$

Solve
The energy transferred in the reaction is

$$q_{solution} = \left(100.0 \text{ mL solution} \times \frac{1.01 \text{ g}}{\text{mL}}\right) \times \frac{4.18 \text{ J}}{\text{g} \cdot °C} \times \left(33.4\,°C - 22.4\,°C\right) = 4.644 \times 10^3 \text{ J}$$

The enthalpy of the reaction per mole of Mg is

$$\Delta H_{rxn} = \frac{4.644 \times 10^3 \text{ J}}{\left(0.243 \text{ g Mg} \times \dfrac{\text{mol}}{24.305 \text{ g}}\right)} = 4.64 \times 10^5 \text{ J/mol, or } 464 \text{ kJ/mol}$$

Because this reaction is exothermic, the enthalpy of reaction is –464 kJ/mol.

Think about It
Always be sure to determine the sign of enthalpy by considering whether the reaction is exothermic or endothermic.

9.67. **Collect and Organize**
Compare Hess's law with the law of conservation of energy.

Analyze

The law of conservation of energy states that energy cannot be created or destroyed; it can be converted from one form into another. Hess's law states that the enthalpy change for a reaction can be obtained by summing the enthalpies of constituent reactions.

Solve

When we apply Hess's law, all the energy is accounted for in the reaction; energy is neither created nor destroyed.

Think about It

Hess's law makes it easy for us to calculate energy changes for chemical reactions from those for other chemical reactions.

9.69. Collect and Organize

To calculate ΔH_f° for SO_2 from the equations given, we use Hess's law.

Analyze

The equation for ΔH_f° of SO_2 has S and O_2 as the reactants and SO_2 as the product. The sum of the other two reactions must add up to the overall ΔH_f°. In both reactions, SO_3 is produced. If we reverse the first equation and add the second equation, the overall reaction will consist of S and O_2 as the reactants and SO_2 as the product. When the first reaction is reversed, the ΔH_{rxn}° will change from exothermic to endothermic.

Solve

$$2\,SO_3(g) \rightarrow 2\,SO_2(g) + O_2(g) \qquad \Delta H_{rxn}^\circ = 196 \text{ kJ}$$
$$\underline{\tfrac{1}{4}\,S_8(s) + 3\,O_2(g) \rightarrow 2\,SO_3(g) \qquad \Delta H_{rxn}^\circ = -790 \text{ kJ}}$$
$$\tfrac{1}{4}\,S_8(s) + 2\,O_2(g) \rightarrow 2\,SO_2(g) \qquad \Delta H_{rxn}^\circ = -594 \text{ kJ}$$

This will be twice that of the ΔH_f° for the formation reaction (for 1 mol of SO_2 formed):

$$\tfrac{1}{8}S_8(s) + O_2(g) \rightarrow SO_2(g)$$

Therefore, $\Delta H_f^\circ = -297$ kJ/mol.

Think about It

Remember that enthalpy is stoichiometric. If 5 mol of SO_2 was formed, then $\Delta H_f^\circ = -1485$ kJ.

9.71. Collect and Organize

The two equations when added in the appropriate way describe the conversion of α-spodumene into β-spodumene.

Analyze

Because α-spodumene is the reactant in the conversion, we have to reverse the first equation. That reaction will then be endothermic. Hess's law then states that we can add the equations and their corresponding ΔH values to give the overall equation and its enthalpy.

Solve

$$2\,\alpha\text{-LiAlSi}_2O_6(s) \rightarrow Li_2O(s) + 2\,Al(s) + 4\,SiO_2(s) + \tfrac{3}{2}\,O_2(g) \quad \Delta H_{rxn}^\circ = 1870.6 \text{ kJ}$$
$$\underline{Li_2O(s) + 2\,Al(s) + 4\,SiO_2(s) + \tfrac{3}{2}\,O_2(g) \rightarrow 2\,\beta\text{-LiAlSi}_2O_6(s) \qquad \Delta H_{rxn}^\circ = -1814.6 \text{ kJ}}$$
$$2\,\alpha\text{-LiAlSi}_2O_6(s) \rightarrow 2\,\beta\text{-LiAlSi}_2O_6(s) \qquad \Delta H_{rxn}^\circ = 56.0 \text{ kJ}$$

This is for the conversion of 2 mol of the α form into the β form. For 1 mol:

$$\alpha\text{-LiAlSi}_2O_6(s) \rightarrow \beta\text{-LiAlSi}_2O_6(s) \qquad \Delta H_{rxn}^\circ = 28.0 \text{ kJ/mol}$$

Think about It

Because the conversion of α-spodumene into β-spodumene is endothermic, we can say that the α form is more stable (by enthalpy) than the β form.

9.73. Collect and Organize

The two chemical reactions must add up to the overall reaction in which NOCl decomposes to nitrogen, oxygen, and chlorine. We can use Hess's law to find the enthalpy of decomposition of NOCl.

Analyze

NOCl must be on the reactants side, so the second reaction must be reversed. This reaction will then be endothermic ($\Delta H^\circ_{rxn} = 38.6$ kJ). The first reaction also has to be reversed because we need to have N_2 and O_2 on the product side of the overall equation. This will be an exothermic reaction ($\Delta H^\circ_{rxn} = -90.3$ kJ).

Solve

$$NO(g) \rightarrow \tfrac{1}{2} N_2(g) + \tfrac{1}{2} O_2(g) \qquad\qquad \Delta H^\circ_{rxn} = -90.3 \text{ kJ}$$
$$\underline{NOCl(g) \rightarrow NO(g) + \tfrac{1}{2} Cl_2(g) \qquad\qquad \Delta H^\circ_{rxn} = 38.6 \text{ kJ}}$$
$$NOCl(g) \rightarrow \tfrac{1}{2} N_2(g) + \tfrac{1}{2} O_2(g) + \tfrac{1}{2} Cl_2(g) \qquad\qquad \Delta H^\circ_{rxn} = -51.7 \text{ kJ}$$

Multiplying this chemical reaction by 2, we obtain the ΔH°_{rxn} for the desired overall equation:

$$2\, NOCl(g) \rightarrow N_2(g) + O_2(g) + Cl_2(g) \qquad\qquad \Delta H^\circ_{rxn} = -103 \text{ kJ}$$

Think about It

This reaction, because it is exothermic, releases energy in the decomposition of NOCl into its constituent elements.

9.75. Collect and Organize

We are asked to explain why the standard heat of formation of carbon monoxide as a gas is difficult to measure experimentally.

Analyze

Carbon monoxide is formed from the combustion of carbon. Another product, however, also forms when carbon reacts with oxygen: CO_2.

Solve

The enthalpy of formation of CO is difficult to measure because the competing reaction to form CO_2 is favorable, so isolating just the enthalpy due to the formation of carbon monoxide is hard.

Think about It

The enthalpy of formation of carbon dioxide is more exothermic (−412.9 kJ/mol) and therefore more favorable by enthalpy than the formation of carbon monoxide (−393.5 kJ/mol).

9.77. Collect and Organize

The standard enthalpy of formation is the energy absorbed or evolved when 1 mol of a substance is formed from the elements, all in their standard states. Here we compare the enthalpy of formation of O_2 to that of O_3.

Analyze

Standard conditions are 1 atm and some specified temperature. Both ozone (O_3) and elemental oxygen (O_2) exist under these conditions.

Solve

Because ozone and elemental oxygen are different forms of oxygen, their standard enthalpies of formation are different. From Appendix 4, ΔH°_f for O_2 is 0 kJ/mol (because it is an element in its most stable form under standard conditions) and ΔH°_f for O_3 is 142.7 kJ/mol.

Think about It

Because ΔH_f° for O_3 is more positive than that for O_2, ozone is less stable than O_2.

9.79. Collect and Organize

In calculating an estimate of the enthalpy change for a reaction by using bond energies, we are to explain why we need to know the stoichiometry of the reaction.

Analyze

Bond breaking is endothermic, and bond formation is exothermic. The stoichiometry of the reaction tells us how many bonds break and how many form.

Solve

We must account for all the bonds that break and all the bonds that form in the reaction. To do so we must start with a balanced chemical reaction. If we miss a bond that breaks, our calculated enthalpy of reaction would be too negative. If we miss a bond that forms, our calculated enthalpy of reaction would be too positive.

Think about It

Before using an equation to calculate enthalpy change, whether from enthalpies of formation or from bond energies, always start with a balanced chemical equation.

9.81. Collect and Organize

We are to explain why the phase of the reactants is important in enthalpy calculations, even in those involving bond energies—in particular, why the reactants and products should all be in the gas phase when we use bond energies to estimate the enthalpy of a reaction.

Analyze

The bond energy is the enthalpy change required to break 1 mol of bonds in a substance in the *gas phase*.

Solve

If the compounds are in the solid or liquid phase, interactions between molecules may slightly change the bond energy for a given bond.

Think about It

Having bond energy data tabulated only for the gaseous phase ensures that the measured energies are for the bonds breaking only and do not include any intermolecular interactions. Later, you will learn more about intermolecular forces. Some can be very strong (ion–ion forces), and others are quite weak (van der Waals forces).

9.83. Collect and Organize

The heat of formation is reflected in a reaction when (1) 1 mol of the substance is produced, (2) the substance is produced under standard-state conditions, and (3) it is produced from the substance's constituent elements in their standard state.

Analyze

Each reaction must meet all the criteria for its ΔH_{rxn}° to be classified as a heat of formation.

Solve

(a) One mole of CO_2 is produced from elemental carbon and oxygen, so ΔH_{rxn}° for this reaction represents ΔH_f°.
(b) Because 2 mol of CO is produced from CO_2 (which is not an element) and C, this reaction does not represent ΔH_f°.
(c) Because two substances are produced and one of the reactants (CO_2) is not an element, this reaction does not represent ΔH_f°.
(d) One mole of CH_4 is produced from elemental carbon and hydrogen; therefore, this reaction represents ΔH_f°.

Think about It

Heat of formation must involve the reaction of the *elements* to form compounds. Remember, though, that some elements, such as O_2, H_2, and N_2, are diatomic in their elemental state.

9.85. Collect and Organize

The heat of a reaction can be computed by finding the difference between the sum of the heats of formation of the products and the sum of the heats of formation of the reactants.

Analyze

We have to take into account the moles of products formed and the moles of reactants used as well, because enthalpy is a stoichiometric quantity.

$$\Delta H^\circ_{rxn} = \sum n_{products} \Delta H^\circ_{f,products} - \sum n_{reactants} \Delta H^\circ_{f,reactants}$$

Values for ΔH°_f for the reactants and products are found in Appendix 4.

Solve

$$\Delta H^\circ_{rxn} = \left[(1 \text{ mol } CH_4)(-74.8 \text{ kJ/mol}) + (2 \text{ mol } H_2O)(-241.8 \text{ kJ/mol}) \right]$$
$$- \left[(4 \text{ mol } H_2)(0 \text{ kJ/mol}) + (1 \text{ mol } CO_2)(-393.5 \text{ kJ/mol}) \right]$$
$$\Delta H^\circ_{rxn} = -164.9 \text{ kJ}$$

Think about It

Be careful to note and find the appropriate ΔH°_f for a compound that may exist in different phases. For example, ΔH°_f of $H_2O(g) = -241.8$ kJ/mol, but ΔH°_f of $H_2O(\ell) = -285.8$ kJ/mol.

9.87. Collect and Organize

To calculate ΔH°_{rxn} for the decomposition of NH_4NO_3 to N_2O and H_2O vapor, we need the balanced equation because the enthalpy of the reaction depends on the moles of reactants consumed and moles of products formed in the reaction.

Analyze

From the balanced chemical equation and the values of ΔH°_f of the reactants and products, we use

$$\Delta H^\circ_{rxn} = \sum n_{products} \Delta H^\circ_{f,products} - \sum n_{reactants} \Delta H^\circ_{f,reactants}$$

Because the reaction is run at 250–300°C, the water product is in the gaseous phase.

Solve

The balanced equation for this reaction is
$$NH_4NO_3(s) \rightarrow N_2O(g) + 2 H_2O(g)$$
We use the coefficients in the equation for ΔH°_{rxn}:
$$\Delta H^\circ_{rxn} = \left[(1 \text{ mol } N_2O)(82.1 \text{ kJ/mol}) + (2 \text{ mol } H_2O)(-241.8 \text{ kJ/mol}) \right]$$
$$- \left[(1 \text{ mol } NH_4NO_3)(-365.6 \text{ kJ/mol}) \right]$$
$$\Delta H^\circ_{rxn} = -35.9 \text{ kJ}$$

Think about It

The reaction is exothermic, releasing 36 kJ for every mole of NH_4NO_3 decomposed.

9.89. Collect and Organize

We are given the balanced chemical equation for the explosive reaction of fuel oil with ammonium nitrate in the presence of oxygen.

Analyze

To calculate ΔH°_{rxn} we use

$$\Delta H^{\circ}_{rxn} = \sum n_{products}\, \Delta H^{\circ}_{f,products} - \sum n_{reactants}\, \Delta H^{\circ}_{f,reactants}$$

Solve

$$\Delta H^{\circ}_{rxn} = \left[(3 \text{ mol N}_2)(0.0 \text{ kJ/mol}) + (17 \text{ mol H}_2\text{O})(-241.8 \text{ kJ/mol}) + (10 \text{ mol CO}_2)(-393.5 \text{ kJ/mol}) \right]$$
$$- \left[(3 \text{ mol NH}_4\text{NO}_3)(-365.6 \text{ kJ/mol}) + (1 \text{ mol C}_{10}\text{H}_{22})(249.7 \text{ kJ/mol}) + (14 \text{ mol O}_2)(0.0 \text{ kJ/mol}) \right]$$
$$\Delta H^{\circ}_{rxn} = -7198 \text{ kJ}$$

Think about It

This is a very exothermic reaction that occurs very fast and is therefore explosive.

9.91. Collect and Organize

We can use average bond energy data in Table A4.1 to estimate the enthalpy of three reactions.

Analyze

The enthalpy of a reaction as estimated from bond energies is given as

$$\Delta H_{rxn} = \sum \Delta H_{bond\ breaking} + \sum \Delta H_{bond\ forming}$$

where $\Delta H_{bond\ breaking}$ and $\Delta H_{bond\ forming}$ are average bond energies for the bonds in the reactants and products, respectively. In computing $\Delta H_{bond\ breaking}$ and $\Delta H_{bond\ forming}$ we have to take into account the number (or moles) of a particular type of bond that breaks or forms. We must also keep in mind that bond breaking requires energy ($+\Delta H$), whereas bond formation releases energy ($-\Delta H$).

Solve

(a) $\Delta H_{rxn} = [(2 \times 945 \text{ kJ/mol}) + (3 \times 436 \text{ kJ/mol})] + [-(6 \times 391 \text{ kJ/mol})] = 852 \text{ kJ}$

$$:N\equiv N: \ + \ 3 \ H\text{—}H \longrightarrow 2 \ H\text{—}\overset{\cdot\cdot}{\underset{\underset{H}{|}}{N}}\text{—}H$$

(b) $\Delta H_{rxn} = [(1 \times 945 \text{ kJ/mol}) + (2 \times 436 \text{ kJ/mol})] + [-(1 \times 163 \text{ kJ/mol}) - (4 \times 391 \text{ kJ/mol})] = 90 \text{ kJ}$

$$:N\equiv N: \ + \ 2 \ H\text{—}H \longrightarrow \ \overset{H}{\underset{H}{\diagdown\!\diagup}}:N\text{—}N:\overset{H}{\underset{H}{\diagup\!\diagdown}}$$

(c) $\Delta H_{rxn} = [(2 \times 945 \text{ kJ/mol}) + (1 \times 498 \text{ kJ/mol})] + [-(2 \times 945 \text{ kJ/mol}) - (2 \times 201 \text{ kJ/mol})] = 96 \text{ kJ}$

$$2:N\equiv N: \ + \ \overset{\cdot\cdot}{\underset{\cdot\cdot}{O}}\!=\!\overset{\cdot\cdot}{\underset{\cdot\cdot}{O}} \longrightarrow 2:N\equiv N\text{—}\overset{\cdot\cdot}{\underset{\cdot\cdot}{O}}:$$

Think about It

We have to use the "best" Lewis structure for these calculations of reaction enthalpy. In part c, an alternate form (but contributing less to the bonding by formal charge arguments) for N_2O would be

$$2:N\equiv N: \quad \overset{\cdot\cdot}{\underset{\cdot\cdot}{O}}\!=\!\overset{\cdot\cdot}{\underset{\cdot\cdot}{O}} \longrightarrow 2\,\overset{\cdot\cdot}{\cdot}N\!=\!N\!=\!\overset{\cdot\cdot}{\underset{\cdot\cdot}{O}}\cdot$$

$\Delta H_{rxn} = [(2 \times 945 \text{ kJ/mol}) + (1 \times 498 \text{ kJ/mol})] + [-(2 \times 418 \text{ kJ/mol}) - (2 \times 607 \text{ kJ/mol})] = 338 \text{ kJ}$

9.93. Collect and Organize

We can use bond energies to compare the reaction enthalpies of the two reactions

$$C_2H_6 + \tfrac{5}{2} O_2 \rightarrow 2 \, CO + 3 \, H_2O$$
$$C_2H_6 + \tfrac{7}{2} O_2 \rightarrow 2 \, CO_2 + 3 \, H_2O$$

Analyze

From the Lewis structures and the average bond energy values in Table A4.1, we can estimate the reaction enthalpies. The enthalpy of a reaction as estimated from bond energies is given as

$$\Delta H_{rxn} = \sum \Delta H_{\text{bond breaking}} + \sum \Delta H_{\text{bond forming}}$$

where $\Delta H_{\text{bond breaking}}$ and $\Delta H_{\text{bond forming}}$ are average bond energies for the bonds in the reactants and products, respectively.

Solve

For the incomplete combustion of C_2H_6 to CO:

$\Delta H_{rxn} = [(6 \times 413 \text{ kJ/mol}) + (1 \times 348 \text{ kJ/mol}) + (5/2 \times 498 \text{ kJ/mol})] + [-(2 \times 1072 \text{ kJ/mol}) - (6 \times 463 \text{ kJ/mol})]$
$\Delta H_{rxn} = -851 \text{ kJ/mol}$

For the complete combustion of C_2H_6 to CO_2:

$\Delta H_{rxn} = [(6 \times 413 \text{ kJ/mol}) + (1 \times 348 \text{ kJ/mol}) + (7/2 \times 498 \text{ kJ/mol})] + [-(4 \times 799 \text{ kJ/mol}) - (6 \times 463 \text{ kJ/mol})]$

$\Delta H_{rxn} = -1405 \text{ kJ/mol}$

The complete combustion reaction releases 554 kJ more energy than the incomplete combustion reaction.

Think about It

Although weaker $C=O$ bonds are formed in the complete combustion reaction, two such bonds are formed in CO_2, which outweighs the strong $C\equiv O$ bond in carbon monoxide in the incomplete combustion reaction.

9.95. **Collect and Organize**

For the reaction of ammonia with oxygen to give water and nitrogen dioxide, we can use the bond energies of the N—H (391 kJ/mol), O=O (498 kJ/mol), N=O (607 kJ/mol), N—O (201 kJ/mol), and O—H (463 kJ/mol) bonds to estimate the enthalpy of the reaction.

Analyze

To be sure which bonds are breaking and which bonds are being formed, drawing the Lewis structures of each of the products and reactants will help us. The enthalpy of a reaction as estimated from bond energies is given as

$$\Delta H_{rxn} = \sum \Delta H_{\text{bond breaking}} + \sum \Delta H_{\text{bond forming}}$$

where $\Delta H_{\text{bond breaking}}$ and $\Delta H_{\text{bond forming}}$ are average bond energies for the bonds in the reactants and products, respectively.

Solve

$\Delta H_{rxn} = [(12 \times 391 \text{ kJ/mol}) + (7 \times 498 \text{ kJ/mol})] + [-(4 \times 201 \text{ kJ/mol}) - (4 \times 607 \text{ kJ/mol}) - (12 \times 463 \text{ kJ/mol})]$

$\Delta H_{rxn} = -610 \text{ kJ}$

Think about It

The bonding in NO_2 is not strictly one single bond and one double bond, as shown by the resonance structures

For calculations using bond energies, however, we can use one of the "frozen" resonance structures to assign bond energy values.

9.97. Collect and Organize / Analyze
We are asked to define and describe the term *fuel value*.

Solve
We often are concerned about the energy a fuel provides per mass; fuel values give the energy per gram that a fuel releases upon burning.

Think about It
For some fuels, such as gasoline, thinking of energy per volume (liter or gallon) might be more convenient.

9.99. Collect and Organize
For this question we compare the fuel values (without making any calculations) of CH_4 and H_2 on a per-mole and a per-gram basis.

Analyze
The balanced equations for the combustion reactions are
$$CH_4(g) + 2\,O_2(g) \rightarrow CO_2(g) + 2\,H_2O(g)$$
$$H_2(g) + \tfrac{1}{2}O_2(g) \rightarrow H_2O(g)$$
The heats of formation for these reactants and products are
$$CH_4(g) = -74.8 \text{ kJ/mol}$$
$$O_2(g) = 0.0 \text{ kJ/mol}$$
$$CO_2(g) = -393.5 \text{ kJ/mol}$$
$$H_2O(g) = -241.8 \text{ kJ/mol}$$
$$H_2(g) = 0.0 \text{ kJ/mol}$$

Solve
(a) In examining the two reactions and the associated heats of formation, we can see easily that the combustion of 1 mol of CH_4 gives off more energy than the combustion of 1 mol of H_2.
(b) However, because 1 g is 1/16 mol of CH_4, whereas 1 g is 1/2 mol of H_2 on a per-gram basis, H_2 releases more energy upon combustion per gram.

Think about It
The high-energy combustion reaction of hydrogen on a per-gram basis makes it an attractive fuel source to develop.

9.101. Collect and Organize
To determine the amount of water that could be heated from 20.0°C to 45.0°C when 1.00 pound of propane is burned, we use the fuel value of propane and the heat capacity equation for water.

Analyze
First, to compute the energy (q, in kilojoules) that 1.00 pound of propane generates, we multiply the fuel value (46.35 kJ/g) by the mass of propane (after converting pounds to grams, using 1 lb = 453.6 g). Then we use the molar heat capacity equation
$$q = nc_P\Delta T$$
where $c_P = 75.3$ J/mol · °C, $\Delta T = 25.0$°C, to find the moles (n) and finally mass (m) of water that can be heated 25.0°C by 1.00 pound of propane.

Solve
Energy generated by propane:
$$1.00 \text{ lb} \times \frac{453.6 \text{ g}}{1 \text{ lb}} \times \frac{46.35 \text{ kJ}}{\text{g}} = 2.10 \times 10^4 \text{ kJ}$$

Mass of water heated 25.0°C by this q:

$$2.10 \times 10^4 \text{ kJ} \times \frac{1000 \text{ J}}{1 \text{ kJ}} = n \times 75.3 \frac{\text{J}}{\text{mol} \cdot °C} \times 25.0°C$$

$$n = 1.11 \times 10^4 \text{ mol}$$

This is $1.11 \times 10^4 \text{ mol} \times \frac{18.02 \text{ g}}{\text{mol}} = 2.01 \times 10^5$ g, or 201 kg

Think about It
Propane's relatively high fuel value makes it an efficient fuel.

9.103. **Collect and Organize**
Once we compute the fuel value of C_5H_{12}, we use it to calculate the energy released when 1.00 kg of C_5H_{12} is burned and how much C_5H_{12} is needed to heat 1.00 kg of water 70.0°C.

Analyze
(a) The fuel value can be calculated by dividing the absolute value of the given $\Delta H°_{comb}$ (–3535 kJ/mol) by the molar mass of C_5H_{12} (72.15 g/mol).
(b) The energy released when 1.00 kg of C_5H_{12} is burned can be found by multiplying the mass in grams by the fuel value.
(c) The molar heat equation is

$$q = nc_P\Delta T$$

where moles (n) can be determined from m = 1.00 kg (1000 g) water, c_P = 75.3 J/mol · °C, and ΔT = 70.0°C. This gives us the energy (in joules) required to heat the water. The amount of C_5H_{12} needed to heat the water can then be calculated by dividing the q value by the fuel value for C_5H_{12}.

Solve
(a) Fuel value of $C_5H_{12} = \frac{3535 \text{ kJ}}{\text{mol}} \times \frac{1 \text{ mol}}{72.15 \text{ g}}$ = 48.99 kJ/g

(b) Heat released by 1.00 kg C_5H_{12} = 1000 g $\times \frac{48.99 \text{ kJ}}{\text{g}} = 4.90 \times 10^4$ kJ

(c) Energy needed to raise 1.00 kg water from 20.0°C to 90.0°C:
$$q = 1000 \text{ g} \times \frac{1 \text{ mol}}{18.02 \text{ g}} \times \frac{75.3 \text{ J}}{\text{mol} \cdot °C} \times 70.0°C = 2.925 \times 10^5 \text{ J, or 293 kJ}$$

Mass of C_5H_{12} needed to generate this energy = 292.5 kJ $\times \frac{1 \text{ g}}{48.99 \text{ kJ}}$ = 5.97 g

Think about It
Only about 6 g of fuel is required from the camper's stove to heat the water. The white gas has a relatively high fuel value.

9.105. **Collect and Organize**
The sublimation occurring for wet laundry drying outside in the winter is
$$H_2O(s) \rightarrow H_2O(g)$$

Analyze
The internal energy is expressed by the equation
$$\Delta E = q + w$$
where q = energy and w = work.

Solve
We are given that ΔE for this process is less than q absorbed ($\Delta E < q$). If so, for the equality
$$\Delta E = q + w$$

to be maintained, w must be negative. A negative value of w must mean that work is done by the system on the surroundings.

Think about It

Because water is subliming from the solid phase into the gas phase, w is indeed negative. The volume is increasing, so ΔV will be positive, making w in the following equation negative:

$$w = -P\Delta V$$

9.107. Collect and Organize

When a sodium hydroxide solution is mixed with a sulfuric acid solution, the solution gets hot. We are asked to find the ΔH_{rxn} for the reaction.

Analyze

(a) This is a neutralization reaction that produces water and sodium sulfate.
(b) To determine the molar ratio (to see whether any reactant is in excess), we multiply the volume of reactant by its concentration.
(c) The water absorbs all the energy generated by the reaction, causing the temperature to rise. The energy then is

$$q = mc_S \Delta T$$

where m = total mass of the solution (100 g + 50.0 g), c_S is the specific heat of water (4.184 J/g · °C), and ΔT is the change in temperature ($T_f - T_i$).

Solve

(a) $2\,NaOH(aq) + H_2SO_4(aq) \rightarrow 2\,H_2O\,(\ell) + Na_2SO_4(aq)$

(b) Stoichiometry of the reaction:

$$\text{mol NaOH} = 100.0 \text{ mL} \times \frac{1.0 \text{ mol}}{1000 \text{ mL}} = 0.10 \text{ mol NaOH}$$

$$\text{mol H}_2\text{SO}_4 = 50.0 \text{ mL} \times \frac{1.0 \text{ mol}}{1000 \text{ mL}} = 0.050 \text{ mol H}_2\text{SO}_4$$

From the balanced equation, 0.050 mol H_2SO_4 would require 0.100 mol NaOH. Therefore, neither NaOH nor H_2SO_4 is left over after the reaction and 0.10 mol H_2O is produced in the reaction.

(c) $q = mc_S \Delta T = 150 \text{ g} \times \dfrac{4.184 \text{ J}}{\text{g} \cdot {}^\circ\text{C}} \times \left(31.4\,{}^\circ\text{C} - 22.3\,{}^\circ\text{C}\right) = 5.71 \times 10^3 \text{ J, or } 5.71 \text{ kJ}$

This is for the reaction of 0.10 mol H_2O which is produced in this particular reaction. For 1 mol H_2O, therefore,

$$\frac{5.71 \text{ kJ}}{0.10 \text{ mol H}_2\text{O}} = 57.1 \text{ kJ/mol H}_2\text{O}$$

Because the reaction transfers energy (the mixture gets hot), this reaction is exothermic and ΔH_{rxn} = −57.1 kJ/mol H_2O.

Think about It

We can assign the sign of ΔH at the end of our calculation. If temperature rises, the reaction is exothermic and the sign of enthalpy is negative.

9.109. Collect and Organize

When a hot sample of copper is dropped into water, energy is transferred from the metal to the water until thermal equilibrium is established.

Analyze

The energy lost by the copper sample is

$$q_{lost} = m_{Cu} \times c_S \times \left(T_f - T_i\right)$$

where $m_{Cu} = 7.25$ g, $c_S = 0.385$ J/g · °C, and $T_i = 100.1\,°C$.
The energy gained by the water is

$$q_{gained} = n_{H_2O} \times c_P \times \left(T_f - T_i\right)$$

where $n_{H_2O} = 50.0$ g/(18.02 g/mol), $c_P = 75.3$ J/mol · °C, and $T_i = 25.0$°C.

The law of conservation of energy gives

$$-q_{lost,Cu} = q_{gained,water}$$

Solve

$$-q_{lost,Cu} = q_{gained,water}$$

$$-7.25 \text{ g} \times \frac{0.385 \text{ J}}{\text{g} \cdot °\text{C}} \left(T_f - 100.1°\text{C}\right) = 50.0 \text{ g} \times \frac{1 \text{ mol}}{18.02 \text{ g}} \times \frac{75.3 \text{ J}}{\text{mol} \cdot °\text{C}} \times \left(T_f - 25.0°\text{C}\right)$$

$$-2.79 \frac{\text{J}}{°\text{C}} \times T_f + 279 \text{ J} = 209 \frac{\text{J}}{°\text{C}} \times T_f - 5223 \text{ J}$$

$$-211.8 \frac{\text{J}}{°\text{C}} \times T_f = -5502 \text{ J}$$

$$T_f = 26.0°\text{C}$$

Think about It

Because the heat capacity of the copper is so small and the heat capacity of water is so large, very little increase in the temperature of water occurs: only 1°C.

9.111. Collect and Organize

We are asked to calculate the standard heat of combustion of acetylene and determine its fuel value.

Analyze

(a) To calculate the molar enthalpy of combustion, we need to write a balanced chemical equation and then use the following equation to calculate ΔH°_{rxn}

$$\Delta H^\circ_{rxn} = \sum n_{products} \Delta H^\circ_{f,products} - \sum n_{reactants} \Delta H^\circ_{f,reactants}$$

(b) The fuel value is the energy released per gram of the fuel, so we will divide our answer in part a by the molar mass of acetylene.

Solve

(a) The balanced chemical equation for the combustion of 1 mol of C_2H_2 is

$$C_2H_2(g) + \tfrac{5}{2}O_2(g) \rightarrow 2 CO_2(g) + H_2O(g)$$

The standard enthalpy for burning 1 mol of C_2H_2 is

$$\Delta H^\circ_{rxn} = \left[\left(2 \text{ mol } CO_2 \times -393.5 \text{ kJ/mol}\right) + \left(1 \text{ mol } H_2O \times -241.8 \text{ kJ/mol}\right)\right]$$
$$- \left[\left(1 \text{ mol } C_2H_2 \times 226.7 \text{ kJ/mol}\right) + \left(\tfrac{5}{2} \text{ mol } O_2 \times 0.0 \text{ kJ/mol}\right)\right]$$

$$\Delta H^\circ_{rxn} = -1255.5 \text{ kJ/mol } C_2H_2$$

(b) The fuel value of acetylene is

$$\frac{1255.5 \text{ kJ}}{\text{mol}} \times \frac{1 \text{ mol}}{26.037 \text{ g}} = 48.22 \text{ kJ/g}$$

Think about It

Some other examples of endothermic compounds:

Inorganic compounds = B_2H_6, CS_2, HI, N_2O, O_3
Organic compounds = C_2H_4, C_6H_6, $(CH_3)_2C{=}C(CH_3)_2$

9.113. Collect and Organize

We are asked to determine, using average bond energy value, whether the formation of polyethylene from ethylene is endothermic, is exothermic, or has no change in energy.

Analyze

The enthalpy of a reaction as estimated from bond energies is given as

$$\Delta H_{rxn} = \sum \Delta H_{bond\ breaking} + \sum \Delta H_{bond\ forming}$$

where $\Delta H_{bond\ breaking}$ and $\Delta H_{bond\ forming}$ are average bond energies for the bonds in the reactants and products, respectively. In computing $\Delta H_{bond\ breaking}$ and $\Delta H_{bond\ forming}$ we have to take into account the number (or moles) of a particular type of bond that breaks or forms. We must also keep in mind that bond breaking requires energy $(+\Delta H)$, whereas bond formation releases energy $(-\Delta H)$.

Solve

The number of C–H bonds does not change, so we need not consider these in the calculation, but rather we can focus on the change in the carbon–carbon bonds.

For the formation of polyethylene from ethylene, the heat of reaction is

$$n\, H_2C{=}CH_2 \longrightarrow {-}{\Big[}CH_2{-}CH_2{\Big]}_n$$

$$\Delta H_{rxn} = [(n \times 614\ kJ/mol)] + [-(2 \times 348\ kJ/mol)]$$

where we will consider $n = 1$

$$\Delta H_{rxn} = -82\ kJ/mol$$

This reaction is exothermic.

Think about It

This finding may be unexpected in that we are breaking a double bond, but remember: From that double bond we are forming two single bonds to each carbon atom. Two single bonds added together is stronger than a double bond.

9.115. Collect and Organize

From the balanced equation and the ΔH°_{rxn} we are to determine whether energy is consumed or produced in the reaction and how much energy is involved when 60.0 g of CH_3OH is used in the reaction.

Analyze

(a) We can balance this reaction by inspection.

(b) We are given that the reaction requires 164 kJ/mol (of methanol) of energy, so this is an endothermic reaction.

(c) To calculate the energy needed to transform 60.0 g of methanol, we need only determine the moles of CH_3OH in 60.0 g and then multiply that result by the energy required in the reaction for 1 mol of CH_3OH (164 kJ/mol).

Solve

(a) $CH_3OH(g) + N_2(g) \rightarrow HCN(g) + NH_3(g) + \frac{1}{2} O_2(g)$

(b) Because this is an endothermic reaction, the energy is a reactant:

$$164\ kJ + CH_3OH(g) + N_2(g) \rightarrow HCN(g) + NH_3(g) + \tfrac{1}{2} O_2(g)$$

(c) The moles of CH_3OH used is

$$60.0\ g \times \frac{1\ mol}{32.04\ g} = 1.87\ mol$$

The enthalpy for the reaction using this amount of CH_3OH is

$$1.87\ mol \times \frac{164\ kJ}{1\ mol} = 307\ kJ$$

Think about It

The energy required or evolved in a reaction is an extensive property; it depends on the amount of reactants involved in the reaction.

9.117. Collect and Organize

We combine three reactions to give the overall reaction for the formation of $PbCO_3$.

Analyze

Because $PbCO_3$ is a product in the overall equation, reaction 3 has to be reversed. Neither reaction 1 nor reaction 2 needs to be changed.

Solve

$$Pb(s) + \tfrac{1}{2}O_2(g) \rightarrow PbO(s) \qquad \Delta H^\circ_{rxn} = -219 \text{ kJ}$$

$$C(s) + O_2(g) \rightarrow CO_2(g) \qquad \Delta H^\circ_{rxn} = -394 \text{ kJ}$$

$$\underline{PbO(s) + CO_2(g) \rightarrow PbCO_3(s) \qquad \Delta H^\circ_{rxn} = -86 \text{ kJ}}$$

$$Pb(s) + \tfrac{3}{2}O_2(g) + C(s) \rightarrow PbCO_3(s) \qquad \Delta H^\circ_{rxn} = -699 \text{ kJ}$$

This is for 1 mol of $C(s)$. For 2 mole of carbon in the target equation, the energy evolved in this reaction is

$$2 \text{ mol} \times \frac{-699 \text{ kJ}}{\text{mol}} = -1400 \text{ kJ}$$

Think about It

All the reactions that were added together are exothermic. The overall reaction, therefore, must also be exothermic. The overall enthalpy of reaction is also the enthalpy of formation of $PbCO_3$.

9.119. **Collect and Organize**

Using the ΔH°_f values for the reactants and products we are asked to calculate the ΔH°_{rxn} for the decomposition of 1 mol of $NaHCO_3$.

Analyze

The overall balanced decomposition reaction is

$$2\, NaHCO_3(s) \rightarrow Na_2CO_3(s) + CO_2(g) + H_2O(g)$$

To calculate the enthalpy of the combustion, use the equation

$$\Delta H^\circ_{rxn} = \sum n_{products} \Delta H^\circ_{f,products} - \sum n_{reactants} \Delta H^\circ_{f,reactants}$$

Solve

$$\Delta H^\circ_{rxn} = \big[(1 \text{ mol } CO_2 \times -393.5 \text{ kJ/mol}) + (1 \text{ mol } H_2O \times -241.8 \text{ kJ/mol}) + (1 \text{ mol } Na_2CO_3 \times -1130.7 \text{ kJ/mol})\big]$$
$$- \big[(2 \text{ mol } NaHCO_3 \times -950.8 \text{ kJ/mol})\big]$$

$$\Delta H^\circ_{rxn} = 135.6 \text{ kJ}$$

For the formation of 1 mol of $NaHCO_3(s)$:

$$\Delta H^\circ_f = \frac{135.6 \text{ kJ}}{2 \text{ mol}} = 67.8 \text{ kJ/mol}$$

Think about It

Remember that enthalpy is stoichiometric. You may have to adjust the ΔH°_{rxn} according to what the problem asks for. Here the enthalpy of decomposition of 1 mol of $NaHCO_3$ was specified.

9.121. **Collect and Organize**

Using ΔH°_f values for urea, carbon dioxide, water, and ammonia we calculate ΔH°_{rxn} for the conversion of urea into ammonia.

Analyze

The ΔH°_{rxn} can be found from the enthalpy of formation values by using

$$\Delta H^\circ_{rxn} = \sum n_{products} \Delta H^\circ_{f,products} - \sum n_{reactants} \Delta H^\circ_{f,reactants}$$

Solve

$$\Delta H^{\circ}_{\text{rxn}} = \left[(1 \text{ mol CO}_2 \times -412.9 \text{ kJ/mol}) + (2 \text{ mol NH}_3 \times -80.3 \text{ kJ/mol})\right]$$
$$- \left[(1 \text{ mol urea} \times -319.2 \text{ kJ/mol}) + (1 \text{ mol H}_2\text{O} \times -285.8 \text{ kJ/mol})\right]$$
$$\Delta H^{\circ}_{\text{rxn}} = 31.5 \text{ kJ}$$

Think about It
The overall reaction is slightly endothermic.

9.123. **Collect and Organize**
We are given balanced chemical reactions for the combustion of two fuels, dimethylhydrazine and hydrogen, along with their enthalpy of combustion values to help us determine which fuel releases more energy per pound.

Analyze
The ΔH values are given on a per-mole-of-fuel basis. We can convert these to a per-gram basis by dividing the absolute value of the enthalpy of the combustion by the molar mass of the fuel. This energy per gram of fuel can then be converted into energy per pound by using the conversion 1 lb = 453.6 g.

Solve
For dimethylhydrazine:

$$\frac{1694 \text{ kJ}}{\text{mol}} \times \frac{1 \text{ mol}}{60.10 \text{ g}} \times \frac{453.6 \text{ g}}{1 \text{ lb}} = 12{,}790 \text{ kJ/lb}$$

For hydrogen:

$$\frac{286 \text{ kJ}}{\text{mol}} \times \frac{1 \text{ mol}}{2.02 \text{ g}} \times \frac{453.6 \text{ g}}{1 \text{ lb}} = 64{,}200 \text{ kJ/lb}$$

Pound for pound, therefore, hydrogen is a better fuel.

Think about It
Even though the combustion of hydrogen is less exothermic on a per-mole basis, its use as a fuel on a per-weight basis yields more energy than dimethylhydrazine.

CHAPTER 10 | Properties of Gases: The Air We Breathe

10.1. Collect and Organize

Four illustrations representing molecules in a balloon are shown in Figure P10.1. The spheres represent gas atoms, and we are asked to choose the drawing that best shows how the gas is distributed in the balloon.

Analyze

Gases are characterized by having no definite shape or volume. They fill the container they are in and occupy the container's entire volume. Also, the atoms or molecules in gases are far apart from each other.

Solve

Drawing (c) accurately reflects the distribution of helium atoms in a balloon. The other representations either show clusters of gas atoms (b and d) or have the gas atoms attached to the wall of the balloon (a) and therefore the helium gas does not occupy the entire volume.

Think about It

What Figure P10.1 does not show, but is good to keep in mind, is that gas molecules are in constant motion.

10.3. Collect and Organize

We are to explain how the decrease in volume of the gas by downward movement of the piston in Figure P10.2 will affect the root-mean-square speed of the gas molecules in the cylinder.

Analyze

The root-mean-square speed of a gas is described by the formula

$$u_{rms} = \sqrt{\frac{3RT}{\mathcal{M}}}$$

where R is the gas constant, T is the temperature, and $\mathcal{M}$ is the molar mass of the gas.

Solve

Because neither pressure nor volume affects the root-mean-square speed (u_{rms}) of the gas (they do not appear in the equation), and the temperature, which does affect the u_{rms}, is held constant for the change in volume in Figure P10.2, the root-mean-square speed is not affected.

Think about It

If the temperature were raised, the root-mean-square speed would increase.

10.5. Collect and Organize

When the number of gas particles in a cylinder is doubled, we are to consider how the pressure is affected, how the frequency of collisions of the particles with the walls of the pistons changes, and by how much the probable speed of the gas particles in the cylinder might change.

Analyze

Avogadro's law states that pressure of a gas is directly proportional to the number of gas particles in the container. The pressure is a measure of the frequency of collisions of the gas particles with the walls of the container; as pressure goes up, the frequency of the collisions also increases. Finally, the most probably speed of the gas particles, like the root-mean-square speed, is affected only by a change in temperature.

Solve

(a) If the volume of the cylinder does not change (that is, the piston does not move), increasing the number of gas particles in the cylinder will increase the pressure proportionately. Because the number of gas particles is doubled, the pressure will also double.

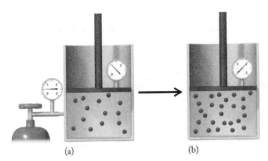

(b) The pressure is a measure of the frequency of collisions of the gas particles with the walls of the container and is directly proportional to the number of particles. Therefore, the frequency of collisions of the gas particles with the walls of the container will double because the number of particles and the pressure double.

(c) The most probable speed of the gas particles in the container does not depend on the number of gas particles present; the most probable speed is not affected.

Think about It

If the piston moves to increase the volume of the piston by a factor of 2 upon doubling the number of gas particles in the cylinder, the pressure and the frequency of collisions will not change.

10.7. **Collect and Organize**

For the two gas samples in which molecules of A are represented by the red spheres confined to cylinders with movable pistons in Figure P10.7 with the same volumes and at the same temperature, we are asked to determine for which sample the mole fraction of A, the partial pressure of A, and the total pressure is greater.

Analyze

The mole fraction of a component is determined by dividing the number of moles or particles of the component of interest in the mixture by the total number of moles or particles present in the mixture. Each gas in a mixture exerts its own contribution to the total pressure of the mixture. The partial pressure of a component in the gas mixture is proportional to the mole fraction of its gas particles in the mixture. Finally, the greater the total number of gas particles present in a mixture, the higher the pressure.

Solve

(a) Cylinder (a) contains 8 red spheres and 4 blue spheres. The mole fraction of A in this cylinder is 8/12 = 0.67. Cylinder (b) contains 11 red spheres and 17 blue spheres. The mole fraction in this cylinder is 11/28 = 0.39. Therefore, the red spheres have the higher mole fraction in cylinder (a).

(b) More red spheres are in cylinder (b) than in cylinder (a), so the pressure exerted by the red spheres will be higher in cylinder (b) than in cylinder (a).

(c) The total number of gas particles in cylinder (a) is 12, whereas the total number of gas particles in cylinder (b) is 28. Therefore, the pressure inside cylinder (b) will be 2.33 times as great as that in cylinder (a).

Think about It

If the pressure were to be equal for these two cylinders, the volume of cylinder (b) would be 2.33 times that of cylinder (a).

10.9. **Collect and Organize**

Effusion is the leaking of gas through a small hole in a container. We are asked which change in Figure P10.9 shows effusion of helium.

Analyze

The balloon contains fewer He atoms after effusion has taken place and, because of the presence of fewer He atoms in the balloon, the pressure inside the balloon decreases, so the balloon will shrink.

Solve

Both (a) and (b) show fewer atoms of He after effusion; however, outcome (a) is the correct choice since the balloon in (a) shrinks, whereas the balloon in (b) expands.

Think about It

We witness this happening to helium balloons in our everyday experience: a helium balloon made from latex usually shows noticeable shrinkage after being left overnight.

10.11. **Collect and Organize**

For CO_2 and SO_2 the number of molecules versus molecular speed is plotted in Figure P10.11. We are asked to identify which curve belongs to CO_2 and which belongs to SO_2 and then to determine which curve would also describe the distribution of molecular speeds for propane (C_3H_8).

Analyze

The formula that describes molecular speed (u_{rms}) is

$$u_{rms} = \sqrt{\frac{3RT}{\mathcal{M}}}$$

where R is the universal gas constant, T is the absolute temperature in kelvins, and $\mathcal{M}$ is the molar mass of the gaseous compound. The larger the molar mass, the slower the u_{rms}. Curve 1 shows more molecules at lower speeds, whereas curve 2 shows more molecules at higher speeds.

Solve

The molar masses of CO_2, SO_2, and C_3H_8 are 44, 64, and 44 g/mol, respectively. Because SO_2 has a higher molar mass than either CO_2 or C_3H_8, it is represented by curve 1. Curve 2 represents both CO_2 and C_3H_8 because they have the same molar mass.

Think about It

For heavier molecules, the distribution of speeds is narrower than for lighter molecules.

10.13. **Collect and Organize**

Three barometers are shown in Figure P10.13. We are to match the barometers with their respective locations.

Analyze

As altitude increases, the atmospheric pressure decreases. We can combine this knowledge with the fact that the barometer will show a lower column of mercury at lower pressures.

Solve

The locations in order of increasing pressure (higher to lower altitude) are Mount Everest < San Diego < gold mine. The barometers in order of increasing pressure are (a) < (b) < (c). Therefore, barometer (a) is sensing the atmospheric pressure on Mount Everest, barometer (b) is for San Diego, and barometer (c) is for the gold mine.

Think about It

The atmospheric pressure at sea level (ignoring the effects of the local weather) would be expected to be the same worldwide.

10.15. **Collect and Organize**

The plot in Figure P10.14 shows the volume (V) as a function of the inverse of pressure ($1/P$). Line 2 in the plot diverges from line 1 at the origin and is above line 1. If the lines represent two different quantities of gas, we are asked to determine which line is the plot for the greater quantity of gas.

Analyze

Because V is inversely proportional to P, the plot of V versus $1/P$ will give a straight line for a sample of gas. According to Avogadro's law, a gas sample with more particles (or moles) of gas will occupy a greater volume at constant pressure at higher temperatures and has a larger volume than that of a gas sample with fewer particles of gas.

Solve

A gas sample with more particles has a larger volume at a given $1/P$ value than one with fewer particles. Therefore, line 2 represents the gas sample with more particles of gas.

Think about It

The lines converge at the origin because at infinite pressure the volume of any quantity of a gas will be zero.

10.17. **Collect and Organize**

The plot in Figure P10.17 shows two lines for the relationship between volume as a function of temperature. We are asked which line is not consistent with the ideal gas law.

Analyze

By Charles's law, volume and temperature are directly proportional. This means that as temperature (T) increases, the volume (V) of the gas increases. This relationship is also evident in the ideal gas law,

$$PV = nRT$$

if we rearrange the equation to

$$V = \frac{nRT}{P} \quad \text{or} \quad V = cT$$

where c = constant.

Solve

Line 2 in Figure P10.17 is the line inconsistent with the ideal gas law because it shows that as temperature increases, the volume decreases. Line 2 is consistent with the ideal gas law because it shows the directly and linear proportionality between T and V.

Think about It

The line labeled as 2 would be correct if either P were plotted on the y-axis and V were plotted on the x-axis.

10.19. **Collect and Organize**

In considering Figure P10.19 for this problem, we are to choose the image that best describes how the solubility of a gas is affected by pressure.

Analyze

In the middle of the diagram the gas and the liquid contained in a cylinder are shown before the pressure is increased by moving the piston down in the cylinder. The middle diagram shows 12 molecules in the gas phase and 12 molecules in the liquid phase. As the pressure is increased, we expect some of the molecules in the gas phase (according to Henry's law) to become dissolved into the liquid phase to reduce the gas pressure in the cylinder.

Solve

Diagram (a) has more gas molecules (11) than molecules in the liquid phase (10), which shows that with increased pressure molecules evaporated from the solution. This is not correct. Diagram (b), however, has fewer molecules in the gas phase (8) and more molecules in the liquid phase (16). This is what we expect, so choice (b) is correct.

Think about It

Choice (a) would result in higher pressure in the cylinder, and we would therefore expect the piston to move up.

10.21. **Collect and Organize / Analyze**

We are asked to define the root-mean-square speed of gas particles.

Solve

The root-mean-square speed, u_{rms}, is the speed of a particle in a gas that has the average kinetic energy of all the particles of the sample.

Think about It

The root-mean-square speed is not exactly the same as the most probable speed, which is the speed corresponding to the peak in the distribution diagram. Nor is it the same as the average speed, which is a simple average of all the particle speeds.

10.23. **Collect and Organize**

We are asked whether pressure changes affect the value of u_{rms} for a gas sample.

Analyze

The root-mean-square speed equation is

$$u_{rms} = \sqrt{\frac{3RT}{\mathcal{M}}}$$

Solve

Pressure does not appear in the equation describing the root-mean-square speed; therefore, a change in pressure has no effect on u_{rms}.

Think about It

Only temperature and molar mass affect u_{rms}.

10.25. **Collect and Organize**

We are to rank the various gases according to the root-mean-square speeds at 0°C.

Analyze

The equation for root-mean-square speed shows an inverse dependence of u_{rms} of the molar mass of the gas:

$$u_{rms} = \sqrt{\frac{3RT}{\mathcal{M}}}$$

Solve

According to the u_{rms} equation, the lower the molar mass, the greater the root-mean-square speed. The molar masses of NO, NO_2, N_2O_4, and N_2O_5 are 30, 46, 92, and 108 g/mol, respectively. Therefore, N_2O_5 has the lowest u_{rms}, and NO has the highest u_{rms}. The rank order in terms of increasing root-mean-square speed is $N_2O_5 < N_2O_4 < NO_2 < NO$.

Think about It

We did not need to compute the root-mean-square speeds here. We needed only to rank the gases in order of decreasing molar mass.

10.27. **Collect and Organize**

Knowing that H_2 (molar mass = 2.02 g/mol) effuses four times faster than an unknown gas, X, we are to calculate the molar mass of X.

Analyze

The effusion equation needed is

$$\frac{r_{H_2}}{r_X} = \sqrt{\frac{\mathcal{M}_X}{\mathcal{M}_{H_2}}} = \frac{4}{1}$$

Rearranging to solve for $\mathcal{M}_X$ gives

$$\mathcal{M}_X = \mathcal{M}_{H_2} \times \left(\frac{r_{H_2}}{r_X}\right)^2$$

Solve

$$\mathcal{M}_X = 2.02 \text{ g/mol} \times (4)^2 = 32.3 \text{ g/mol}$$

Think about It
This gas might be oxygen, whose molar mass is 32.0 g/mol.

10.29. **Collect and Organize**
We can compare u_{rms} for an unknown gas (X) to H_2 to determine the gas's molar mass.

Analyze
The ratio of $u_{rms,X}/u_{rms,H_2}$ is given as 1/3. The relevant equation is

$$\frac{u_{rms,X}}{u_{rms,H_2}} = \sqrt{\frac{\mathcal{M}_{H_2}}{\mathcal{M}_X}} = \frac{1}{3}$$

Rearranging to solve for $\mathcal{M}_X$ gives

$$\mathcal{M}_X = \mathcal{M}_{H_2} \times \left(\frac{u_{rms,H_2}}{u_{rms,X}}\right)^2$$

Solve

$$\mathcal{M}_X = \frac{2.02\ \text{g}}{\text{mol}} \times (3)^2 = 18.2\ \text{g/mol}$$

Think about It
If the gas diffuses slower than H_2, its molar mass must be greater than that of H_2. A common molecule with a molar mass of ~18 g/mol is water, H_2O, so this gas might be water vapor.

10.31. **Collect and Organize**
We consider which gas, H_2 or He, effuses more rapidly from a blimp.

Analyze
The rate of effusion for a gas depends on its molar mass.

$$u_{rms} = \sqrt{\frac{3RT}{\mathcal{M}}}$$

Gases with lower molar masses effuse more rapidly than those with higher molar masses.

Solve
The molar mass of H_2 (2.02 g/mol) is less than the molar mass of He (4.00 g/mol), so hydrogen would effuse more rapidly from the blimp.

Think about It
Because the molar mass of hydrogen is half that of helium, it will effuse 1.42 times faster according to the ratio calculation:

$$\frac{u_{rms,H_2}}{u_{rms,He}} = \sqrt{\frac{4.003\ \text{g/mol}}{2.02\ \text{g/mol}}} = 1.42$$

10.33. **Collect and Organize**
Force and pressure are often used interchangeably in physics describing speed, but what is their difference in meaning in the context of gases?

Analyze

The mathematical equations describing force and pressure are

$$F = ma$$
$$P = F/A$$

Solve

Force is the product of the mass of an object and the acceleration due to gravity. Pressure uses force in its definition: it is the force an object exerts over a given area.

Think about It

A large force over a small area results in high pressure, but that same large force distributed over a very large area results in low pressure.

10.35. Collect and Organize

Differences in density of the liquid determine how high the liquid climbs in the tube of a Torricelli barometer. We are asked which liquid (water, ethanol, or mercury) leads to the tallest column in the barometer.

Analyze

Because the force of gravity on the liquid in the column of a barometer opposes the atmospheric pressure forcing the liquid up the column, the less dense the liquid, the less the liquid is affected by gravity, so atmospheric pressure raises the liquid higher in the column.

Solve

Among ethanol, water, and mercury liquids, ethanol has the lowest density, so it has the highest column of liquid in a barometer.

Think about It

Mercury, having the highest density of the liquids, has the shortest column in a barometer.

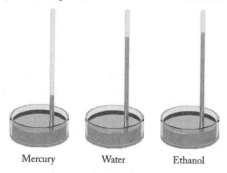

Mercury   Water   Ethanol

10.37. Collect and Organize

We are asked to explain the difference in pressure that an ice skater places on ice with a dull versus a sharp skate blade.

Analyze

Pressure is force over a unit area. The force of the ice skater on the ice is due to the skater's mass. The mass stays constant for this comparison. What must be different is the area between the skate blade and the ice.

Solve

A sharpened blade has a smaller area over which the force is distributed than that of a dull blade. Because $P = F/A$, as area (A) decreases, pressure must increase since the force due to the skater's mass is constant.

Think about It

The pressure also increases if we increase the mass of the ice skater.

10.39. Collect and Organize

We are to convert pressures expressed in kilopascals and millimeters of mercury to atmospheres.

Analyze

We need the following conversion factors:
$$1 \text{ atm} = 101.325 \text{ kPa} = 101,325 \text{ Pa}$$
$$1 \text{ atm} = 760 \text{ mmHg}$$

Solve

(a) $2.0 \text{ kPa} \times \dfrac{1 \text{ atm}}{101.325 \text{ kPa}} = 0.020 \text{ atm}$

(b) $562 \text{ mmHg} \times \dfrac{1 \text{ atm}}{760 \text{ mmHg}} = 0.739 \text{ atm}$

Think about It

A pascal also is equivalent to 1 N/m^2. This makes sense because the newton (N) is a unit of force. That force divided by area (in square meters) gives the units of pressure.

10.41. Collect and Organize

The pressure due to gravity for a cube of tin 5.00 cm on a side is given by
$$P = \frac{F}{A} = \frac{ma}{A}$$
where m = mass of the tin cube, a = acceleration due to gravity, and A = area over which the force is distributed.

Analyze

To find the mass of the cube of tin, we will multiply its volume $(5.00 \text{ cm})^3$ by the density of tin given in Appendix 3 (7.31 g/cm^3). We have to be sure to use consistent units in this calculation of the pressure exerted by the bottom face of the tin. The acceleration due to gravity is 9.8 m/s^2, so we want to express the area of the cube face in square meters.

Solve

The mass of the tin cube is
$$\left(5.00 \text{ cm}\right)^3 \times \frac{7.31 \text{ g}}{\text{cm}^3} = 913.8 \text{ g, or } 0.9138 \text{ kg}$$
The pressure due to gravity of the bottom face of the cube is
$$P = \frac{0.9138 \text{ kg} \times 9.80665 \text{ m/s}^2}{\left(5.00 \text{ cm}\right)^2 \times \left(\dfrac{1 \text{ m}}{100 \text{ cm}}\right)^2} = 3.58 \times 10^3 \; \frac{\text{kg}}{\text{m} \cdot \text{s}^2} = 3.58 \times 10^3 \text{ Pa}$$

Think about It

We can also express this pressure in atmospheres:
$$3.58 \times 10^3 \text{ Pa} \times \frac{1 \text{ atm}}{1.01325 \times 10^5 \text{ Pa}} = 3.54 \times 10^{-2} \text{ atm}$$

10.43. Collect and Organize

We are to express the highest recorded atmospheric pressure of 108.6 kPa in millimeters of mercury, atmospheres, and millibars.

Analyze

We need the following conversion factors:

$$1 \text{ atm} = 101.325 \text{ kPa} = 101,325 \text{ Pa}$$

$$1 \text{ atm} = 760 \text{ mmHg}$$

$$1 \text{ kPa} = 10 \text{ mbar}$$

Solve

(a) $108.6 \text{ kPa} \times \dfrac{1 \text{ atm}}{101.325 \text{ kPa}} \times \dfrac{760 \text{ mmHg}}{1 \text{ atm}} = 814.6 \text{ mmHg}$

(b) $108.6 \text{ kPa} \times \dfrac{1 \text{ atm}}{101.325 \text{ kPa}} = 1.072 \text{ atm}$

(c) $108.6 \text{ kPa} \times \dfrac{10 \text{ mbar}}{1 \text{ kPa}} = 1086 \text{ mbar}$

Think about It

The highest recorded atmospheric pressure is just a little above 1 atm at 1.072 atm.

10.45. Collect and Organize

Amontons's law states that pressure and temperature are directly related: as temperature increases, so does pressure. We are asked to interpret this relationship from the kinetic molecular theory perspective.

Analyze

Pressure originates from the collision of gas particles with the walls of a container. The more collisions between gas particles and the container, the greater the pressure. Temperature is a measure of how fast molecules are moving in the gas.

Solve

The higher the temperature, the faster the gas particles move. The faster they move, the more often they collide with the walls of the container and the greater the force with which gas particles hit the walls. Both of these result in increased pressure as temperature is raised.

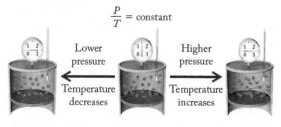

Think about It

At absolute zero, no molecular motion, and thus no pressure, would exist.

10.47. Collect and Organize

A balloonist needs to decrease her rate of ascent. How should she change the temperature of the gas in the balloon?

Analyze

A balloon rises because the air inside the balloon is less dense than the air outside. This means that fewer air molecules are inside the balloon than in an identical volume outside the balloon. Warmer gas molecules move faster and with more force, which results in a higher pressure, allowing them to escape from the bottom of the balloon.

Solve

To allow more air molecules in the balloon so as to increase the mass and therefore the density of air inside the balloon, the balloonist should decrease the temperature. Fewer "hot" gas molecules will escape, and the open design of the balloon will allow an increase in amount of cooler gas molecules that enter. This will slow the ascent of the balloon.

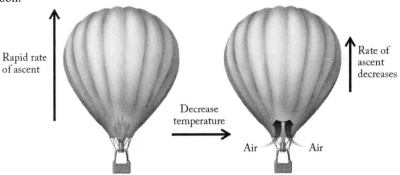

Think about It

You will see this effect if you ever have a chance to ride in a hot-air balloon. To avoid going too high, the balloonist will stop firing the burners.

10.49. Collect and Organize

Using Boyle's law, find the pressure of a gas when 1.00 mol at 1.00 atm in 3.25 L is compressed to 2.24 L.

Analyze

The equation for Boyle's law for the compression (or expansion) of a gas is

$$P_1V_1 = P_2V_2$$

For this gas compression, neither the number of moles of gas nor the temperature changes, so we do not need them in the calculation.

Solve

$$1.00 \text{ atm} \times 3.25 \text{ L} = P_2 \times 2.24 \text{ L}$$
$$P_2 = 1.45 \text{ atm}$$

Think about It

Because the volume was reduced, the pressure increased proportionately.

10.51. Collect and Organize

We are asked to find the pressure of an underwater site, knowing how much expansion a balloon undergoes when rising from the site to the surface. From that pressure and the fact that for every 10 m change in depth the pressure increases by 1.0 atm, we can calculate the diver's depth.

Analyze

We can use Boyle's law ($P_1V_1 = P_2V_2$) to find P_1. Once we know the pressure we can multiply it by 10 m/1 atm to arrive at the depth of the diver.

Solve

(a and b) The pressure at the site of the diver's work is

$$P_1 \times 115 \text{ L} = 1.00 \text{ atm} \times 352 \text{ L}$$
$$P_1 = 3.06 \text{ atm}$$

The pressure includes atmospheric pressure (1.00 atm), so

$$P_{\text{additional}} = 3.06 \text{ atm} - 1.00 \text{ atm} = 2.06 \text{ atm}$$

$$2.06 \text{ atm} \times \frac{10 \text{ m}}{1.0 \text{ atm}} = 21 \text{ m}$$

Think about It
If the diver had been working deeper, the balloon would have undergone a greater expansion upon reaching the surface.

10.53. Collect and Organize
A 4.66 L sample of gas is heated from 273 K to 398 K without changing the pressure, and we are asked to predict the final volume of the gas. We would expect that the final volume would be greater than the initial volume according to Charles's law.

Analyze
To find V_2, use Charles's law,

$$\frac{V_1}{T_1} = \frac{V_2}{T_2}$$

where $V_1 = 4.66$ L, $T_1 = 273$ K, and $T_2 = 398$ K.

Solve

$$\frac{4.66 \text{ L}}{273 \text{ K}} = \frac{V_2}{398 \text{ K}}$$
$$V_2 = 6.79 \text{ L}$$

Think about It
As expected, the gas did expand upon heating.

10.55. Collect and Organize
Balloons filled indoors at a warmer temperature have a greater volume than the same balloons placed outside at a colder temperature. We are to calculate the volume of balloons filled indoors at 20°C to 5.0 L and then hung outside at –25°C, assuming constant pressure inside and outside the house.

Analyze
Use Charles's law,

$$\frac{V_1}{T_1} = \frac{V_2}{T_2}$$

where $V_1 = 5.0$ L, $T_1 = 20$°C (293 K), and $T_2 = -25$°C (248 K).

Solve

$$\frac{5.0 \text{ L}}{293 \text{ K}} = \frac{V_2}{248 \text{ K}}$$
$$V_2 = 4.2 \text{ L}$$

Think about It
The volume of the balloons decreased, as would be expected when they are placed outside in the colder temperature.

10.57. Collect and Organize
We compare the effect of decreasing pressure on a gas sample (from 760 to 700 mmHg) to the effect of raising the temperature (from 10°C to 35°C) on the volume of a gas sample.

Analyze

Boyle's law describes the effect of decreasing pressure on the volume where P/V = constant. If we decrease the pressure by 50%, we have to increase the volume by 50%. Charles's law shows the direct relationship between temperature and volume. Here $\%\Delta V = \%\Delta T$.

Solve

(a) Lowering the pressure from 760 mmHg to 700 mmHg gives a percent change in V of

$$\frac{760 \text{ mmHg} - 700 \text{ mmHg}}{760 \text{ mmHg}} \times 100 = 7.9\% \text{ change in volume}$$

This will give a 7.9% increase in volume.

(b) The percent change in temperature is

$$\frac{308 \text{ K} - 273 \text{ K}}{273 \text{ K}} \times 100 = 12.8\%$$

This will give a 12.8% increase in volume.

Therefore, an increase in the temperature from 10°C to 35°C (b) gives the greatest increase in volume.

Think about It

Remember to convert temperatures to the Kelvin scale. If we had not converted to the Kelvin scale, it would have appeared that the volume in part b increased by 75%.

10.59. **Collect and Organize**

For various changes in temperature and external pressure, we are to predict how the volume of a gas sample changes.

Analyze

We must keep in mind the direct proportionality between V and T, as shown by Charles's law, and the inverse proportionality between V and P, as shown by Boyle's law.

Solve

(a) When the absolute temperature doubles, the volume doubles. When the pressure is doubled, the volume is halved. Combining these yields no change in the volume of the gas.

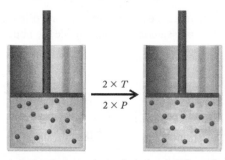

(b) When the absolute temperature is halved, the volume is halved. When the pressure is doubled, the volume is halved. Combining these gives a decrease in volume of gas sample to ¼ the original volume.

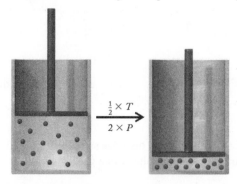

(c) Combining these effects is best looked at mathematically:

$$V_2 = \frac{PV_1 \times 1.75T_1}{T_1 \times 1.50P_1} = 1.17V_1, \text{ or an increase of 17\%}$$

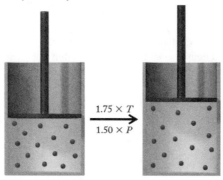

Think about It
The way to simplify this problem is to consider each change separately and then "add" the effects.

10.61. **Collect and Organize**
We are to calculate the volume of a weather balloon after 24 hr, during which helium leaks out.

Analyze
Because volume and the amount of gas are directly proportional, the appropriate form of Avogadro's law is

$$\frac{V_1}{n_1} = \frac{V_2}{n_2}$$

We are given $V_1 = 150.0$ L and $n_1 = 6.1$ mol of He and told that the helium leaks from the balloon at the rate of 10 mmol/hr for 24 hr.

Solve
The amount of gas leaked from the balloon is

$$24 \text{ hr} \times \frac{10 \text{ mmol}}{1 \text{ hr}} = 240 \text{ mmol} = 0.24 \text{ mol}$$

The amount of He in the balloon after 24 hr is

$$6.1 \text{ mol} - 0.24 \text{ mol} = 5.86 \text{ mol}$$

The volume (V_2) of the balloon is

$$\frac{150.0 \text{ L}}{6.1 \text{ mol}} = \frac{V_2}{5.86 \text{ mol}}$$
$$V_2 = 144 \text{ L}$$

Think about It
As expected, fewer moles of gas in the balloon takes up less volume.

10.63. **Collect and Organize**
When the bicycle tire cools, we would expect the pressure to decrease according to Amontons's law.

Analyze
Amontons's law states that pressure and temperature are directly proportional:

$$\frac{P_1}{T_1} = \frac{P_2}{T_2}$$

We are given $P_1 = 7.1$ atm. We have to be sure to express $T_1 = 27°C$ and $T_2 = 5.0°C$ as absolute temperatures.

Solve

$$\frac{7.1 \text{ atm}}{300 \text{ K}} = \frac{P_2}{278.2 \text{ K}}$$

$$P_2 = 6.6 \text{ atm}$$

Think about It

The pressure of air in the tire did decrease as we expected when the temperature decreased.

10.65. Collect and Organize

Define standard temperature and pressure conditions and define the volume of 1 mol of an ideal gas at those conditions.

Analyze

We can use the ideal gas law, $PV = nRT$, to calculate the volume (V) of 1 mol of gas (n) at standard temperature (T) and pressure (P).

Solve

STP is defined as 1 atm and 0°C (273 K).
The volume of 1 mol of gas at STP is

$$1 \text{ atm} \times V = 1.00 \text{ mol} \times 0.08206 \, \frac{\text{L} \cdot \text{atm}}{\text{mol} \cdot \text{K}} \times 273 \text{ K}$$

$$V = 22.4 \text{ L}$$

Think about It

The molar volume of gas at STP does not vary much depending on the identity of the gas.

10.67. Collect and Organize

Use the ideal gas law to determine the moles of air present in a bicycle tire with a volume of 2.36 L at 6.8 atm and 17.0°C.

Analyze

The ideal gas law is

$$PV = nRT$$

Rearranging to solve for n, number of moles of air, gives

$$n = \frac{PV}{RT}$$

With R in units of L·atm/mol·K, V must be in liters, pressure in atmospheres, and temperature in kelvins.

Solve

$$n = \frac{6.8 \text{ atm} \times 2.36 \text{ L}}{0.08206 \text{ L} \cdot \text{atm/mol} \cdot \text{K} \times 290 \text{ K}} = 0.67 \text{ mol}$$

Think about It

If we were to pump more moles of gas into the bicycle tire, the pressure would increase.

10.69. Collect and Organize

Given the volume of a hyperbaric chamber, the mass of oxygen in the chamber, and the temperature in the chamber, we can use the ideal gas law to calculate the pressure inside the chamber.

Analyze
Rearranging the ideal gas equation to solve for pressure, we get

$$P = \frac{nRT}{V}$$

We first have to determine the moles (n) of O_2 present in 5.00 kg of O_2.

Solve

$$\text{moles } (n) \text{ } O_2 \text{ present} = 5000.00 \text{ g } O_2 \times \frac{1 \text{ mol } O_2}{31.998 \text{ g}} = 156.3 \text{ mol}$$

The pressure in the chamber due to oxygen is

$$P = \frac{156.3 \text{ mol} \times 0.08206 \text{ L} \cdot \text{atm}/\text{mol} \cdot \text{K} \times 298 \text{ K}}{4.85 \times 10^3 \text{ L}} = 0.788 \text{ atm}$$

Think about It
Hyper comes from the Greek meaning *over*. Thus, a hyperbaric chamber will have an *overpressure* of oxygen. Our answer therefore makes sense because the normal pressure of oxygen in the air is about 0.21 atm.

10.71. ### Collect and Organize
In this problem we compare the moles of oxygen a skier breathes in at the top of a ski run with that breathed in at the bottom of the ski run. We are given that the pressure and temperature at the top of the ski run are 713 mmHg and –5°C, and at the bottom of the ski run the pressure and temperature are 734 mmHg and 0°C.

Analyze
We can use the combined gas law to solve this problem for the ratio of moles of air breathed in by the skier at the bottom of the run to that at the top of the run.

$$\frac{P_1 V_1}{n_1 T_1} = \frac{P_2 V_2}{n_2 T_2}$$

Because the volume of the skier's lungs does not change, $V_1 = V_2$, the equation reduces to

$$\frac{P_1}{n_1 T_1} = \frac{P_2}{n_2 T_2}$$

Rearranging this equation to give the ratio of moles of air the skier breathes in gives

$$\frac{n_2}{n_1} = \frac{P_2 T_1}{P_1 T_2}$$

where P_1 = 713 mmHg, T_1 = –5°C (268 K), P_2 = 734 mmHg, and T_2 = 0°C (273 K). We can then express the ratio as a percentage.

Solve

$$\frac{n_2}{n_1} = \frac{734 \text{ mmHg} \times 268 \text{ K}}{713 \text{ mmHg} \times 273 \text{ K}} = 1.01, \text{ or } 101\%$$

The skier breathes in 1% more air at the bottom of the ski run than he breathes in at the top of the run.

Think about It
The question specifically asks about how many more moles of *oxygen* the skier breathes in. We, however, calculated the increase in the percentage of *air* that the skier takes in. The answer will be the same when expressed as a percentage because the composition of air (21% oxygen) would be expected to be the same at the bottom of the run as at the top of the run.

10.73. **Collect and Organize**

We are to calculate the mass of methane contained in a 250 L tank at a pressure of 255 bar and a temperature of 20°C.

Analyze

We can use the ideal gas law for this problem, but we will have to be careful to make our units consistent. Rearranging the ideal gas equation to solve for moles of methane (which we can convert to mass later by using the moar mass of methane, 16.04 g/mol), we have

$$n = \frac{PV}{RT}$$

where P is 255 bar (to be converted to atmospheres with the conversion 1 atm = 1.01325 bar). $V = 250$ L, and T is 20°C (293 K).

Solve

The moles of gas present in the tank is

$$n = \frac{\left(255 \text{ bar} \times \dfrac{1 \text{ atm}}{1.01325 \text{ bar}}\right) \times 250 \text{ L}}{\dfrac{0.08206 \text{ L} \cdot \text{atm}}{\text{mol} \cdot \text{K}} \times 295 \text{ K}} = 2.60 \times 10^3 \text{ mol of methane}$$

The mass of methane in the tank is

$$2.62 \times 10^3 \text{ mol CH}_4 \times \frac{16.04 \text{ g}}{\text{mol}} = 4.19 \times 10^4 \text{ g or } 41.9 \text{ kg}$$

Think about It

Remember to always convert the temperature into kelvins when using the ideal gas law.

10.75. **Collect and Organize**

Using data for the volume as a function of the temperatures of a 4.0 g gas sample at 1.00 atm pressure, we are asked to determine the moles of gas in the sample and then identify the gas from its molar mass.

Analyze

The relationship between temperature and volume is described by Charles's law:

$$V \propto T, \text{ or } \frac{V}{T} = \text{constant, or } V = T \times \text{constant}$$

and a plot of volume versus temperature from the rearranged ideal gas law would be

$$V = \frac{nRT}{P} = \frac{nR}{P} \times T$$

where $x = T$ and $y = V$, so the slope of the line will be nR/P. From the slope of the line we can find the number of moles of the gas in the sample

$$\text{slope} = \frac{nR}{P}, \text{ or } n = \frac{\text{slope} \times P}{R}$$

where $P = 1.00$ atm.

Solve

(a) The plot of temperature versus volume for this gas sample gives a slope of 0.0821.

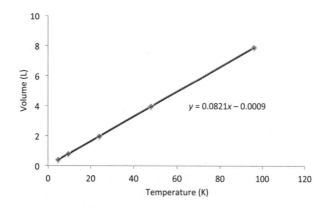

The number of moles of the gas in the sample then is

$$n = \dfrac{\dfrac{0.0821 \text{ L}}{\text{K}} \times 1.00 \text{ atm}}{\dfrac{0.08206 \text{ L} \cdot \text{atm}}{\text{mol} \cdot \text{K}}} = 1.00 \text{ mol}$$

(b) The molar mass of the gas is

$$\dfrac{4.0 \text{ g}}{1.00 \text{ mol}} = 4.0 \text{ g/mol}$$

The gas is helium.

Think about It
The graph does indeed show the direct linear relationship between the temperature and volume, as predicted by Charles's law. We see clearly on the graph that as temperature increases, the volume increases.

10.77. ### Collect and Organize
The density of a gas is defined as its mass per unit volume. If gases are at the same T and P, must they have the same density?

Analyze
The density of gas is derived from the ideal gas equation,

$$PV = nRT$$

where "molar density" would be given by

$$\frac{n}{V} = \frac{P}{RT}$$

The number of moles of gas n is related to its mass by

$$n = \frac{m}{\mathcal{M}}$$

where $\mathcal{M}$ = molar mass.

Solve
Substituting $n = m/\mathcal{M}$ into the molar density equation and rearranging to give $m/V = d$ gives

$$\frac{m/\mathcal{M}}{V} = \frac{P}{RT}$$

$$\frac{m}{V} = \frac{P\mathcal{M}}{RT} = d$$

Because each gas has a different molar mass, the densities of different gases are not necessarily the same for a particular temperature and pressure.

Think about It

From the equation above for density, we can see that as the molar mass of the gas increases, the density increases.

10.79. **Collect and Organize**

Density changes as a function of pressure and temperature. We are to predict how.

Analyze

The equation describing the density of gas is

$$d = \frac{\mathcal{M}P}{RT}$$

Solve

From the equation we see that density is directly proportional to pressure and inversely proportional to temperature. This means that density (a) increases with increasing pressure and (b) increases with decreasing temperature.

Think about It

Notice from the equation that density also increases as the molar mass of the gas increases.

10.81. **Collect and Organize**

We use the equation for the density of a gas to calculate the density of radon. Will radon concentrations be higher in the basement or on the top floor of a building?

Analyze

The density of the radon can be calculated from

$$d = \frac{\mathcal{M}P}{RT}$$

where $\mathcal{M}$ = 222 g/mol, P = 1 atm, and T = 298 K. We can compare the radon density to air's density (1.2 g/L).

Solve

(a) $d = \dfrac{222 \text{ g/mol} \times 1 \text{ atm}}{0.08206 \text{ L} \cdot \text{atm/mol} \cdot \text{K} \times 298 \text{ K}} = 9.08 \text{ g/L}$

(b) The density of radon is greater than the density of air (1.2 g/L), so radon is more likely to be concentrated in the basement.

Think about It

Radon testing kits all measure radon levels in basements of homes and buildings because that is where radon is most concentrated.

10.83. **Collect and Organize**

Given the mass of an oxide of sulfur gas (0.078 g) in a known volume (30.0 mL) measured at a particular temperature (22°C) and pressure (750 mmHg), we are to determine the identity as SO_2 or SO_3.

Analyze

We can use the gas density equation to calculate $\mathcal{M}$:

$$d = \frac{m}{V} = \frac{\mathcal{M}P}{RT}$$

$$\mathcal{M} = \frac{mRT}{VP}$$

We have to be sure to use units of volume in liters, pressure in atmospheres, and temperature in kelvins.

Solve

$$M = \frac{0.078 \text{ g} \times 0.08206 \text{ L} \cdot \text{atm/mol} \cdot \text{K} \times 295 \text{ K}}{0.0300 \text{ L} \times \left(750 \text{ mmHg} \times \dfrac{1 \text{ atm}}{760 \text{ mmHg}} \right)} = 64 \text{ g/mol}$$

The molar mass of SO_2 is 64.1 g/mol and the molar mass of SO_3 is 80.1 g/mol. The gas in the flask, therefore, is SO_2.

Think about It
Remember that consistent units are very important when using any equation.

10.85. **Collect and Organize**
For a gas we are given the density (1.107 g/L) at a particular temperature (300 K) and pressure (740 mmHg). We are to determine whether the gas could be CO or CO_2.

Analyze
Use the gas density equation to calculate M:

$$d = \frac{m}{V} = \frac{MP}{RT}$$

$$M = \frac{mRT}{VP} = \frac{dRT}{P}$$

Solve

$$M = \frac{1.107 \text{ g/L} \times 0.08206 \text{ L} \cdot \text{atm/mol} \cdot \text{K} \times 300 \text{ K}}{\left(740 \text{ mmHg} \times \dfrac{1 \text{ atm}}{760 \text{ mmHg}} \right)} = 28.0 \text{ g/mol}$$

The molar masses of CO and CO_2 are 28.01 and 44.01 g/mol, respectively. The unknown gas could be CO.

Think about It
Be careful in this problem to convert millimeters of mercury to atmospheres for the pressure.

10.87. **Collect and Organize**
We are given the balanced chemical equation for the conversion of CaC_2 to C_2H_2. We are asked to calculate the moles of C_2H_2 required to light the lamp for 1 hr given that the lamp uses 4.8 L of acetylene per hour at 1.02 atm and 25°C, and then calculate the mass of CaC_2 to provide 4 hr of light.

Analyze
(a) The ideal gas law can be used to calculate $n_{C_2H_2}$ where $P = 1.02$ atm, $V = 4.8$ L/hr, and $T = 25°C$ (298 K).

(b) Once we know how much C_2H_2 is required for 1 hr, we can multiply it by 4 to arrive at the moles of C_2H_2 required for 4 hr. Because 1 mol of C_2H_2 is produced from 1 mol of CaC_2, this is also the moles of CaC_2 required. The mass of CaC_2 can then be found by multiplying $n_{C_2H_2}$ by the molar mass of CaC_2.

Solve
(a) Moles of C_2H_2 used per hour:

$$n = \frac{1.02 \text{ atm} \times 4.8 \text{ L/hr}}{0.08206 \text{ L} \cdot \text{atm/mol} \cdot \text{K} \times 298 \text{ K}} = 0.20 \text{ mol/hr}$$

(b) For a 4-hour shift:

$$4 \text{ hr} \times \frac{0.20 \text{ mol C}_2\text{H}_2}{\text{hr}} \times \frac{1 \text{ mol CaC}_2}{1 \text{ mol C}_2\text{H}_2} \times \frac{64.10 \text{ g CaC}_2}{1 \text{ mol}} = 51 \text{ g CaC}_2 \text{ needed}$$

Think about It
Because the ideal gas law allows us to compute the moles of gas, we can use the result in subsequent stoichiometry calculations.

10.89. **Collect and Organize**
We are given the balanced chemical equation for the decomposition of $KClO_3$ to $O_2(g)$. We are asked to calculate the mass of $KClO_3$ needed to generate 200.0 L of $O_2(g)$ at 0.85 atm and 273 K.

Analyze
We first need to use the ideal gas law to calculate n_{O_2} generated, where $P = 0.85$ atm, $V = 200.0$ L, and $T = 273$ K. Because the stoichiometric ratio of O_2 produced to $KClO_3$ used is 3:2, we have to multiply n_{O_2} by $^2/_3$ to give n_{KClO_3}. The mass of $KClO_3$ then can be found by multiplying n_{KClO_3} by its molar mass (122.5 g/mol).

Solve
Moles of O_2 generated:
$$n_{O_2} = \frac{0.85 \text{ atm} \times 200.0 \text{ L}}{0.08206 \text{ L} \cdot \text{atm/mol} \cdot \text{K} \times 273 \text{ K}} = 7.6 \text{ mol } O_2$$

Mass of $KClO_3$ required:
$$7.6 \text{ mol } O_2 \times \frac{2 \text{ mol } KClO_3}{3 \text{ mol } O_2} \times \frac{122.5 \text{ g } KClO_3}{1 \text{ mol}} = 6.2 \times 10^2 \text{ g } KClO_3$$

Think about It
The amount of $KClO_3$ needed is large because the volume of oxygen is quite large.

10.91. **Collect and Organize**
We are given the balanced chemical reaction for changing CO_2 into O_2 by using Na_2O_2. We are asked to calculate the amount of Na_2O_2 needed on the submarine per sailor in 24 hr given the rate of CO_2 exhaled by each sailor (125 mL/min) at 1.02 atm and 23°C.

Analyze
Use the ideal gas equation to calculate moles of CO_2 exhaled by a sailor in 1 min, where $P = 1.02$ atm, $V = 125$ mL (0.125 L), and $T = 23°C$ (296 K). Then, convert this into n_{CO_2} exhaled in 1 d (24 hr) by using 60 min = 1 hr. Finally, use the stoichiometric equation to calculate the mass of Na_2O_2 required for each sailor (molar mass of $Na_2O_2 = 77.98$ g/mol).

Solve
Moles of CO_2 exhaled in 1 min:
$$n_{CO_2} = \frac{1.02 \text{ atm} \times 0.125 \text{ L/min}}{0.08206 \text{ L} \cdot \text{atm/mol} \cdot \text{K} \times 296 \text{ K}} = 5.25 \times 10^{-3} \text{ mol/min } CO_2$$

Moles of CO_2 exhaled in 1 d:
$$\frac{5.25 \times 10^{-3} \text{ mol } CO_2}{1 \text{ min}} \times \frac{60 \text{ min}}{1 \text{ hr}} \times 24 \text{ hr} = 7.56 \text{ mol } CO_2$$

Mass of Na_2O_2 required for 24-hr period per sailor:
$$7.56 \text{ mol } CO_2 \times \frac{2 \text{ mol } Na_2O_2}{2 \text{ mol } CO_2} \times \frac{77.98 \text{ g } Na_2O_2}{1 \text{ mol}} = 590 \text{ g } Na_2O_2$$

Think about It
Because the ideal gas law allows us to compute the moles of gas, we can use the result in subsequent stoichiometry calculations.

10.93. **Collect and Organize / Analyze**
We are asked to define the partial pressure of a gas.

Solve
The partial pressure of a gas is the pressure that a particular gas contributes to the total pressure.

Think about It
The sum of the partial pressures of all the gases in a mixture adds up to the total pressure.

10.95. **Collect and Organize**
The mole fraction of a gas is the ratio of moles of a gas divided by the total number of moles in the gas mixture.

Analyze
To get the mole fraction for each gas, we first sum the moles of all the gaseous components (0.70 mol N_2 + 0.20 mol H_2 + 0.10 mol CH_4) to calculate the total moles of gas in the mixture. The individual mole fraction for H_2 is

$$x_{H_2} = \frac{n_{H_2}}{n_{total}}$$

where n_{H_2} is the number of moles of hydrogen and n_{total} is the sum of the moles of all components in the mixture.

Solve
Total moles of gas in the mixture equals $(0.70 + 0.20 + 0.10) = 1.00$ mol.

$$x_{H_2} = \frac{0.20 \text{ mol}}{1.00 \text{ mol}} = 0.20$$

Think about It
The mole fraction of N_2 would be 0.70 and the mole fraction of CH_4 would be 0.10. The sum of the mole fractions for all the components in the mixture adds up to 1.

10.97. **Collect and Organize**
The mole fractions of the gases in Problem 10.95 are $x(N_2) = 0.70$, $x(H_2) = 0.20$, and $x(CH_4) = 0.10$. We are to use this information to calculate the partial pressure of each gas and the total pressure of the gas mixture when the volume is 0.75 L at 10°C (283 K).

Analyze
The partial pressure of each gas is related to the total pressure: $P_x = x_x P_{total}$. We can calculate P_{total} from the ideal gas law, where $V = 0.75$ L, n = total moles of gas in the mixture, and $T = 283$ K.

Solve

$$P_{total} = \frac{1.00 \text{ mol} \times 0.08206 \text{ L} \cdot \text{atm/mol} \cdot \text{K} \times 283 \text{ K}}{0.75 \text{ L}} = 30.96 \text{ atm}$$

$$P_{N_2} = 0.70 \times 30.96 \text{ atm} = 22 \text{ atm}$$

$$P_{H_2} = 0.20 \times 30.96 \text{ atm} = 6.2 \text{ atm}$$

$$P_{CH_4} = 0.10 \times 30.96 \text{ atm} = 3.1 \text{ atm}$$

Think about It
The sum of the partial pressures equals P_{total}.

10.99. **Collect and Organize**
Because the oxygen is collected over water, a portion of the volume includes gaseous water. We are given the volume of the $O_2(g)$ and $H_2O(g)$ mixture, the temperature, and the pressure. We are asked to calculate how many moles of O_2 are present in the mixture.

Analyze

At 25°C (298 K), the vapor pressure due to water is 23.8 mmHg (Table 10.4). The pressure of O_2 in the sample is

$$P_{O_2} = P_{total} - P_{H_2O} = 760 - 23.8 \text{ mmHg} = 736 \text{ mmHg}$$

Then, we can use the ideal gas equation ($PV = nRT$) to calculate the number of moles of oxygen gas where $P = 736$ mmHg (we have to convert this to atmospheres), $V = 0.480$ L, and $T = 298$ K.

Solve

$$n_{O_2} = \frac{\left(736 \text{ mm} \times \dfrac{1 \text{ atm}}{760 \text{ mm}}\right) \times 0.480 \text{ L}}{0.08206 \text{ L} \cdot \text{atm/mol} \cdot \text{K} \times 298 \text{ K}} = 0.0190 \text{ mol } O_2$$

Think about It

Water vapor contributes little to the total pressure, so oxygen is the major gaseous component in the mixture.

10.101. **Collect and Organize**

We are given the balanced chemical equations for three reactions in which reactants and products are all gases. From the moles of gas consumed and the moles of gas produced, we are to determine how the pressure changes for each reaction.

Analyze

The greater the moles of gas in a sealed rigid container, the higher the pressure. If the reaction produces more moles of gas than it consumes, the pressure after the reaction is complete must be greater than the pressure before the reaction took place. However, if a reaction produces fewer moles of gas than it consumes, the pressure must be lower. If no change occurs in the moles of gas between reactants and products, the pressure does not change.

Solve

(a) Two moles of gas is consumed and 5 mol of gas is produced; $\Delta n = n_{products} - n_{reactants} = 3$, and the pressure is greater at the end of the reaction.
(b) Three moles of gas is consumed and 2 mol of gas is produced; $\Delta n = -1$, and the pressure is lower at the end of the reaction.
(c) Six moles of gas is consumed and 7 mol of gas is produced; $\Delta n = 1$, and the pressure is greater at the end of the reaction.

Think about It

Mathematically, if $\Delta n = n_{products} - n_{reactants}$ is positive, the pressure increases; if $\Delta n = 0$, the pressure stays the same; if Δn is negative, the pressure decreases.

10.103. **Collect and Organize**

Using $PV = nRT$, we can calculate the moles of O_2 present in a human lung where the pressure is 266 mmHg with pure O_2 to compare to the oxygen content at sea level (760 mmHg) breathing in air, so as to determine how much more oxygen the high-altitude, pure-oxygen breath has.

Analyze

We will be comparing moles of oxygen, so rearranging the ideal gas equation to solve for n gives

$$n = \frac{PV}{RT}$$

At sea level, $P = 1.00$ atm and the mole fraction of oxygen in air is 0.2095. Therefore, the partial pressure of O_2 at sea level is $P_{O_2} = 1.00 \text{ atm} \times 0.2095 = 0.2095$ atm. At an altitude that has an atmospheric pressure of 266 mmHg, the climber is breathing 100% O_2 with $P = 266$ mmHg/760 mmHg $= 0.35$ atm. We are not given the values of V and T, so we can treat these as constants. As we are comparing n_{O_2} values in a ratio of

$n_{O_2,8000m}\big/n_{O_2,\text{sea level}}$, we see that we do not need these values. In fact, we can even leave R, the gas constant, out of our final calculation.

Solve

$$n_{O_2,8000m} = \frac{0.35\ \text{atm} \times V}{RT} \qquad n_{O_2,\text{sea level}} = \frac{0.2095\ \text{atm} \times V}{RT}$$

The ratio $n_{O_2,8000m}\big/n_{O_2,\text{sea level}}$ is

$$\frac{\left(\dfrac{0.35\ \text{atm} \times V}{RT}\right)}{\left(\dfrac{0.2095\ \text{atm} \times V}{RT}\right)} = \frac{0.35\ \text{atm}}{0.2095\ \text{atm}} = 1.7$$

This means that the climber at high altitude breathing pure oxygen is breathing in 70% more oxygen than at sea level.

Think about It
Breathing pure O_2 at that great altitude more than compensates for the pressure difference. The climber actually has more oxygen in her lungs at the higher altitude than at sea level.

10.105. ### Collect and Organize
The reaction of carbon monoxide with oxygen to form CO_2 is described by the equation

$$2\ CO(g) + O_2(g) \rightarrow 2\ CO_2(g)$$

From the information given (650 mmHg of CO and 325 mmHg of O_2 at the beginning of the reaction), we are to calculate the final pressure of the gases in the sealed vessel at the end of the reaction.

Analyze
We need to determine the moles of CO_2 produced from the CO and O_2. We can express the moles of CO and O_2 by using the ideal gas equation:

$$n_{CO} = \frac{650\ \text{mmHg} \times V}{RT} \quad \text{and} \quad n_{O_2} = \frac{325\ \text{mmHg} \times V}{RT}$$

From the balanced equation we see that 2 mol of CO is required to react with 1 mol of O_2.

Solve
Notice that n_{CO} is twice that of n_{O_2}. This agrees exactly with the stoichiometric ratio of $CO:O_2$ in the balanced equation. If we assume 100% yield, both reactants will be consumed in the reaction to give CO_2 as the only product. We will have the same number of moles of CO_2 as we had moles of CO at the start of the reaction. Therefore, the pressure of CO_2 at the end of the reaction will be the same as the pressure that the reactant CO exerted at the beginning of the reaction, namely, 650 mmHg.

Think about It
In answering this question, we didn't have to perform any calculations; rather, we just had to relate the stoichiometry to the pressures of the gases.

10.107. ### Collect and Organize
The balanced chemical equation for the production of ammonia from nitrogen and hydrogen is

$$N_2(g) + 3\ H_2(g) \rightarrow 2\ NH_3(g)$$

We are given the initial partial pressures of the reactants N_2 and H_2 (3.6 and 2.4 atm, respectively), and we are to calculate the percent decrease in the pressure when half the H_2 is used to produce NH_3.

Analyze
The initial pressure inside the vessel can be calculated by using the ideal gas equation, where n = total moles of H_2 and N_2. To find the pressure when half the N_2 is consumed, we first have to determine the moles of H_2, N_2,

and NH_3 present in the vessel by using the reaction stoichiometry. Then we calculate the pressure from the total moles of gas in the vessel. Because we are looking for a percent decrease, we can express pressures with the unspecified "variables" R, T, and V.

Solve
The initial pressure inside the reaction vessel is all due to the presence of H_2 and N_2. So the total pressure at the start of the reaction is
$$(3.6 + 2.4) \text{ atm} = 6.0 \text{ atm}$$
Because the pressure of a gas is directly proportional to the number of moles of gas, we can think of the partial pressures like moles. So if half the hydrogen reacts, the new partial pressure of hydrogen will be
$$2.4 \text{ atm} \div 2 = 1.2 \text{ atm of } H_2 \text{ remaining after the reaction is complete.}$$
Because we need only 1/3 of the moles of N_2 to react with the 1.2 atm of H_2 to form NH_3, the reaction will use 1.2 atm $\div$ 3 = 0.4 atm of N_2, which will leave
$$3.6 \text{ atm} - 0.4 = 3.2 \text{ atm of } N_2 \text{ remaining after the reaction is complete.}$$
Now we consider what partial pressure of NH_3 is produced. The stoichiometry of the reaction says that for every mole of N_2 used, 2 mol of NH_3 is produced. We have seen above that 0.4 atm of N_2 is used, which means that
$$0.4 \times 2 = 0.8 \text{ atm of } NH_3 \text{ is produced after the reaction is complete.}$$
So, the total pressure at the end of the reaction is
$$1.2 \text{ atm } H_2 + 3.2 \text{ atm } N_2 + 0.8 \text{ atm } NH_3 = 5.2 \text{ atm}$$
The difference between the final pressure and the initial pressure is
$$5.2 \text{ atm} - 6.0 \text{ atm} = -0.8 \text{ atm}$$
The percent decrease in pressure for this reaction is
$$\frac{0.8 \text{ atm}}{6.0 \text{ atm}} \times 100 = 13\%$$

Think about It
We observe a decrease in pressure as this reaction proceeds, which we expect because 4 mol of reactants produces 2 mol of products in the balanced chemical equation.

10.109. Collect and Organize
We are to explain why Henry's law constant for CO_2 is so much larger than that for N_2 or O_2.

Analyze
We are given a hint that CO_2 reacts with water. This reaction gives carbonic acid:
$$H_2O(\ell) + CO_2(g) \rightarrow H_2CO_3(aq)$$

Solve
The higher the Henry's law constant, the greater the solubility of the gas at that temperature. The reaction of CO_2 with water changes dissolved CO_2 into carbonic acid. Once this occurs, more CO_2 can dissolve in water.

Think about It
N_2 and O_2 simply dissolve in the water. Without reactions with water to give another species, the water becomes saturated with these gases.

10.111. Collect and Organize
We are to describe the intermolecular interactions that allow methane to have some solubility in water.

Analyze
Water is a polar molecule with hydrogen bonding and dipole–dipole interactions dominating its intermolecular interactions. Methane is nonpolar, so it uses only London dispersion (van der Waals) forces in its intermolecular interactions.

Solve
Methane is slightly soluble in water owing to the dispersion–dipole forces between polar water and nonpolar methane.

Think about It
However, the solubility of CH_4 in H_2O is limited because for methane to dissolve in water, the dispersion–dipole interactions between them must overcome the stronger hydrogen bonds between the water molecules and the strong dispersion forces between the methane molecules.

10.113. **Collect and Organize**
Given that the mole fraction of O_2 in air is 0.209 and that arterial blood has 0.025 g of O_2 per liter at 37°C and 1 atm, we can calculate k_H for O_2 in blood by using Henry's law.

Analyze
Henry's law is defined as
$$C_{gas} = k_H P_{gas}$$
where C_{gas} is the concentration of dissolved gas, k_H is Henry's law constant, and P_{gas} is the pressure of the gas. Rearranging the equation to solve for k_H gives
$$k_H = \frac{C_{gas}}{P_{gas}}$$
The units of k_H are usually expressed as moles per liter per atmosphere (mol/L · atm).
The concentration of O_2 in blood in moles per liter (mol/L) is
$$\frac{0.25 \text{ g } O_2}{L} \times \frac{1 \text{ mol}}{32.00 \text{ g}} = 7.81 \times 10^{-3} \text{ mol/L}$$
The partial pressure of O_2 in the air is
$$0.209 \times 1 \text{ atm} = 0.209 \text{ atm}$$

Solve
$$k_H = \frac{7.81 \times 10^{-3} \text{ mol/L}}{0.209 \text{ atm}} = 3.7 \times 10^{-2} \text{ mol/L·atm}$$

Think about It
As the temperature changes, so too does k_H. As temperature increases, less O_2 is soluble and the value of k_H decreases.

10.115. **Collect and Organize**
Using the k_H value of 3.7×10^{-2} mol/L · atm from Problem 10.113, we are to calculate the solubility of O_2 in the blood of a climber on Mt. Everest ($P_{atm} = 0.35$ atm) and a scuba diver ($P = 3.0$ atm).

Analyze
The concentration (solubility) of O_2 in the blood can be calculated by using Henry's law:
$$C_{O_2} = k_H P_{O_2}$$
For each case we need the pressure of O_2 in the atmosphere. If we assume that the mole fraction of O_2 stays at 0.209, the partial pressure of O_2 for each is as follows:
$$\text{For the alpine climber, } P_{O_2} = 0.209 \times 0.35 \text{ atm} = 7.32 \times 10^{-2} \text{ atm}$$
$$\text{For the scuba diver, } P_{O_2} = 0.209 \times 3 \text{ atm} = 0.627 \text{ atm}$$

Solve
(a) For the alpine climber
$$C_{O_2} = \frac{3.7 \times 10^{-2} \text{ mol}}{L \cdot atm} \times 7.32 \times 10^{-2} \text{ atm} = 2.7 \times 10^{-3} \text{ } M$$

(b) For the scuba diver

$$C_{O_2} = \frac{3.7 \times 10^{-2} \text{ mol}}{\text{L} \cdot \text{atm}} \times 0.627 \text{ atm} = 2.3 \times 10^{-2} \ M$$

Think about It
The scuba diver has more than eight times the concentration of O_2 in her arterial blood than the alpine climber.

10.117. Collect and Organize
For methane we are to determine the root-mean-square speed at 298 K.

Analyze
The root-mean-square speed is

$$u_{rms} = \sqrt{\frac{3RT}{M}}$$

We need to use $R = 8.314$ kg $\cdot$ m^2/s^2 (mol $\cdot$ K) and molar mass of methane (16.04 g/mol) in the units of kilograms per mole (0.01604 kg/mol).

Solve

$$u_{rms} = \sqrt{\frac{3 \times 8.314 \text{ kg} \cdot \text{m}^2/\text{s}^2 (\text{mol} \cdot \text{K}) \times 298 \text{ K}}{0.01604 \text{ kg/mol}}} = 681 \text{ m/s}$$

Think about It
Methane has a fairly low molar mass for a gas, and so its root-mean-square speed is relatively fast.

10.119. Collect and Organize
We are to calculate the root-mean-square speed for Ar atoms at a temperature at which their KE_{avg} is 5.18 kJ/mol.

Analyze
The equation relating KE_{avg} to u_{rms} is $KE_{avg} = \frac{1}{2} mu_{rms}^2$. Rearranging the equation and solving for u_{rms} gives

$$u_{rms} = \sqrt{\frac{2KE_{avg}}{m}}$$

where m is the mass of 1 mol of Ar atoms (39.948 g/mol, or 0.039948 kg/mol) and 1 kJ = 1000 kg $\cdot$ m^2/s^2, so $KE_{avg} = 5180$ kg $\cdot$ m^2/s^2 $\cdot$ mol.

Solve

$$u_{rms} = \sqrt{\frac{2 \times 5180 \text{ kg} \cdot \text{m}^2/\text{s}^2 \cdot \text{mol}}{0.039948 \text{ kg/mol}}} = 509 \text{ m/s}$$

Think about It
Writing the units associated with each quantity in a formula is a good habit so that you can easily see that you have converted the units appropriately.

10.121. Collect and Organize
By comparing the rates of diffusion of the two gases, we can calculate the molar mass of HX, which will enable us to identify the element X.

Analyze

The ratio of the rates of diffusion is given by

$$\frac{r_{NH_3}}{r_{HX}} = \sqrt{\frac{\mathcal{M}_{HX}}{\mathcal{M}_{NH_3}}}$$

The rate of diffusion of each gas is defined as how far in the tube the gas travels before it reacts with the other gas to form solid NH_4X. In this experiment, NH_3 travels 68.5 cm and HX travels 100 cm − 68.5 cm = 31.5 cm.

Solve

Because distance is directly proportional to rate of travel, we can use the ratio of distances in place of the ratio of rates in Graham's law:

$$\frac{r_{NH_3}}{r_{HX}} = \frac{68.5 \text{ cm}}{31.5 \text{ cm}} = \sqrt{\frac{\mathcal{M}_{HX}}{17.03 \text{ g/mol}}} = 2.17$$

$$\mathcal{M}_{HX} = (2.17)^2 \times 17.03 \text{ g/mol} = 80.5 \text{ g/mol}$$

The molar mass of X will be $\mathcal{M}_{HX} - \mathcal{M}_H = 80.5 - 1.00 = 79.5$ g/mol. The element that forms HX (a halogen, in group 17 of the periodic table) and has a molar mass close to 79.5 is bromine, Br.

Think about It

Despite the simple nature of the experiment, the molar mass of an unknown gaseous compound can be fairly accurately determined.

10.123. Collect and Organize / Analyze

We are to explain why real gases deviate from ideal behavior at low temperatures and high pressures.

Solve

At low temperatures the gas particles move more slowly, and their collisions become inelastic; they stick together because of the weak attractive forces between them. The particles, therefore, do not act separately to contribute to the pressure in the container, and the pressure is lower than would be expected from the ideal gas law. Also, the gas particles take up real volume in the container and as the pressure increases, the volume of the particles takes up a greater volume of the free space in the container. This has the effect of raising the pressure–volume above what we would expect from the ideal gas law (in a plot of PV/RT versus P).

Think about It

Gases at low pressures and not-too-cold temperatures behave most ideally.

10.125. Collect and Organize

The van der Waals constant b is associated with the volume of the gas particles. We are asked why the value of b increases as the atomic number of noble gas elements increases.

Analyze

As atomic number increases, the number of electrons and the size of the atoms increase.

Solve

Because b is a measure of the volume that the gas particles occupy, b increases as the sizes of the particles increase.

Think about It

Table 10.7 shows that the units of b are in liters per mole (L/mol). This is the volume that 1 mol of the gas particles occupies in the volume of the gas container. As the size increases from He to Ar, for example, b does indeed increase.

10.127. **Collect and Organize**

The van der Waals constant a is associated with the interactions between gas particles. We are asked why the value of a for Ar is greater than the value of a for He.

Analyze

As molar mass increases, the sizes of the atoms increase and have more electrons. These electrons can have greater imbalances in their distributions around the atoms (they are more polarizable).

Solve

As the imbalance in electron distribution increases (polarizability) with greater molar mass, the weak interactions between gas particles become stronger and the value of a increases. Therefore, Ar, with 18 electrons, has a larger value of a than He, with only 4 electrons.

Think about It

Table 10.7 shows that the value of a does indeed increase as the molar mass increases in other related molecules. Compare, for example, H_2, N_2, and O_2.

10.129. **Collect and Organize**

Given that the plot in Figure 10.38 of PV/RT versus P for CH_4 is different from the plot for H_2 in describing how they deviate from ideal behavior, we are to consider for which gas the volume of the gas particles is more important than the attractive interactions between them at a pressure of 200 atm.

Analyze

In Figure 10.38 we see that the curve for H_2 always deviates above the ideal gas line, whereas the curve for CH_4 first deviates below the ideal gas line at lower pressures and then deviates above the line at higher pressures. A line diverging above the ideal gas line indicates that the volume of the real molecules in the gas sample is no longer approximately equal to zero, so that the free volume no longer is a good estimate of the total volume. A line that diverges below the ideal gas line indicates attractive forces between the molecules that cause them to stick together, which decreases the force of collisions with the wall of the container; therefore, the pressure decreases in relation to ideal behavior.

Solve

Figure 10.38 at $P = 200$ atm shows that CH_4 has attractive forces that cause it to deviate from ideal behavior at lower pressures but that for H_2, deviation is caused only by the real volume of the molecules. From this behavior we can say that for H_2 the effect of the volume occupied by the gas molecules is more important than the attractive forces between them.

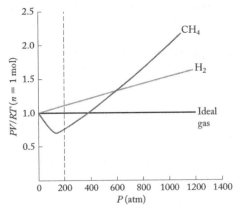

Think about It

In a plot of PV/RT versus P, we can see that CO_2 has an even larger attractive-forces effect than that of CH_4 because its negative deviation from ideal behavior (at pressures of 0–100 atm) is even greater than that for CH_4.

10.131. **Collect and Organize**

We are to calculate the pressure of 50.0 g of H_2 at 20°C (293 K) in a 1.00 L vessel by using the van der Waals equation for real gases and then using the ideal gas equation.

Analyze

The van der Waals equation is

$$\left(P + \frac{n^2 a}{V^2}\right)(V - nb) = nRT$$

where $a = 0.244$ $L^2 \cdot atm/mol^2$ and $b = 0.0266$ L/mol for H_2. We first have to determine the number of moles of H_2 in 50.0 g by using the molar mass of H_2 (2.02 g/mol).

Solve

(a) Moles of H_2: 50.0 g × 1 mol/2.02 g = 24.75 mol H_2
Pressure calculation using the van der Waals equation:

$$\left(P + \frac{(24.75 \text{ mol})^2 \times 0.244 \text{ L}^2 \cdot \text{atm/mol}^2}{(1.00 \text{ L})^2}\right)\left(1.00 \text{ L} - 24.75 \text{ mol} \times 0.0266 \text{ L/mol}\right)$$

$$= 24.75 \text{ mol} \times 0.08206 \text{ L} \cdot \text{atm/mol} \cdot \text{K} \times 293 \text{ K}$$

$$\left(P + 149.5 \text{ atm}\right) = 1741.8 \text{ atm}$$

$$P = 1590 \text{ atm}$$

(b) Pressure calculation using the ideal gas equation:

$$P = \frac{nRT}{V} = \frac{24.75 \text{ mol} \times 0.08206 \text{ L} \cdot \text{atm/mol} \cdot \text{K} \times 293 \text{ K}}{1.00 \text{ L}} = 595 \text{ atm}$$

Think about It

At these high pressures, hydrogen deviates a great deal from ideal behavior, as shown by the very different pressures calculated through the ideal gas equation and the van der Waals equation.

10.133. **Collect and Organize**

For a sports car engine cylinder with a volume of 633 mL in which compression achieves an increase in pressure of 9.0 times, we are asked to calculate the volume of the air and gasoline mixture after compression. We then are asked to evaluate the assumption that during compression no change in temperature occurs.

Analyze

In the compression we are simply reducing the volume by a factor of 9 to increase the pressure by a factor of 9 (since pressure and volume are inversely proportional).

Solve

(a) The volume of the air–gasoline mixture in the cylinder after compression is

$$\frac{633 \text{ mL}}{9} = 70.3 \text{ mL}$$

(b) The assumption that the temperature is constant during the compression is not realistic because when gases are compressed the temperature increases, according to Charles's law.

Think about It

If the initial temperature is 298 K, let's calculate the temperature of the gasoline–air mixture upon compression by using Charles's law:

$$\frac{V_1}{V_2} = \frac{T_1}{T_2}$$

$$\frac{633 \text{ mL}}{70.3 \text{ mL}} = \frac{298 \text{ K}}{T_2}, \text{ so } T_2 = 331 \text{ K}$$

10.135. Collect and Organize

We are to calculate u_{rms} for argon atoms at 0.00010 K.

Analyze

The u_{rms} is calculated through

$$u_{rms} = \sqrt{\frac{3RT}{M}}$$

Solve

$$u_{rms} = \sqrt{\frac{3 \times 8.314 \text{ kg} \cdot \text{m}^2/\text{s}^2(\text{mol} \cdot \text{K}) \times 0.00010 \text{ K}}{39.948 \text{ g/mol} \times \dfrac{1 \text{ kg}}{1000 \text{ g}}}} = 0.25 \text{ m/s}$$

Think about It

Helium atoms at the same temperature would have a greater root-mean-square speed (0.79 m/s) because they are lighter gas particles.

10.137. Collect and Organize

We can use the ideal gas equation to calculate the moles of air (and then the mass of air) that must be compressed into a scuba tank so that it will deliver 80 ft³ of air at 72°F and 1.00 atm pressure.

Analyze

To find the moles of air in 80 ft³ we use $PV = nRT$ rearranged to $n = PV/RT$, where $V = 80$ ft³ (which must be converted to liters by using 1 ft = 0.3048 m and 1 m³ = 1000 L), $P = 1.00$ atm, and $T = 72°F$ (which must be converted to kelvins by using °C = 5/9(°F − 32) and K = °C + 273.15). Using the molar mass of air (which we can calculate from the mole fractions and the molar mass of each component), we can convert the moles of air into grams and then add to the weight of the 15 kg scuba tank.

Solve

Moles of air required:

$$n = \frac{1 \text{ atm} \times \left(80 \text{ ft}^3 \times \dfrac{(0.3048 \text{ m})^3}{1 \text{ ft}^3} \times \dfrac{1000 \text{ L}}{1 \text{ m}^3} \right)}{0.08206 \text{ L} \cdot \text{atm/mol} \cdot \text{K} \times \left(\dfrac{5}{9}(72 - 32) + 273.15 \right)} = 93.5 \text{ mol}$$

Molar mass of dry air (data from Table 6.1):

$$M_{air} = (0.7808 \times 28.01 \text{ g/mol}) + (0.2095 \times 32.00 \text{ g/mol}) + (0.00934 \times 39.948 \text{ g/mol})$$

$$+ (0.00033 \times 44.01 \text{ g/mol}) + (0.000002 \times 16.04 \text{ g/mol}) + (0.0000005 \times 2.02 \text{ g/mol}) = 28.96 \text{ g/mol}$$

Mass of air in the tank:

$$93.5 \text{ mol} \times \frac{28.96 \text{ g}}{\text{mol}} = 2.71 \times 10^3 \text{ g, or } 2.71 \text{ kg}$$

Total mass of the tank: 2.71 kg + 15 kg = 18 kg.

Think about It

The air inside the tank does not add much to the mass. The tank, though, must be thick and heavy to withstand the 3000 psi of pressure needed for that amount of air.

10.139. Collect and Organize

We are to calculate the volume that 6.0 mL of liquid halothane ($d = 1.87$ g/mL) would occupy in the gaseous state at 37°C and 1.00 atm pressure. Then, we are to calculate the density of this gas at that temperature and pressure.

Analyze

From the volume of the liquid halothane and its density and molar mass ($C_2HBrClF_3$, 197.4 g/mol), we can calculate the moles of halothane present in the sample. Then, using $PV = nRT$, we can determine the volume that the gas occupies. From the gas density equation $d = \mathcal{M}P/RT$, we can calculate the density of the gas at 37°C and 1 atm pressure. Remember that we must convert temperature in this problem to kelvins.

Solve

(a) Moles of halothane in 6.0 mL of liquid:

$$6.0 \text{ mL} \times \frac{1.87 \text{ g}}{\text{mL}} \times \frac{1 \text{ mol}}{197.4 \text{ g}} = 0.0568 \text{ mol}$$

Volume that 6.0 mL of liquid halothane occupies as a gas at 37°C:

$$V = \frac{0.0568 \text{ mol} \times 0.08206 \text{ L} \cdot \text{atm/mol} \cdot \text{K} \times 310 \text{ K}}{1.00 \text{ atm}} = 1.45 \text{ L}$$

(b) Density of the halothane gas at 37°C:

$$d = \frac{197.4 \text{ g/mol} \times 1.00 \text{ atm}}{0.08206 \text{ L} \cdot \text{atm/mol} \cdot \text{K} \times 310 \text{ K}} = 7.76 \text{ g/L, or } 0.00776 \text{ g/mL}$$

Think about It

As the temperature decreased, the density of the gas increased as expected because density and temperature are inversely proportional in the gas density equation.

10.141. Collect and Organize

We are asked to analyze the effect of molar mass on the position of the product ring formed by the reaction of either HCl or CH_3CO_2H with the three amines CH_3NH_2, $(CH_3)_2NH$, and $(CH_3)_3N$, which we can do by using Graham's law (refer to Figure P10.140).

Analyze

Graham's law of effusion may be used to approximately describe situations involving diffusion. It shows that the rate of diffusion (which is directly related to how far along the tube the gas travels) is inversely related to the molar mass of the gas (lighter gases travel faster).

$$\frac{r_x}{r_y} = \sqrt{\frac{\mathcal{M}_y}{\mathcal{M}_x}}$$

To answer this question, we need the molar masses of the acids and amine bases: HCl (36.46 g/mol), CH_3CO_2H (60.05 g/mol), CH_3NH_2 (31.06 g/mol), $(CH_3)_2NH$ (45.08 g/mol), and $(CH_3)_3N$ (59.11 g/mol).

Solve

(a) When the white ring of the product is seen exactly halfway between the two ends, it means that the gases diffused the same distance and therefore at the same rate. This would occur for gases that have nearly equal molar masses: CH_3CO_2H and $(CH_3)_3N$.

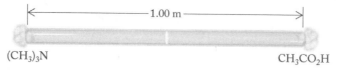

(b) The combination of gases that would produce the white ring closest to the amine end of the tube would be fast-diffusing HCl and slow-diffusing $(CH_3)_3N$.

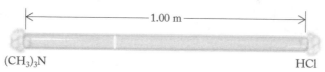

(c) Any combination that would give the product at the same location as another (within 1 cm) would have to have the same ratio of r_{acid}/r_{amine}. These ratios from Graham's law are as follows:

Amine Base	Acid	r_{acid}/r_{amine}
CH_3NH_2	HCl	0.923
$(CH_3)_2NH$	HCl	1.11
$(CH_3)_3N$	HCl	1.27
CH_3NH_2	CH_3CO_2H	0.719
$(CH_3)_2NH$	CH_3CO_2H	0.866
$(CH_3)_3N$	CH_3CO_2H	0.992

To be within 1 cm of each other, the r_{acid}/r_{amine} ratio would have to be within 0.01. None of the combinations in this list would form the product at the same position as any other combination.

Think about It
This "crude" experiment can accurately identify the amine or the acid used.

10.143. Collect and Organize
We can calculate the partial pressure of H_2, He, and CH_4 in Uranus's atmosphere, knowing each gas's percentage by volume and the total pressure (130 kPa).

Analyze
The percent composition by volume gives us the mole fraction in percent because the volume is directly related to the number of moles of gas through the ideal gas equation. Therefore, the mole fractions of the gases are 0.83 H_2, 0.15 He, and 0.02 CH_4. The partial pressure of each gas can be calculated by using $P_X = x_X \times P_{total}$.

Solve
$$P_{H_2} = 0.83 \times 130 \text{ kPa} = 108 \text{ kPa}$$
$$P_{He} = 0.15 \times 130 \text{ kPa} = 20 \text{ kPa}$$
$$P_{CH_4} = 0.02 \times 130 \text{ kPa} = 3 \text{ kPa}$$

Think about It
The sum of the partial pressures adds up to the total pressure. This is a good way to check for any calculation errors.

10.145. Collect and Organize
We are given the balanced equation for ammonium nitrite decomposing to nitrogen and liquid water. We are asked to calculate the change in pressure in a 10.0 L vessel due to N_2 formation for 1.00 L of a 1.0 M NH_4NO_2 solution decomposing at 25°C.

Analyze
Because N_2 is the only gas involved in the reaction, all the pressure increase will be due to the production of N_2 in the reaction. From the stoichiometric equation we can calculate the moles of N_2 that will be produced (assuming 100% decomposition) and then we can use the ideal gas equation ($PV = nRT$) to calculate the pressure change.

Solve
$$\text{moles of } N_2 \text{ produced: } 1.00 \text{ L} \times \frac{1.0 \text{ mol NH}_4\text{NO}_2}{1 \text{ L}} \times \frac{1 \text{ mol N}_2}{1 \text{ mol NH}_4\text{NO}_2} = 1.0 \text{ mol}$$

$$P_{N_2} = \frac{1.0 \text{ mol} \times 0.08206 \text{ L} \cdot \text{atm/mol} \cdot \text{K} \times 298 \text{ K}}{9.0 \text{ L}} = 2.7 \text{ atm}$$

Think about It
Because the molar ratio of N_2 to NH_4NO_2 is 1:1, the moles of N_2 produced in the reaction equals the moles of NH_4NO_2 consumed.

10.147. **Collect and Organize**
From the balanced chemical equation and given the amount of nitrate that enters the swamp in one day (200.0 g), we are asked first to calculate the volume of N_2 and CO_2 that would form at 17°C (290 K) and 1.00 atm and then to calculate the density of the gas mixture at that temperature and pressure.

Analyze
Once we calculate the moles of NO_3^- (from the molar mass of $NO_3^- = 62.00$ g/mol), we can calculate the moles of N_2 and CO_2 produced by using the stoichiometric ratios from the balanced equation (2 NO_3^- : 1 N_2, 2 NO_3^- : 5 CO_2). Using the ideal gas equation, we can calculate the volume of each gas produced. We can then calculate the density of the gas mixture by determining the mass of CO_2 and N_2 produced (from the molar amounts already calculated) and dividing the total mass by the total volume the gases occupy.

Solve
(a) and (b) Volume of gases produced in the swamp:

$$\text{mol NO}_3^- = 200.0 \text{ g} \times \frac{1 \text{ mol}}{62.00 \text{ g}} = 3.226 \text{ mol}$$

$$\text{mol N}_2 \text{ produced} = 3.226 \text{ mol NO}_3^- \times \frac{1 \text{ mol N}_2}{2 \text{ mol NO}_3^-} = 1.613 \text{ mol N}_2$$

$$\text{volume of N}_2 = \frac{nRT}{P} = \frac{1.613 \text{ mol} \times 0.08206 \text{ L} \cdot \text{atm/mol} \cdot \text{K} \times 290 \text{ K}}{1.00 \text{ atm}} = 38.4 \text{ L}$$

$$\text{mol CO}_2 \text{ produced} = 3.226 \text{ mol NO}_3^- \times \frac{5 \text{ mol CO}_2}{2 \text{ mol NO}_3^-} = 8.065 \text{ mol CO}_2$$

$$\text{volume of CO}_2 = \frac{nRT}{P} = \frac{8.065 \text{ mol} \times 0.08206 \text{ L} \cdot \text{atm/mol} \cdot \text{K} \times 290 \text{ K}}{1.00 \text{ atm}} = 192 \text{ L}$$

Total volume of gases at 1.00 atm and 290 K: 38.4 L + 192 L = 230 L
(c) The density of this gas is as follows:

$$\text{mass of N}_2 \text{ produced} = 1.613 \text{ mol} \times \frac{28.01 \text{ g}}{1 \text{ mol}} = 45.18 \text{ g}$$

$$\text{mass of CO}_2 \text{ produced} = 8.065 \text{ mol} \times \frac{44.01 \text{ g}}{1 \text{ mol}} = 354.9 \text{ g}$$

$$\text{total mass of gases} = 45.18 \text{ g} + 354.9 \text{ g} = 400.1 \text{ g}$$

$$\text{density of gas mixture} = \frac{400.1 \text{ g}}{230 \text{ L}} = 1.74 \text{ g/L, or } 0.00174 \text{ g/mL}$$

Think about It
The calculation of density here drew on the simple definition of density as mass divided by volume.

10.149. **Collect and Organize**
We are asked how many grams of N_2H_4 is needed to make the same amount of N_2 as in Problem 10.74. From Problem 10.74, we know that we need 5.25×10^3 mol of N_2 to produce 1.38×10^5 L of N_2 to power the car. From the balanced equation, we see that 1 mol of hydrazine produces 1 mol of $N_2(g)$.

Analyze
The amount of hydrazine required is 5.25×10^3 mol. Multiplying this by the molar mass of hydrazine (32.05 g/mol) will give us the mass of N_2H_4 needed.

Solve

$$5.25 \times 10^3 \text{ mol N}_2\text{H}_4 \times \frac{32.05 \text{ g}}{\text{mol}} = 1.68 \times 10^5 \text{ g, or 168 kg}$$

Think about It

Although this is a lot of hydrazine, it may be easier to handle than 1.39×10^5 L of N_2.